Numerical
Methods
in FORTRAN

John M. McCormick

Columbia University

Mario G. Salvadori

Columbia University

Prentice-Hall, Inc.

Englewood Cliffs, New Jersey

Numerical
Methods
in FORTRAN

PRENTICE-HALL INTERNATIONAL, INC. London
PRENTICE-HALL OF AUSTRALIA, PTY., LTD. Sydney
PRENTICE-HALL OF CANADA, LTD. Toronto
PRENTICE-HALL OF INDIA (PRIVATE) LTD. New Delhi
PRENTICE-HALL OF JAPAN, INC. Tokyo

Prentice-Hall Applied Mathematics Series

Third printing.............August, 1965

Numerical Methods in FORTRAN
by John M. McCormick and Mario G. Salvadori

Preface

The increasing availability of digital computers has caused a basic change in the presentation of courses on numerical analysis. Programming of numerical methods can be immediately emphasized as part of such courses, with a three-fold advantage accruing to the student:

a) the student knows he has mastered a given numerical method when he is able to program it successfully;

b) the learning of programming techniques is better motivated when the student can apply them immediately to the coding of an equally fresh numerical method, rather than to some extraneous example;

c) the student can solve more interesting and complicated problems by combining numerical analysis and programming, thus becoming more conscious of the power of modern computational procedures.

This book attempts to fill the needs of a textbook for such a modern course, but can also be used for either an elementary course on numerical analysis or a course on FORTRAN programming.

Chapter 1 is a concise introduction to the digital computer and the FORTRAN language; it links the first half of the book, an introduction to numerical methods, with the second half, a collection of 53 complete, working programs. Most of the programs are based on the numerical methods introduced in the first half of the book and are intended to be easily understood by the beginner.

Each program is complete, and has been successfully run on one or more computers. Each program includes typical numerical results, and is accompanied by a flow chart, explanatory notes, and beginner's hints. These programs contain almost every kind of FORTRAN statement, from simple arithmetic statements to sophisticated subprograms. A reference table gives the programs where any FORTRAN statement may be found, and the notes where it is explained. This "program library" should prove useful to anyone learning FORTRAN (whether by himself or in class) and to anyone in need of simple, tested programs for the solution of the problems most commonly encountered in practice.

Chapters 2 through 8 present fundamental methods of numerical analysis, with most analytical derivations based on a single technique: the Taylor series expansion of functions of one or two real variables. They cover

a) interpolation and extrapolation;
b) algebraic and transcendental equations;
c) simultaneous linear equations;
d) initial-value, characteristic-value, and boundary-value problems;
e) partial differential equations of the hyperbolic, parabolic, and elliptic types.

These chapters can be used without reference to programming techniques, and contain over 320 illustrative examples and problems. Answers to half the problems are included in the book.

Chapters 2 through 8 may be used for an elementary, 3-point course on numerical analysis at the junior or senior level, since they require of the student only a working knowledge of the calculus and a mere awareness of the existence of differential equations and their scientific significance. These chapters are also well suited to self-study, thanks especially to the examples which illustrate each numerical technique.

It is regrettable that such a short book cannot present practical applications of numerical techniques; but, for the interested reader, there are references to a more advanced book on numerical methods,[*] which contains such applications.

The programs are numbered to correspond to the chapter of the book where that particular programmed numerical technique is discussed. Thus, Gauss's method is presented in Chapter 5 and coded in Program 5.2.

The programs whose numbers begin with a 9 are based on techniques beyond the scope of the analytical part of this book. They are included to make the book more valuable as a handbook of useful FORTRAN programs.

---

[*] M. G. Salvadori and M. L. Baron, *Numerical Methods in Engineering*, Second Edition (Englewood Cliffs, N.J.: Prentice-Hall, Inc., 1961).

The authors are deeply indebted

to Dr. M. L. Baron and Mr. J. P. Wright for their critical reading of the manuscript;

to Dr. W. R. Spillers and Mr. C. P. Lecht for their advice on the programs;

to Miss K. A. Anner for her help in running the programs;

to Mrs. A. C. McCormick and Mrs. T. L. Wright for their care in typing the manuscript;

to Mr. N. C. Romanelli and Mr. R. Carola of Prentice-Hall for their skill in producing the book.

John M. McCormick
Mario G. Salvadori

Notes

1. The following book is referred to in the text by the abbreviation N.M.:

Numerical Methods in Engineering, Second Edition, by M. G. Salvadori and M. L. Baron, published by Prentice-Hall, Inc., Englewood Cliffs, N.J., 1961.

2. Numbers enclosed in square brackets, e.g., [.00323], denote exact solutions in Examples and Problems.

Table
of Contents

FORTRAN Programs,
Flow Charts,
Beginner's Hints,
and Examples

On the Programs, 147

Reference to FORTRAN statements, 148

Numerical
Methods
in FORTRAN

Computers
and Programming

Chapter One

1.1 The Digital Computer

The developments of modern science have confronted the scientist and the engineer with a variety of problems which are best solved by approximate methods. Hence the widening interest in *numerical analysis,* a branch of mathematics which leads to approximate solutions by repeated application of the four basic operations of algebra. Numerical analysis has been applied to scientific and technological problems from the very beginning of applied science, but has been given new impetus by the development of the *electronic digital computer.* The increasing number of problems being solved on digital computers includes both those for which the exact solution is not available and those which the machine can more efficiently solve by recomputing the solution each time rather than by searching for it among previous results. For example, although tables of the elementary functions are readily available, modern computers "generate" such functions each time they are needed.

The high-speed digital computer, in essence, can perform only a few simple operations, such as distinguishing between a "plus" and a "minus" physical state. Thus, it can determine whether a switch is open or not, whether a magnetic core is magnetized or not, whether a low-temperature metal is conducting or not. Next, the computer can transfer this information on "pluses" and "minuses," and keep track of it. These and other operations are done automatically within the computer.

The user need only realize that an electronic computer, when properly instructed, can

(a) perform basic algebraic operations,

(b) make simple tests, such as determining whether a number is negative, zero, or positive, or whether a switch is off or on,

(c) perform more complex operations by repetition of basic operations and simple tests,

(d) follow a predetermined sequence of instructions concerning the operations to be performed,

(e) change the instructions to be followed, depending upon the results of intermediate operations, i.e., make "logical decisions," and

(f) store in the memory for future reference the results of the operations.

The possibility of logical decisions makes of the electronic computer an essentially new and amazingly powerful tool in the field of numerical calculations.

The memory of a digital computer is the place where information is stored. The memory may consist of magnetic cores, a magnetic drum, electrical relays, or any other device that has two identifiable physical states, i.e., on or off, magnetized or unmagnetized, current flowing or not flowing, plus or minus, zero or one, etc. Stored information must be accessible so that it can be referred to and replaced when desired. The information stored can be original data, instructions, reference tables, and intermediate or final results. Each storage location is identified by a location number called an *address*. By means of these numerical addresses, a computer can locate the data and the instructions needed in the solution of a problem. The speed of a computer is largely dependent on its *access time* — the length of time required to obtain data from storage and make it available to other units of the computer system.

The other units of the computer vary from system to system but all have some input-output device that "accepts" — that is, can use — numbers, letters, and symbols. Information is usually fed into the system from punched cards, paper or magnetic tape, a keyboard, or switches. After performing the required operations, the computer can produce answers in many forms. Results may be punched into cards or paper tapes, recorded on magnetic tape, printed or typed on paper, or left in memory for use in subsequent problems. Printers provide high-speed output by printing an entire line of information at one time.

The *operating unit* of the computer actually performs the required operations. It is usually subdivided into an *arithmetic and logic unit*, which executes the calculations and makes decisions, and a *control unit*, which gives orders to the arithmetic unit according to predetermined instructions.

1.2 Programming the Computer

The computer must be given directions for the solution of a problem. The sequence of steps to be performed must be translated into detailed instructions written in a code, which the computer can "understand." A series of such instructions is called a *program*. When it is retained in a storage device during the calculations, it is called a *stored program*. In such a program the coded, stored instructions are available, as needed, to direct an entire sequence of complicated operations.

Special instructions enable the computer to make decisions based on intermediate results, allowing the automatic selection of the proper course among various alternatives, and the handling of exceptions to standard procedures.

For each problem it is to solve, the computer must be given the detailed series of instructions that tell the computer what to do with the data it will subsequently receive under every possible combination of circumstances. The number of instructions required for the complete solution of a problem may be only a few, or many thousands, depending upon the complexity of the problem. These instructions may be coded in the "language" the machine is capable of understanding, the so-called *natural* or *machine language* of the computer, or in any number of *problem-oriented languages*. These last "languages" make use of words and symbols similar to those familiar to the user, so that a user well-versed in the solution of certain types of problems can program them in roughly the words and symbols of his own language. Since problem-oriented languages are not directly understood by the computers, special computer programs, called processors or *compilers*, are needed so that the computer itself can "translate" the "problem-oriented" program into a machine-language program, which can be run on the computer. Special languages have found great acceptance in the business-accounting and science-engineering worlds, because they greatly facilitate the use of computers by nonprofessional programmers.

The two most popular scientific languages are ALGOL and FORTRAN. The ALGOL language is quite general and is widely used by professional programmers and researchers in programming. But the very generality of this language makes it more difficult to create compilers that may be easily adaptable to a large variety of standard computers.

On the other hand the FORTRAN language, developed by IBM, is quite simple. It is easily learned and remembered by engineers and scientists who may need it only sporadically. The great majority of present-day computers have FORTRAN compilers (or close cousins). Moreover, since FORTRAN is, in a sense, a particular type of ALGOL, it is convenient to learn FORTRAN first, even if eventually one will wish to write in ALGOL. It is easier to learn ALGOL once one has mastered FORTRAN.

All the programs presented in this book have been coded in FORTRAN II. They have all been successfully executed, and typical results obtained by their use are printed with each program.

It is assumed that, while studying this book, the reader will consult some of the many excellent references available on FORTRAN. A list of such references is given at the end of this chapter. Hence, the following section will not try to give a complete course on FORTRAN, but only a concise introduction to the subject.

1.3 A Concise Introduction to FORTRAN

The FORTRAN (FORmula TRANslation) system consists of a language and a compiler. The system enables the scientist or engineer to communicate problems to the computer in an *almost* mathematical language. The compiler is itself a program which tells the computer how to translate the program written in the FORTRAN language into a program written in machine language.

The FORTRAN language is a compromise between machine language and mathematical language. It uses symbols understood by the computer, and requires that certain rules be *rigidly* followed. But it also uses many of the ordinary symbols of mathematics and relieves the user almost entirely of programming computer control operations.

The problem to be solved is usually described by the user in a program written in FORTRAN language, called the *source program*. The source program is then "read," i.e., put into the computer memory along with the FORTRAN compiler. The computer, following instructions from the compiler, converts the source program into a program in machine language, the *object program*, ready to be run on the computer.

The FORTRAN language is largely independent of the computer to be used; hence, the same source program, with slight variations, can be used on different computers, even though generally the object programs produced by different compilers from the same source program will be entirely different.

The printer and the typewriter associated with a computer usually print only in capital letters, have a limited number of special characters (such as /, $+$, $-$, *), and are incapable of properly showing exponents and subscripts. Nonetheless, many formulas retain their familiar appearance in FORTRAN. The following FORTRAN expressions are identical with their algebraic counterparts:

Addition	A $+$ B
	J $+$ 2
Subtraction	C $-$ D
	5 $-$ L
Division	E/F
	N/4
Value of a constant	1.414
	539

Other expressions are only slightly changed in FORTRAN:

	Mathematics	FORTRAN
Multiplication	$A \cdot B$	A*B
	$2 \cdot J$	2*J
Elementary functions	$\cos x$	COSF(X)
	$\sin x$	SINF(X)
	$\log x$	LOGF(X)

In other cases, FORTRAN expressions differ in appearance from the corresponding mathematical expressions, but their meaning remains clear:

Mathematics	FORTRAN
$\sqrt{x}$	SQRTF(X)
e^x	EXPF(X)
$\arctan x$	ATANF(X)
$|x|$	ABSF(X)

The expression for exponentiation in FORTRAN contains a double asterisk:

Mathematics	FORTRAN
A^B	A**B
x^3	X**3

The sentences of the FORTRAN language are called *statements*. *Arithmetic statements* look like statements of equality: their left-hand side always represents a single variable; their right-hand side is always an expression which may involve parentheses, operation symbols, constants, variables, and functions, combined in accordance with a set of rules very much like those of ordinary algebra. For example,

Mathematics	FORTRAN
$X = A + B \cdot C$	X = A + B*C
$I = (J/2)^4$	I = (J/2)**4
$Z = \sqrt{\sin x}$	Z = SQRTF(SINF(X))

Parentheses are used as in algebra to specify the order of operations. For example,

Mathematics	FORTRAN
$(X \cdot B)^D$	(X*B)**D
$X \cdot (B^D)$	X*(B**D)
$A \cdot (B + C)$	A*(B+C)
$(A \cdot B) + C$	(A*B)+C

If parentheses are not used to specify the order of operations, the order is assumed to be

1. exponentiation,
2. multiplication and division,
3. addition and subtraction.

Thus,

Mathematics	FORTRAN
$(A^B) \cdot C$	A**B*C
A^{BC}	A**(B*C)
$\dfrac{D^E}{F} - G$	D**E/F−G
$D^{E/(F-G)}$	D**(E/(F−G))

FORTRAN distinguishes between numbers that must be integers and those which may have a decimal point. *Fixed-point numbers* are always integers, and are used primarily to count operations or to identify statements. Such numbers are used in FORTRAN as they are in algebraic expressions:

Statement	Result
I = 2 + 3	5
N = 4 − 1	3
K = 10/5	2
L = 4*3	12
M = 2**2	4

Notice that, in spite of their name, fixed-point numbers are written *without* a decimal point, because the decimal point is always "fixed" at the right end of the number, and thus can be omitted.

We distinguish two types of fixed-point numbers — constants and variables — both of which can have only integer values. The expressions above contain a mixture of fixed-point constants and variables. *Fixed-point constants* may have a + or − sign:

$$3$$
$$-7$$
$$0$$
$$+401$$
$$-2828$$

Variables are represented in FORTRAN by one to six alphabetic or numeric characters (integers). The *first* character must be a *letter* and no special characters (/, *, +, etc.) may be used. In particular, *fixed-point variables* must use one of the letters I, J, K, L, M, N for their first letter. The following are correct representations of fixed-point variables:

I
J1
MIKE
K123
NUMBER

The following are incorrect representations of fixed-point variables:

ANNE	(begins with character other than I, J, K, L, M, N)
L/K	(special character / is used)
NUMBER1	(longer than 6 characters)

Floating-point numbers are numbers that are not necessarily integers. Such numbers are used in FORTRAN as they are in algebraic expressions:

Statement	*Result*
ANGLE = 2.3 + 7.1	9.4
BETA = 3.1416 − .1414	3.0002
C = 10./4.	2.5
SUMZND = 4.2*3.1 + PI	13.02 + PI
Y = 1.5**2.*THETA1	2.25(THETA1)

The statements above contain a mixture of floating-point constants and variables, including the integer 2. written in *floating-point mode*. (Fixed-point and floating-point are referred to as the two *modes* in which a number or a constant may be written.) An integer in floating-point mode will be treated by the computer as if it had as many decimal figures as specified for the other floating-point numbers. Notice that *floating-point variables* must begin with a letter *other* than I, J, K, L, M, N.

Subscripted variables are indicated by placing the subscript, or subscripts, in parentheses after the variable name:

TITLE(1)

ARRAY(3,I)

NUM(I+1, INDEX, 2*JN−9)

The variable may have from one to three subscripts. The subscripts can only be positive fixed-point constants or variables, or expressions of the form

a positive integer constant

times a nonsubscripted integer variable

plus an integer constant.

NUMBER(4*I−5) is an example of a correctly subscripted variable. This *strict* rule (without which the compiler would not be able to provide an optimized object program) presents pitfalls for the beginner. Some common mistakes in subscripting are

A(0)	0 is not allowed as a subscript
A(2+I)	constant plus variable not allowed; I+2 is correct
A(I*2)	constant must precede variable; 2*I is correct
A(X+2.)	neither a floating-point variable (X) nor a floating-point constant (2.) is allowed
A(I(2))	a subscript cannot be subscripted
A(I/2)	no division allowed.

Arithmetic statements define numerical calculations. They very much resemble conventional arithmetic formulas, but two important restrictions must be noticed in this connection:

(1) The equal sign (=) means "is to be replaced by" rather than "is equal to." Thus, the algebraically meaningless statement

N = N + 1

is meaningful in FORTRAN, and is used all the time to increment a variable N by 1. It means "take the value stored under the name N, add 1 to it, and store the result under the name N again."

(2) The quantities on the right-hand side of the equal sign must be of the same *mode*, with the exception that fixed-point numbers may appear as subscripts or exponents in an otherwise floating-point expression. Thus the statement

X = 2*PI + 7

is unacceptable because PI is a floating-point variable and 2 and 7 are fixed-point constants. One must write

X = 2.*PI + 7.

Similarly,

N = 1 + X

is incorrect; it may be written correctly as

N = 1 + IX

in fixed-point mode, or

N = 1. + X

in floating-point mode.

Notice, from the last example, that the quantity on the left-hand side need not be in the same mode as the expression on the right-hand side. However, the result will be "fixed" or "floated" according to whether the *left-hand member* is a fixed- or floating-point variable. Thus the result of the two statements

PI = 3.1415927
N = 2. + PI

is the number 5, since all figures to the right of the decimal point are lost when the result is put into fixed-point mode, as required by its name N.

A similar alteration of the number occurs when doing division in fixed-point mode. The result of the statement

X = 2*(3/4)

is the floating-point number 0., since the operation "3 divided by 4" yields 0 in fixed-point mode, and this operation precedes the multiplication by 2; the floating-point variable on the left causes the decimal point to be added to the zero. If decimal figures are wanted, one must write

X = 2.*(3./4.)

The computer has the ability of automatic *looping*, that is, it can automatically repeat the same operations with different data. Looping may be obtained in FORTRAN in several ways: one of the most common is the use of an IF statement. The IF statement allows the programmer to change the sequence of operations, depending upon whether the value of an expression is negative, zero, or positive. For example, the factorial of an integer N may be computed by means of the following program which contains an IF statement.

```
        . . .
        . . .
        I = 0
        NFACT = 1
   10   I = I + 1
        NFACT = NFACT*I
        IF(I − N)   10, 20, 20
   20   . . .
        . . .
```

The first two statements in the program set the initial values of I equal to 0 and of NFACT equal to 1. Statement 10 increases I by 1. The next statement computes NFACT for the new value of I. The IF statement checks whether I − N is less than, greater than, or equal to zero, i.e., whether I is less than, greater than, or equal to N. If I < N, control is transferred to statement 10 and the calculation is continued until N! is obtained. When the value of I becomes N, control is transferred to statement 20, and the program will continue on to other statements.

A second way to accomplish looping is to use a DO loop. The statement

DO 20   I = 1, N

causes the program to repeatedly execute the statements that follow it, *up to* and *including* statement 20, for values of the integer I running from 1 to N. Thus the part of a program for computing N! could also be written

. . .

. . .

```
        NFACT = 1
        DO 20  I = 2, N
  20    NFACT = NFACT*I
```

. . .

. . .

The DO statement

```
        DO 20  I = 1, N, M
```

increments the running integer I by M; when M = 1, as in the previous example, it is not written explicitly. It is possible to *nest* DO loops, that is, to place one or more loops within another loop. For the details of nesting and for other restrictions, the reader is referred to FORTRAN instruction books and the programs in this book.

The FORTRAN language consists of

(a) arithmetic statements

(b) control statements

(c) input/output statements

(d) specification statements

(e) subprogram statements

(f) special statements.

In this brief introduction, we have exhibited many arithmetic statements. We have also illustrated two control statements (IF and DO). There are many others. Several control statements (the unconditional and the computed GO TO, IF(SENSE SWITCH), CONTINUE, PAUSE, STOP, and END), several forms of input/output statements (FORMAT, READ, READ INPUT TAPE, PUNCH, PRINT, WRITE OUTPUT TAPE), three specification statements (DIMENSION, EQUIVALENCE, COMMON), many "arithmetic-statement" and library functions, and several subprograms (SUBROUTINE and FUNCTION) are used in the programs in the second half of this book, and are explained in the notes accompanying the programs.

In studying the programs, the reader is advised to concentrate his attention, at first, on the central "algorithm" of each program (i.e., on the part of the program that is concerned with the actual computations), and to ignore those instructions that serve to

(a) read the data into the computer,

(b) set the initial values of the variables, and define the constants,

(c) determine when the calculation should be stopped,

(d) print the results.

Each program is accompanied by notes that explain the program and comment on the instructions, by beginner's hints, and by *flow charts* or *block diagrams* that facilitate the writing and reading of programs. The flow chart maps the sequence of operations, clearly showing the alternate paths which the computation may follow without giving operational details. The flow-chart symbols used are the common ones of Figure 1.1.

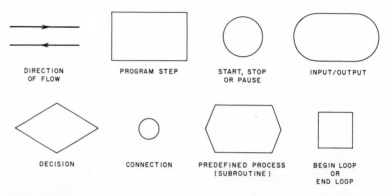

DIRECTION OF FLOW   PROGRAM STEP   START, STOP OR PAUSE   INPUT/OUTPUT

DECISION   CONNECTION   PREDEFINED PROCESS (SUBROUTINE)   BEGIN LOOP OR END LOOP

Figure 1.1

Many of the programs in the second half of the book correspond to techniques introduced in the first half.* (The chapter numbers indicate the correspondence.) The reader may begin to study these programs as soon as he has mastered the basic elements of FORTRAN presented in this book, although the great bulk of detailed information needed to code in FORTRAN requires his careful perusal of references such as those listed below:

Smith, Robert E. and Johnson, Dora E., FORTRAN
Autotester, John Wiley & Sons, Inc., New York, 1962

McCracken, Daniel D., *A Guide to Fortran Programming*,
John Wiley & Sons, Inc., New York, 1961

IBM General Information Manual
FORTRAN

IBM 7090/7094 PROGRAMMING SYSTEMS
FORTRAN II Programming

IBM 1620 FORTRAN II SPECIFICATIONS

160 FORTRAN/REFERENCE MANUAL
Control Data 160 Computer

REFERENCE MANUAL FORTRAN II
for the IBM 704 Data Processing System

REFERENCE MANUAL
709/7090 FORTRAN Programming System

IBM 7090/7094 Programming Systems
FORTRAN IV

* All the programs are written in FORTRAN II. Most are written in the simplest input/output form (e.g., READ instead of READ INPUT TAPE), since most FORTRAN systems are compatible upwards (e.g., most IBM 1620 programs will run without change on an IBM 7094).

Approximate
Computations

Chapter Two

2.1 Successive Approximations

The final results of scientific investigations are often represented by functions or numbers, but these can be evaluated exactly in relatively few cases. It is, therefore, of great practical importance to be able to evaluate approximate results with the accuracy required by the problem at hand. Methods of *successive approximations* are among the most powerful devised to achieve this goal.

It is well known that the roots of an algebraic equation of degree higher than four cannot be evaluated exactly by performing a finite number of operations on its coefficients. All the same, a real root may often be evaluated to any degree of accuracy by the following procedure.

Consider, for example, the fifth-degree equation

$$32x^5 - 64x + 31 = 0, \tag{a}$$

which, like all odd-degree equations with real coefficients, is known to have at least one real root (since complex roots must appear in conjugate pairs).

Lacking any information as to the location of a real root x, we make an initial guess:

$$x^{(0)} = 0; \tag{b}$$

we rewrite (a) as

$$x = \frac{31 + 32x^5}{64}, \tag{c}$$

and start with the initial guess (b) on the right-hand member of (c), which allows the determination of the following successive approximations of the root:

$$x^{(1)} = \frac{31 + 32(x^{(0)})^5}{64} = \frac{31 + 32(0)^5}{64} = .48,$$

$$x^{(2)} = \frac{31 + 32(x^{(1)})^5}{64} = \frac{31 + 32(.48)^5}{64} = .4971,$$

$$x^{(3)} = \frac{31 + 32(x^{(2)})^5}{64} = \frac{31 + 32(.4971)^5}{64} = .49955,$$

$$x^{(4)} = \frac{31 + 32(x^{(3)})^5}{64} = \frac{31 + 32(.49955)^5}{64} = .49997.$$

The fourth approximation $x^{(4)}$ has an error of three units in the fifth decimal digit when compared with the exact root of (a), $x = \frac{1}{2}$.

The procedure used in the preceding example is called an *iterative* method of successive approximations (from the Latin *iterare*, to repeat). The operation required to evaluate an approximation $x^{(k+1)}$ from the preceding approximation $x^{(k)}$ is of the form

$$x^{(k+1)} = F(x^{(k)}), \tag{d}$$

and equation (c) may be seen to be a particular case of (d). The $x^{(k)}$ are called the *iterates* of the unknown x. Iterative calculations are terminated as soon as two successive iterates are identical within the required number of figures.

Approximate values of a function $f(x)$ at a particular value of x may also be obtained by successive approximations, using, for example, the power series expansion of $f(x)$ whenever the expansion exists (see Sec. 2.3). Thus, from the power series for $\sin x$,

$$\sin x = x - \frac{x^3}{6} + \frac{x^5}{120} - \cdots, \tag{e}$$

the values of sin .5 obtained by taking into account one, two, and three terms of the series are, respectively,

$$f^{(1)} = .5,$$

$$f^{(2)} = .5 - \frac{(.5)^3}{6} = .479167,$$

$$f^{(3)} = .5 - \frac{(.5)^3}{6} + \frac{(.5)^5}{120} = .479427.$$

The last value has an error of one unit in the last computed digit.

Power series expansions are often used to tabulate the values of functions that are defined by a differential equation or an integral and cannot be obtained in finite terms by means of elementary functions. Thus, the *elliptic integral* of the first kind, defined by the integral

$$F(k, \varphi) = \int_0^\varphi \frac{dx}{\sqrt{1 + k^2 \sin x}} \qquad (k^2 < 1), \tag{f}$$

or the *Bessel function* of the first kind of order zero, defined by the differential equation

$$\frac{d^2y}{dx^2} + \frac{1}{x}\frac{dy}{dx} + y = 0, \quad \text{with} \quad y(0) = 1, y'(0) = 0, \tag{g}$$

may be evaluated by expanding $1/\sqrt{1 + k^2 \sin x}$ and y, respectively, into power series.

Once the values of a function $f(x)$ are known for a number of values of x, say, $x_0, x_1, x_2, \ldots, x_n$, $f(x)$ may be approximately evaluated at a point $\bar{x}$ lying between two of the previous points by assuming that the graph of $f(x)$ is a straight line, a quadratic parabola, or a higher-order parabola. Such value of $f(\bar{x})$ is said to be obtained by *interpolation*. When $\bar{x}$ lies outside the range of values (x_0, x_n), $f(\bar{x})$ is said to be obtained by *extrapolation*.

In the following chapters we shall present iterative, interpolation, extrapolation, and series methods for the approximate evaluation of one or more unknowns, and of functions of one or more variables. These procedures will be applied to the approximate solution of algebraic, transcendental, ordinary and partial differential equations.

The availability of computing devices of all kinds, from the slide-rule to the electronic computer, has enormously increased the power and popularity of approximate numerical methods. Today, it is often more practical to obtain sufficiently accurate answers by numerical methods than to use analytical means to derive theoretically exact solutions, which eventually must also be evaluated numerically. For example, rather than store in the memory of an electronic computer the values of $y = \cos x$ for a number of values of the variable x, it may be more economical to have the computer "generate" $\cos x$ by evaluation of series approximations.

2.2 Errors

The results of approximate computations are affected by errors. Numerical errors arise from different causes and affect final results in different ways. Hence, it is important to consider the nature of some types of errors before one analyzes computational procedures.

The error due to the representation of a number by a *finite* number of decimal digits is called a *round-off* error. For example, the roots

$$x_{1,2} = \frac{1}{3} \pm i\sqrt{2} \tag{a}$$

of the quadratic equation

$$9x^2 - 6x + 19 = 0 \tag{b}$$

are exact from the viewpoint of mathematical analysis, since they satisfy (b) exactly. But since these roots can be computed only to a finite number of decimals, they are affected by a round-off error whenever written in decimal form. Round-off errors usually affect the last retained digit of the decimal representation, although at times they may actually change many (.99999 + .00001 = 1.00000); their effects on the results can usually, but not always (see Sec. 7.8) be controlled by retaining additional digits.

Whenever a function $f(x)$ is represented by an infinite series (see Sec. 2.3), the error in the value of $f(x)$ due to cutting off its series after a finite number of terms is called a *truncation error*. The magnitude of the truncation error equals the sum of all the discarded terms: it may be large, and may even exceed the sum of the terms retained, thus making the calculated result meaningless. An accurate estimate of truncation errors is, therefore, essential.

If we write a decimal number in the form

$$N = a_0 + \frac{a_1}{10} + \frac{a_2}{10^2} + \frac{a_3}{10^3} + \cdots, \tag{c}$$

where the a_i are one-digit integers, we can see that round-off errors are of the same nature as truncation errors.

Certain numerical procedures, such as the integration of differential equations with initial values (see Sec. 2.1, Eq. (g)), are based on the repetition of a sequence of operations which use the last computed value, say y_n, to obtain the next value y_{n+1} of the requested function y. If the result of each sequence of operations is affected by an error, the errors usually add up and the nth value of y is affected by an *accumulated error*. The importance of accumulated errors depends on their rate of accumulation. If the rate of accumulation decreases so that the error is bounded, the sequence of operations is said to be *stable*. It is *unstable* if the rate increases so that the accumulated error also increases and eventually makes the solution meaningless. On the other hand, even if the accumulated error increases, the accumulated *relative error*, i.e., the error divided by y, may decrease so that the solution may still be meaningful for many applications. The analysis of the stability of a sequence of operations is usually complex, but it is of fundamental importance in numerical analysis.

One should not use an approximate method of calculation unless its inherent error can be estimated. Expressions for errors will be given in the following sections, whenever possible, but most often only *error estimates* are available. These indicate the order of magnitude of the error in terms either of significant or of decimal figures.

The number of digits to be carried in a computation to guarantee a given number of correct significant figures in the results depends essentially on the operations involved and must be carefully gauged in order to avoid numerically meaningless answers. As an elementary example, subtraction of numbers of like magnitude often leads to the loss of many figures. The operation $D = ad - bc$, typical of the evaluation of determinants, is a common source of this trouble. For example, with $a = \frac{5}{17}$, $b = \frac{7}{18}$, $c = \frac{5}{18}$, $d = \frac{7}{19}$, and carrying 5 decimal figures in the calculations, D gives

$$D = (.29411)(.36842) - (.38888)(.27777)$$

$$= .10835 - .10801 = .00034,$$

with a loss of 3 significant figures out of $5 (D = \frac{35}{104652} = .00033444)$.

2.3 Taylor Series Expansions [Program 2.3]

The representation of a function $f(x)$ as an infinite power series of its variable x is one of the basic tools of numerical analysis and will be used frequently in subsequent chapters. Its main features are briefly reviewed in this section.

Let $f(x)$ be a function with derivatives of all orders at $x = x_0$, and assume that in a neighborhood of x_0, $f(x)$ may be represented by the power series in $x - x_0$:

$$f(x) \equiv c_0 + c_1(x - x_0) + c_2(x - x_0)^2 + \cdots = \sum_{n=0}^{\infty} c_n(x - x_0)^n. \qquad \textbf{(a)}$$

Under widely satisfied conditions the derivatives of $f(x)$ may be obtained by differentiating the series (a) term by term:

$$f'(x) = \sum_{n=1}^{\infty} nc_n(x - x_0)^{n-1} = c_1 + 2c_2(x - x_0) + 3c_3(x - x_0)^2$$
$$+ \cdots, \quad \text{(b)}$$

$$f''(x) = \sum_{n=2}^{\infty} n(n - 1)c_n(x - x_0)^{n-2} = 2 \cdot 1c_2 + 3 \cdot 2c_3(x - x_0)$$
$$+ \cdots, \quad \text{(c)}$$

. . . .

$$f^{(m)}(x) = \sum_{n=m}^{\infty} n(n - 1)(n - 2) \cdots (n - m + 1)c_n(x - x_0)^{n-m}$$

$$= \sum_{n=m}^{\infty} \frac{n!}{(n - m)!} c_n(x - x_0)^{n-m} \quad \text{(d)}$$

$$= m! c_m + (m + 1)! c_{m+1}(x - x_0) + \cdots.$$

Setting $x = x_0$ on both sides of (a), (b), (c), and (d), we find

$$f(x_0) = c_0 \quad \text{or} \quad c_0 = f(x_0),$$

$$f'(x_0) = c_1 \quad \text{or} \quad c_1 = f'(x_0),$$

$$f''(x_0) = 2c_2 \quad \text{or} \quad c_2 = \frac{f''(x_0)}{2},$$

. . . .

$$f^{(m)}(x_0) = m! c_m \quad \text{or} \quad c_m = \frac{f^{(m)}(x_0)}{m!},$$

by means of which (a) becomes

$$f(x) = \sum_{n=0}^{\infty} \frac{f^{(n)}(x_0)}{n!} (x - x_0)^n, \quad \text{(2.3.1)}$$

where

$$f^{(n)}(x_0) \equiv \left. \frac{d^n f}{dx^n} \right|_{x=x_0}, \quad f^{(0)}(x_0) \equiv f(x_0) \quad \text{and} \quad 0! = 1.$$

Equation (2.3.1) is the *Taylor series expansion* of $f(x)$ about $x = x_0$, and shows that a complete knowledge of the behavior of $f(x)$ at a point x_0 determines the value of the function at any point x at which the series converges. Thus, the Taylor series *extrapolates* the values of $f(x)$ from a knowledge of the behavior of the function at $x = x_0$.

It is often useful to represent a Taylor series in a slightly different form. If x is replaced by $x_0 + x$, (2.3.1) becomes

$$f(x_0 + x) = \sum_{n=0}^{\infty} \frac{f^{(n)}(x_0)}{n!} x^n. \quad \text{(2.3.2)}$$

In this form, x is the distance between x_0 and the point where the function is to be evaluated. Setting $x_0 = 0$ in either (2.3.1) or (2.3.2), we find the *Maclaurin series expansion*:

$$f(x) = \sum_{n=0}^{\infty} \frac{f^{(n)}(0)}{n!} x^n. \tag{2.3.3}$$

The Maclaurin series expansion applied to $f(x) = (1 + x)^n$ gives the *binomial series*

$$(1 + x)^n = 1 + nx + \frac{n(n-1)}{2} x^2 + \frac{n(n-1)(n-2)}{3 \cdot 2} x^3 + \cdots, \tag{2.3.4}$$

which always converges for $|x| < 1$.

In the numerical evaluation of a function by (2.3.1), the series is truncated after a finite number of terms, say m. It may be shown by the theorem of the mean that the truncation error after the mth term is given by

$$R_m = \frac{f^{(m)}(\bar{x})}{m!} (x - x_0)^m, \qquad x_0 \le \bar{x} \le x, \tag{2.3.5}$$

where the exact location of $\bar{x}$ usually is not known. However, (2.3.5) may be used to obtain an upper bound of the truncation error by replacing $f^{(m)}(\bar{x})$ with an upper bound $M^{(m)}$ to its values in the interval (x_0, x). The truncation error is then bounded by

$$|R_m| \le \left| \frac{M^{(m)}}{m!} (x - x_0)^m \right|. \tag{2.3.6}$$

When a *convergent* power series has terms which decrease in absolute value and alternate in sign, the truncation error after m terms cannot exceed the $(m + 1)$th term. Thus, in particular, for a Taylor series *with alternating signs*, and decreasing terms,

$$|R_m| \le \left| \frac{f^{(m)}(x_0)}{m!} (x - x_0)^m \right|, \tag{2.3.7}$$

in which the mth derivative is computed at x_0 rather than at $\bar{x}$ as in (2.3.5).

Example 2.3.1. Expand $f(x) = \ln x$ into a Taylor series about $x_0 = 1$.

$$f^{(0)}(x_0) = \ln 1 = 0; \quad f^{(n)}(x) = (-1)^{n-1}(n-1)!\, x^{-(n-1)};$$

$$f^{(n)}(x_0) = (-1)^{n-1}(n-1)!(1)^{-(n-1)} = (-1)^{n-1}(n-1)!;$$

$$\frac{1}{n!} f^{(n)}(x_0) = (-1)^{n-1} \frac{(n-1)!}{n!} = (-1)^{n-1} \frac{1}{n};$$

$$\ln x = \sum_{n=1}^{\infty} \frac{(-1)^{n-1}}{n} (x - 1)^n; \quad |R_m| \le \frac{(x-1)^m}{m} \quad \text{[by (2.3.7)]}.$$

To obtain ln 1.1 to three decimal places the remainder must be less than $0.0005 = \frac{1}{2}10^{-3}$ in absolute value. Hence,

$$|R_m| \leq \frac{(1.1 - 1.0)^m}{m} = \frac{(.1)^m}{m} < \frac{1}{2} 10^{-3} \quad \therefore \quad m \geq 3;$$

$$\ln 1.1 = 0. + .1 - \frac{1}{2}(.1)^2 = .095 \quad [.09531];$$

$$R_3 \leq \frac{10^{-3}}{3} = .00033 \quad [.00031].$$

Example 2.3.2. Expand $f(x) = e^x$ into a Maclaurin series and compute $e^{.1}$ to three decimal figures.

$$f^{(n)}(x) = e^x; \quad f^{(n)}(0) = 1; \quad M^{(m)} = e^x;$$

$$e^x = \sum_{n=0}^{\infty} \frac{x^n}{n!}; \quad |R_m| \leq e^x \frac{|x^m|}{m!} \quad [\text{by } (2.3.6)].$$

To compute $e^{.1}$ to three decimal places:

$$R_m \leq e^{.1} \frac{(.1)^m}{m!} \doteq \left[1 + .1 + \frac{1}{2!}(.1)^2 + \cdots + \frac{1}{m!}(.1)^m\right]\frac{(.1)^m}{m!}$$

$$< \frac{1}{2} 10^{-3} \quad \therefore \quad m \geq 3;$$

$$e^{.1} = 1. + .1 + \frac{1}{2}(.1)^2 = 1.105 \quad [1.1052];$$

$$R_3 < .0002 \quad [.0002].$$

Example 2.3.3. Expand $f(x) = \cos x$ into a Maclaurin series and compute $\cos .2$ to four decimal places.

$$f^{(n)}(x) = \begin{cases} (-1)^{n/2} \cos x, & n \text{ even}; \\ (-1)^{(n+1)/2} \sin x, & n \text{ odd}; \end{cases}$$

$$f^{(n)}(0) = \begin{cases} (-1)^{n/2}, & n \text{ even}; \\ 0, & n \text{ odd}. \end{cases}$$

$$\cos x = \sum_{n=0,2,4,\ldots}^{\infty} (-1)^{n/2} \frac{x^n}{n!}; \quad |R_m| \leq \frac{|x^m|}{m!} \quad [\text{by } (2.3.7)].$$

To compute $\cos .2$ to four decimal places:

$$|R_m| \leq \frac{(.2)^m}{m!} = \frac{2^m}{m!} 10^{-m} < \frac{1}{2} 10^{-4} \quad \therefore \quad m \geq 5$$

and, since the term $m = 5$ is zero,

$$\cos .2 = 1. + 0. - \frac{(.2)^2}{2!} + 0. + \frac{(.2)^4}{4!} + 0. = .9800667 \quad [.9800666];$$

$$|R_6| \leq \frac{(.2)^6}{6!} = .9 \times 10^{-7} \quad [1. \times 10^{-7}].$$

Example 2.3.4. Evaluate $\sqrt{1+x}$ to two decimal places at $x = .4$.

$$\sqrt{1+x} = (1+x)^{1/2} = 1 + \frac{1}{2}x - \frac{1}{8}x^2 + \frac{1}{16}x^3 - \frac{5}{128}x^4 + \cdots.$$

To evaluate $\sqrt{1 + .4}$ to two decimal places, by (2.3.7):

$$1 + \frac{1}{2}(.4) - \frac{1}{8}(.4)^2 = 1.18 \quad [1.183];$$

$$|R_3| < \frac{(.4)^3}{16} = .004 \quad [.003].$$

The *Taylor series of a function* $z = f(x, y)$ *of two independent variables* x, y about the point (x_0, y_0) is obtained from (2.3.2) by incrementing *one of the variables at a time*. Indicating the partial derivatives of $z(x, y)$ by

$$f_x = \frac{\partial z}{\partial x}, f_y = \frac{\partial z}{\partial y}, f_{xx} = \frac{\partial^2 z}{\partial x^2}, f_{xy} = \frac{\partial^2 z}{\partial x \, \partial y}, f_{yy} = \frac{\partial^2 z}{\partial y^2}, \cdots, \qquad \text{(e)}$$

(2.3.2) applied to $f(x_0 + x, y_0)$, i.e., to the function f considered as a function of x only while y_0 is kept constant, gives

$$f(x_0 + x, y_0) = f(x_0, y_0) + f_x(x_0, y_0) \frac{x}{1!} + f_{xx}(x_0, y_0) \frac{x^2}{2!} + \cdots,$$

from which, changing y_0 into $y_0 + y$ on both sides of the equation,

$$f(x_0 + x, y_0 + y) = f(x_0, y_0 + y) + f_x(x_0, y_0 + y) \frac{x}{1!}$$

$$+ f_{xx}(x_0, y_0 + y) \frac{x^2}{2!} + \cdots. \qquad \text{(f)}$$

Expanding by means of (2.3.2) the coefficient of each power of x in (f) into a power series in y about y_0, while x_0 is kept constant, we obtain

$$f(x_0, y_0 + y) = f(x_0, y_0) + f_y(x_0, y_0) \frac{y}{1!} + f_{yy}(x_0, y_0) \frac{y^2}{2!} + \cdots,$$

$$f_x(x_0, y_0 + y) = f_x(x_0, y_0) + f_{xy}(x_0, y_0) \frac{y}{1!} + f_{xyy}(x_0, y_0) \frac{y^2}{2!} + \cdots, \qquad \text{(g)}$$

$$f_{xx}(x_0, y_0 + y) = f_{xx}(x_0, y_0) + f_{xxy}(x_0, y_0) \frac{y}{1!} + f_{xxyy}(x_0, y_0) \frac{y^2}{2!} + \cdots$$

. . . .

Substituting (g) in (f), the Taylor series expansion of $f(x, y)$ about x_0, y_0 becomes

$$f(x_0 + x, y_0 + y)$$
$$= f(x_0, y_0) + [f_x(x_0, y_0)x + f_y(x_0, y_0)y]$$
$$+ \frac{1}{2!} [f_{xx}(x_0, y_0)x^2 + 2f_{xy}(x_0, y_0)xy + f_{yy}(x_0, y_0)y^2] \qquad \text{(2.3.8)}$$

$$+ \frac{1}{3!} [f_{xxx}(x_0, y_0)x^3 + 3f_{xxy}(x_0, y_0)x^2y$$
$$+ 3f_{xyy}(x_0, y_0)xy^2 + f_{yyy}(x_0, y_0)y^3] + \cdots.$$

Example 2.3.5. Expand $f(x, y) = \cos xy$ about $x_0 = \pi/2$, $y_0 = \frac{1}{2}$ up to second-order terms.

$$f_x = -y \sin xy; \quad f_y = -x \sin xy; \quad f_{xx} = -y^2 \cos xy;$$

$$f_{xy} = -\sin xy - xy \cos xy; \quad f_{yy} = -x^2 \cos xy;$$

$$f\left(\frac{\pi}{2}, \frac{1}{2}\right) = \frac{\sqrt{2}}{2};$$

$$f_x\left(\frac{\pi}{2}, \frac{1}{2}\right) = -\frac{1}{2}\frac{\sqrt{2}}{2}; \quad f_y\left(\frac{\pi}{2}, \frac{1}{2}\right) = -\frac{\pi}{2}\frac{\sqrt{2}}{2};$$

$$f_{xx}\left(\frac{\pi}{2}, \frac{1}{2}\right) = -\frac{1}{4}\frac{\sqrt{2}}{2}; \quad f_{xy}\left(\frac{\pi}{2}, \frac{1}{2}\right) = -\frac{\sqrt{2}}{2}\left(1 + \frac{\pi}{4}\right);$$

$$f_{yy}\left(\frac{\pi}{2}, \frac{1}{2}\right) = -\frac{\pi^2}{4}\frac{\sqrt{2}}{2};$$

$$f\left(\frac{\pi}{2} + x, \frac{1}{2} + y\right)$$
$$= \frac{\sqrt{2}}{2}\left\{1 - \left(\frac{1}{2}x + \frac{\pi}{2}y\right) - \left[\frac{1}{8}x^2 + \left(1 + \frac{\pi}{4}\right)xy + \frac{\pi^2}{8}y^2\right]\right\}.$$

2.4 Synthetic Substitution [Programs 2.1, 4.7-A]

The evaluation of an nth-degree polynomial, e.g., a power series truncated after its $(n + 1)$th term

$$p_n(x) = a_n x^n + a_{n-1}x^{n-1} + \cdots + a_1 x + a_0, \qquad \text{(2.4.1)}$$

requires $n - 1$ multiplications to obtain the powers of x from x^2 to x^n, which, moreover, must be stored; n multiplications to obtain the $a_m x^m$ ($m = 1, 2, ..., n$); and n additions; or altogether $3n$ operations for large n.

Letting, instead,

$$P_n = a_n; \quad P_{n-1} = P_n x + a_{n-1}; \quad P_{n-2} = P_{n-1} x + a_{n-2}; \quad \ldots, \qquad (2.4.2)$$

$p_n(x)$ may be written in the form of *nested binomials*,

$$p_n(x) = (\cdots ((((a_n)x + a_{n-1})x + a_{n-2})x + a_{n-3})x + \cdots + a_1)x + a_0$$

$$\equiv P_0, \qquad (2.4.3)$$

and evaluated by the recurrence equations (2.4.2), which require n multiplications and n additions, or $2n$ operations, and avoid the storage of intermediate results. The operations indicated in (2.4.3) are those of synthetic substitution, a procedure illustrated in the first three rows of (2.4.4) for $n = 3$ and $x = b$.

$$p_3(x) = a_3 x^3 + a_2 x^2 + a_1 x + a_0. \qquad \text{(a)}$$

	a_3	a_2	a_1	a_0
$x = b$		$a_3 b$	$a_3 b^2 + a_2 b$	$a_3 b^3 + a_2 b^2 + a_1 b$
	a_3	$a_3 b + a_2$	$a_3 b^2 + a_2 b + a_1$	$a_3 b^3 + a_2 b^2 + a_1 b + a_0 = p_3(b)$
$x = b$		$a_3 b$	$2a_3 b^2 + a_2 b$	
	a_3	$2a_3 b + a_2$	$3a_3 b^2 + 2a_2 b + a_1 = p_3'(b)$	
$x = b$		$a_3 b$		(2.4.4)
	a_3	$3a_3 b + a_2 = \dfrac{1}{2!} p_3''(b)$		
$x = b$				
	$a_3 = \dfrac{1}{3!} p_3'''(b)$			

According to (2.4.2), each number on the third row of (2.4.4) is obtained by adding to the corresponding number of the first row the preceding number on the third row multiplied by b. To apply synthetic substitution successively the third row is used as starting row to obtain the fifth row; the fifth as starting row for the seventh, and so forth. The last computed numbers on the third, fifth, $\ldots$, $(2n + 3)$rd rows are equal to $p_n(b)$, $(1/1!)p_n'(b)$, $\ldots$, $(1/n!)p_n^{(n)}(b)$. The coefficients of the powers of x not appearing in $p_n(x)$ must be written as zeros in the scheme for synthetic substitution.

Letting $x = b + z$ and expanding $p_n(b + z)$ into a (finite) power series about $x_0 = b$ by (2.3.2),

$$p_n(x) \equiv p_n(b + z) = p_n(b) + p_n'(b)z + \frac{1}{2!} p_n''(b)z^2 \qquad (2.4.5)$$

$$+ \cdots + \frac{1}{n!} p_n^{(n)}(b)z^n,$$

it is seen that n successive substitutions also give the coefficients of $p_n(b + z)$. For example, in order to obtain the $p_3(b + z)$ corresponding to (a) but lacking the z^2 term, $(1/2!)p_3''(b)$ must be set equal to zero and the corresponding value of b is, by (2.4.4),

$$b = -\frac{a_2}{3a_3}.$$ **(b)**

In general the coefficient of x^{n-1} will vanish in $p_n(b + z)$ if

$$b = -\frac{a_{n-1}}{na_n}.$$ **(2.4.6)**

Example 2.4.1. Reduce to zero the coefficient of x^3 in the equation $p_4(x) = 2x^4 - 8x^3 + 2x + 3$.

$$b = -\frac{-8}{4 \cdot 2} = 1; \quad z = x - 1 \quad \text{[by (2.4.6)]}.$$

	2	−8	0	2	3
$b = 1$		2	− 6	− 6	− 4
	2	−6	− 6	− 4	− 1 = $p_4(1)$
$b = 1$		2	− 4	−10	
	2	−4	−10	−14 = $p_4'(1)$	
$b = 1$		2	− 2		
	2	−2	$-12 = \frac{1}{2!}p_4''(1)$		
$b = 1$		2			
	2	$0 = \frac{1}{3!}p_4'''(1)$			
$b = 1$					
	$2 = \frac{1}{4!}p_4^{iv}(1)$				

$$p_4(x) = 2(x - 1)^4 - 12(x - 1)^2 - 14(x - 1) - 1$$

2.5 Checking of Tables by Differences [Program 2.2]

The results of approximate computations must be checked whenever possible. Approximate roots of algebraic or transcendental equations are checked by direct substitution in the equation. The tabulated values of a function, which so often represent the final result of a series of computations, may be checked by means of *differences*.

Given the values $f_i = f(x_i)$ of a function, tabulated at *pivotal points* x_i evenly spaced by h along the x-axis,

$$x_i = x_0 + ih \qquad (i = 0, 1, 2, 3, \ldots), \tag{2.5.1}$$

we call first, second, third, ... *central* differences of $f(x)$ and indicate by δf, $\delta^2 f$, $\delta^3 f$, ..., the successive differences shown in Table 2.5.1. The odd

Table 2.5.1

i	x_i	f_i	δf_i	$\delta^2 f_i$	$\delta^3 f_i$	$\delta^4 f_i$	$\delta^5 f_i$	$\delta^6 f_i$
0	x_0	f_0						
1/2			$f_1 - f_0$					
1	x_1	f_1		$\delta f_{3/2} - \delta f_{1/2}$				
3/2			$f_2 - f_1$		$\delta^2 f_2 - \delta^2 f_1$			
2	x_2	f_2		$\delta f_{5/2} - \delta f_{3/2}$		$\delta^3 f_{5/2} - \delta^3 f_{3/2}$		
5/2			$f_3 - f_2$		$\delta^2 f_3 - \delta^2 f_2$		$\delta^4 f_3 - \delta^4 f_2$	
3	x_3	f_3		$\delta f_{7/2} - \delta f_{5/2}$		$\delta^3 f_{7/2} - \delta^3 f_{5/2}$		$\delta^5 f_{7/2} - \delta^5 f_{5/2}$
7/2			$f_4 - f_3$		$\delta^2 f_4 - \delta^2 f_3$		$\delta^4 f_4 - \delta^4 f_3$	
4	x_4	f_4		$\delta f_{9/2} - \delta f_{7/2}$		$\delta^3 f_{9/2} - \delta^3 f_{7/2}$		
9/2			$f_5 - f_4$		$\delta^2 f_5 - \delta^2 f_4$			
5	x_5	f_5		$\delta f_{11/2} - \delta f_{9/2}$				
11/2			$f_6 - f_5$					
6	x_6	f_6						

differences are tabulated at the "half-points," the even differences at the "pivotal points." From Table 2.5.1,

$$\delta f_{1/2} = f_1 - f_0; \quad \delta f_{3/2} = f_2 - f_1; \quad \delta f_{5/2} = f_3 - f_2; \quad \ldots;$$
$$\delta^2 f_1 = (f_2 - f_1) - (f_1 - f_0) = f_2 - 2f_1 + f_0;$$
$$\delta^2 f_2 = f_3 - 2f_2 + f_1; \quad \ldots; \tag{2.5.2}$$
$$\delta^3 f_{3/2} = (f_3 - 2f_2 + f_1) - (f_2 - 2f_1 + f_0) = f_3 - 3f_2 + 3f_1 - f_0; \quad \ldots.$$

It is seen from (2.5.2) that the coefficients of the f_i in $\delta^n f$ are those of the binomial expansion of $(a - b)^n$. Hence, for example,

$$\delta^4 f_2 = f_4 - 4f_3 + 6f_2 - 4f_1 + f_0,$$
$$\delta^5 f_{5/2} = f_5 - 5f_4 + 10f_3 - 10f_2 + 5f_1 - f_0. \tag{a}$$

It will be shown in Section 3.2 that $\delta^n f$ is approximately proportional to $h^n f^{(n)}(x)$, the more so the smaller the spacing h. Hence, whenever the magnitude of the derivatives $f^{(n)}(x)$ eventually decreases with an increase of the order n (most functions related to physical problems have this kind of behavior), the $\delta^n f$ in Table 2.5.1 become rapidly smaller with increasing n, particularly if $h \ll 1$.

Example 2.5.1. Table 2.5.2 contains the values of $f(x) = e^x$ at $x = 0.(.1)1.$, that is, for x from 0 to 1 in steps of $h = .1$, and shows how the successive differences

$$\delta^n f(x) \equiv \delta^n e^x \doteq h^n \frac{d^n e^x}{dx^n} = (.1)^n e^x$$

decrease as $(.1)^n$. The erratic values of $\delta^4 f_i$ are due to the rounding off of e^x to four decimal places.

Table 2.5.2

i	x_i	f_i	δf_i	$\delta^2 f_i$	$\delta^3 f_i$	$\delta^4 f_i$
0	0.	1.0000				
1/2			.1052			
1	.1	1.1052		.0110		
3/2			.1162		.0013	
2	.2	1.2214		.0123		−.0002
5/2			.1285		.0011	
3	.3	1.3499		.0134		+.0005
7/2			.1419		.0016	
4	.4	1.4918		.0150		−.0001
9/2			.1569		.0015	
5	.5	1.6487		.0165		+.0003
11/2			.1734		.0018	
6	.6	1.8221		.0183		−.0001
13/2			.1917		.0017	
7	.7	2.0138		.0200		+.0007
15/2			.2117		.0024	
8	.8	2.2255		.0224		−.0002
17/2			.2341		.0022	
9	.9	2.4596		.0246		
19/2			.2587			
10	1.	2.7183				

Let us now assume that the tabulated value f_5 has an error ϵ, i.e., appears as $f_5 + \epsilon$, and let us examine the effect of successively differencing ϵ (Table 2.5.3). The coefficients of ϵ in the nth differences are the coefficients of the binomial expansion of $(a - b)^n$. Hence, the successive differences of ϵ not only do not vanish, but are magnified according to a recognizable pattern. The $\delta^n f$, instead, generally tend to vanish. Therefore, for large enough values of n the $\delta^n(f + \epsilon)$ will in most cases be identical with the $\delta^n \epsilon$ and allow the evaluation of ϵ.

Table 2.5.3

i	ϵ	$\delta\epsilon$	$\delta^2\epsilon$	$\delta^3\epsilon$	$\delta^4\epsilon$
0	0				
1/2		0			
1	0		0		
3/2		0		0	
2	0		0		0
5/2		0		0	
3	0		0		ϵ
7/2		0		ϵ	
4	0		ϵ		-4ϵ
9/2		ϵ		-3ϵ	
5	ϵ		-2ϵ		$+6\epsilon$
11/2		$-\epsilon$		$+3\epsilon$	
6	0		ϵ		-4ϵ
13/2		0		$-\epsilon$	
7	0		0		$+\epsilon$
15/2		0		0	
8	0		0		0

Example 2.5.2. Correct the error in one of the values f_i of Table 2.5.4 by means of differences.

In Table 2.5.4, $f(x) = e^x$, but $f_5 = e^{.5}$ appears as 1.4687, rather than 1.6487, a transposition error easily made in copying numbers. The $\delta^4 f_i$ at $i = 3, 4, 5, 6, 7$ have ratios roughly proportional to $+1, -4, +6, -4, +1$. This indicates the existence of an error ϵ in f_5. The sum of the *absolute* values of the $\delta^4 f_i$ at $i = 3, 4, 5, 6, 7$ $(+2.8783)$ is thus approximately equal to $(1 + 4 + 6 + 4 + 1)|\epsilon| = 16|\epsilon|$, and

$$|\epsilon| = 2.8783/16 = 0.1799.$$

Table 2.5.4

i	x_i	f_i	δf	$\delta^2 f$	$\delta^3 f$	$\delta^4 f$
0	0.	1.0000				
1/2			.1052			
1	.1	1.1052		.0110		
3/2			.1162		.0013	
2	.2	1.2214		.0123		− .0020
5/2			.1285		.0011	
3	.3	1.3499		.0134		−.1795
7/2			+.1419		−.1784	
4	.4	1.4918		−.1650		+ .7199
9/2			−.0231		+.5415	
5	.5	1.4687		+.3765		−1.0797
11/2			.3534		−.5382	
6	.6	1.8221		−.1617		+ .7199
13/2			.1917		+.1817	
7	.7	2.0138		.0200		− .1793
15/2			.2117		.0024	
8	.8	2.2255		.0224		− .0002
17/2			.2341		+.0022	
9	.9	2.4596		−.0246		
19/2			−.2587			
10	1.	2.7183				

Since $\delta^4 f_5 \doteq 6\epsilon = -1.0797$ is negative, $\epsilon = -0.1799$ and $f_5 = 1.4687 - (-0.1799) = 1.6486$, with an error of one unit in the last digit.

Obviously the difference check may fail if two or more near values f_i, f_j, . . . are affected by errors ϵ_i, ϵ_j, . . ., since all the errors spread through the table and eventually interfere with each other, marring the pattern of proportionality of the coefficients of $(a - b)^n$.

PROBLEMS

2.1 From a table for the powers of x, establish the number of *significant* figures n_1, n_2 which must be carried in the computations to evaluate the following functions to three significant figures at $x = 1.1$ and at $x = .5$, respectively, rounding off the final results.

(a) $y = x^4 - x^3$

(b) $\dfrac{x^4 - x^3}{10 - x}$

(c) $y = \dfrac{x^4 - x^2}{x - 1}$

(d) $y = \dfrac{(x - 1)^3}{10 + x}$

2.2 From a table for the exponential function e^x, determine the number of *significant* figures n_1, n_2 which must be carried at all times in the computations to evaluate the following functions to three decimal figures at $x = .1$ and $x = 1.1$, respectively, without rounding off the final results.

(a) $y = .1e^x$

(b) $y = \dfrac{e^x - 1}{e^x + 1}$

(c) $y = \frac{1}{2}(e^x - e^{-x})$

(d) $y = \frac{1}{2}(e^x + e^{-x})$

(e) $y = (e^x - 1)^3$

(f) $y = (e^x - 1)^{1/2}$

2.3 Derive the Maclaurin expansions of the following functions and establish the number of terms n required to obtain their correct values to two decimal figures at $x = .5$.

(a) $y = \sqrt{1 + x}$

(b) $y = \sqrt{1 - x^2}$

(c) $y = \sqrt[4]{1 - x^4}$

(d) $y = 1/\sqrt{1 + x}$

(e) $y = \sinh x$

(f) $y = \tanh x$

(g) $y = \cos 3x$

(h) $y = \sin (\pi/6 + x)$

2.4 Derive the Taylor expansions of the following functions about $x_0 = 1$, and determine the number of terms n required to obtain their correct values to two decimal figures at $x = 1.1$.

(a) $y = e^x$

(b) $y = \dfrac{1}{x}$

(c) $y = \sqrt{x}$

(d) $y = \frac{1}{3} e^{2x}$

2.5 Derive the Taylor expansions of the following functions about $x_0 = 0$, $y_0 = 0$, up to second-order terms; evaluate the expansions at $x = .3$, $y = .2$; and compare them with the values of z at this point.

(a) $z = x^2 - y^2$

(b) $z = \cos (x - y)$

(c) $z = \sin (x^2 - y^2)$

(d) $z = e^{xy}$

(e) $z = xe^y - ye^x$

2.6 Evaluate the following nth-degree polynomials and their first n derivatives at $x = 2$, by repeated synthetic substitution.

(a) $p_3 = 2x^3 + 3x^2 + x - 1$

(b) $p_4 = x^4 - 2x^2 + x + 2$

(c) $p_4 = x^4 - x^3 + 1$

(d) $p_5 = x^5 - 3x^2 + 3x - 1$

2.7 Given the following polynomials $p_n(x)$, evaluate the coefficients of the polynomials $p_n(b + x)$, which have the coefficient of x^{n-1} equal to zero.

(a) $p_3(x) = x^3 + 4x^2 - 2x + 2$

(b) $p_4(x) = 2x^4 + 16x^3 - x + 1$

(c) $p_4(x) = x^4 + x^3 + x^2 + 1$

2.8 Evaluate the first four central differences of the functions $f(x)$ given in the following tables.

(a) f_i	0.	.09531	.18232	.26236	.33647	.40547	
(b) f_i	.43429	.86856	1.30288	1.73718	2.17147	2.60577	3.04006
(c) f_i	2.236	2.345	2.449	2.550	2.646	2.739	2.828
(d) f_i	.3420	.3584	.3746	.3907	.4067	.4226	

2.9 Determine by successive differences the error in one of the tabulated values f_i of the following tables.

(a) f_i	.5000	.5150	.5299	.5646	.5592	.5736	.5878	
(b) f_i	1.000	1.225	1.514	1.581	1.732	1.871	2.000	
(c) f_i	.84270	.88021	.93011	.93401	.95229	.96611	.97635	.98379
(d) f_i	1.5708	1.5828	1.6200	1.7868	1.7868	1.9356	2.1565	2.5046

Differentiation, Integration, Interpolation, and Extrapolation

Chapter Three

3.1 Pivotal Points

The numerical evaluation of a function $f(x)$ is usually required at discrete points x_i of the x-axis. When these *pivotal points* are evenly spaced by h, as is often the case, they are given by

$$x_i = x_0 \pm ih \qquad (i = 0, 1, 2, 3, \ldots), \tag{3.1.1}$$

where $f(x)$ has the *pivotal values* $f_i = f(x_i)$ (Figure 3.1.1). The value f_j of $f(x)$ at any pivotal point x_j can be expressed, in terms of $f(x)$ and its derivatives at another pivotal point x_i, by means of a Taylor series expansion about x_i. Thus, if

$$x_j = x_{i \pm m} = x_i \pm mh, \tag{3.1.2}$$

one obtains by (2.3.2) with $x_0 = x_i$ and $x = \pm mh$

$$f_j = f(x_i \pm mh) = f_i \pm mh f_i' + \frac{(mh)^2}{2!} f_i'' \pm \frac{(mh)^3}{3!} f_i''' + \cdots. \tag{3.1.3}$$

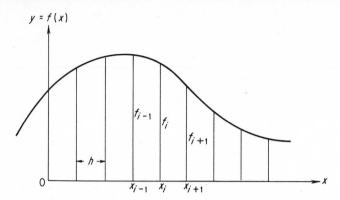

Figure 3.1.1

In particular, with $m = 1$ and $m = 2$, we find the following expressions for $f(x)$ at the two pivotal points on either side of x_i:

$$f_{i-2} = f_i - 2hf_i' + 2h^2f_i'' - \frac{4h^3}{3}f_i''' + \cdots, \tag{3.1.4a}$$

$$f_{i-1} = f_i - hf_i' + \frac{h^2}{2}f_i'' - \frac{h^3}{6}f_i''' + \cdots, \tag{3.1.4b}$$

$$f_{i+1} = f_i + hf_i' + \frac{h^2}{2}f_i'' + \frac{h^3}{6}f_i''' + \cdots, \tag{3.1.4c}$$

$$f_{i+2} = f_i + 2hf_i' + 2h^2f_i'' + \frac{4h^3}{3}f_i''' + \cdots. \tag{3.1.4d}$$

3.2 Differentiation Formulas [Program 3.1]

Approximate expressions for the derivatives of $f(x)$ at x_i, in terms of the values of $f(x)$ at adjoining pivotal points, may be obtained by Taylor series expansions. For example, solution of (3.1.4c) for f_i' gives the exact expression

$$f_i' = \frac{f_{i+1} - f_i}{h} - \left(\frac{h}{2}f_i'' + \frac{h^2}{6}f_i''' + \cdots\right), \tag{3.2.1}$$

from which, neglecting the terms in parentheses, we obtain the approximate expression

$$f_i' \doteq \frac{1}{h}(f_{i+1} - f_i). \tag{3.2.2}$$

The error e_i in (3.2.2) is given by the terms in parentheses in (3.2.1); e_i approaches zero as h approaches zero. Dropping the higher-order terms in h in comparison with the first, the error e_i in (3.2.2) is approximately

$$e_i \doteq -\frac{h}{2}f_i'', \tag{3.2.3}$$

i.e., e_i is of order h.

A second exact expression for f_i' is found by subtracting (3.1.4b) from (3.1.4c):

$$f_i' = \frac{f_{i+1} - f_{i-1}}{2h} - \left(\frac{h^2}{6}f_i''' + \cdots\right). \tag{3.2.4}$$

The approximate expression for f_i',

$$f_i' = \frac{f_{i+1} - f_{i-1}}{2h}, \tag{3.2.5}$$

is thus seen to have an error of order h^2.

Similarly, an expression for f_i'' is found by adding (3.1.4b) and (3.1.4c),

$$f_i'' = \frac{1}{h^2}(f_{i+1} - 2f_i + f_{i-1}) - \frac{h^2}{12}f_i^{iv} + \cdots, \tag{3.2.6}$$

from which the corresponding approximate expression is seen to have an error of order h^2.

Table 3.2.1 contains approximate expressions for derivatives up to order four, involving from two to five pivotal points and *valid at the point with the* **boldface** *coefficient.* The table also gives the corresponding errors.

To illustrate, the 4-point formula for f_i' of (3.2.9) reads

$$f_i' = \frac{1}{6h}(-11f_i + 18f_{i+1} - 9f_{i+2} + 2f_{i+3}),$$

with an error $-h^3 f^{iv}/4$, while the 5-point formula for f_i'' of (3.2.20) reads

$$f_i'' = \frac{1}{12h^2}(11f_{i-1} - 20f_i + 6f_{i+1} + 4f_{i+2} - f_{i+3}),$$

with an error $h^3 f^v/12$. The reader will notice that the coefficients of each of these formulas must add up to zero, since when all the f_i are equal to 1, $f(x)$ is constant, and all the derivatives of a constant are zero. Further, any formula "slanted" to the right (or left) in Table 3.2.1 gives rise to an equivalent formula slanted in the opposite direction by changing the sign of all the coefficients. For example, given the formula slanted to the right of (3.2.24),

$$f_i''' = \frac{1}{h^3}(-f_{i-1} + 3f_i - 3f_{i+1} + f_{i+2}),$$

the corresponding formula slanted to the left is

$$f_i''' = \frac{1}{h^3}(-f_{i-2} + 3f_{i-1} - 3f_i + f_{i+1}).$$

Table 3.2.1

$h^n f^{(n)}$	Multiplier	Differentiation formula coefficients					Error in $f^{(n)}$	Equation
	1	-1	1				$-(1/2)hf''$	3.2.7
	1/2	-3	4	-1			$(1/3)h^2 f'''$	3.2.8
	1/6	-11	18	-9	2		$-(1/4)h^3 f^{\mathrm{iv}}$	3.2.9
	1/12	-25	48	-36	16	-3	$(1/5)h^4 f^{\mathrm{v}}$	3.2.10
hf'	1/2	-1	0	1			$-(1/6)h^2 f'''$	3.2.11
	1/6	-2	-3	6	-1		$(1/12)h^3 f^{\mathrm{iv}}$	3.2.12
	1/12	-3	-10	18	-6	1	$-(1/20)h^4 f^{\mathrm{v}}$	3.2.13
	1/12	1	-8	0	8	-1	$(1/30)h^4 f^{\mathrm{v}}$	3.2.14
	1	1	-2	1			$-hf'''$	3.2.15
	1	2	-5	4	-1		$(11/12)h^2 f^{\mathrm{iv}}$	3.2.16
	1/12	35	-104	114	-56	11	$-(5/6)h^3 f^{\mathrm{v}}$	3.2.17
$h^2 f''$	1	1	-2	1			$-(1/12)h^2 f^{\mathrm{iv}}$	3.2.18
	1	1	-2	1	0		$-(1/12)h^2 f^{\mathrm{iv}}$	3.2.19
	1/12	11	-20	6	4	-1	$(1/12)h^3 f^{\mathrm{v}}$	3.2.20
	1/12	-1	16	-30	16	-1	$(1/90)h^4 f^{\mathrm{v}}$	3.2.21
	1	-1	3	-3	1		$-(3/2)hf^{\mathrm{iv}}$	3.2.22
	1/2	-5	18	-24	14	-3	$(7/4)h^2 f^{\mathrm{v}}$	3.2.23
$h^3 f'''$	1	-1	3	-3	1		$-(1/2)hf^{\mathrm{iv}}$	3.2.24
	1/2	-3	10	-12	6	-1	$(1/4)h^2 f^{\mathrm{v}}$	3.2.25
	1/2	-1	2	0	-2	1	$-(1/4)h^2 f^{\mathrm{v}}$	3.2.26
	1	1	-4	6	-4	1	$-2hf^{\mathrm{v}}$	3.2.27
$h^4 f^{\mathrm{iv}}$	1	1	-4	6	-4	1	$-hf^{\mathrm{v}}$	3.2.28
	1	1	-4	6	-4	1	$-(1/6)h^2 f^{\mathrm{v}}$	3.2.29

Differentiation formulas for higher derivatives are obtained from Table 3.2.1 by "shifting" operators, i.e., by applying, successively, two lower derivative operators. For example, to obtain a centered sixth-derivative formula, apply (3.2.18) for the second derivative to (3.2.29) for the fourth derivative:

$$
\begin{array}{rrrrrrrr}
(1)(1 & -4 & 6 & -4 & 1 & &) \\
(-2)(& 1 & -4 & 6 & -4 & 1 &) \\
(1)(& & 1 & -4 & 6 & -4 & 1) \\
\hline
= \quad (1 & -6 & 15 & -20 & 15 & -6 & 1) = h^6 f^{\mathrm{vi}}.
\end{array}
$$

(3.2.30)

The product of the respective multipliers (in this case $1 \times 1 = 1$) gives the new multiplier.

Formulas derived in this manner are valid at the boldface point of the second operator which is multiplied by the boldface point coefficient of the first operator. Thus, a 7-point, fifth-derivative formula, slanted to the right, may be obtained by applying the first-derivative operator (3.2.8) to the fourth-derivative operator (3.2.29). The new multiplier is $(\frac{1}{2})(1) = \frac{1}{2}$ and the resultant expression is

$$
\begin{array}{l}
(\tfrac{1}{2})(-\mathbf{3})(\quad 1 \quad -4 \quad\quad 6 \quad -4 \quad\quad 1 \quad\quad\quad\quad) \\
(\tfrac{1}{2})(\quad 4)(\quad\quad\quad 1 \quad -4 \quad\quad 6 \quad -4 \quad\quad 1 \quad\quad) \\
(\tfrac{1}{2})(-1)(\quad\quad\quad\quad\quad 1 \quad -4 \quad\quad 6 \quad -4 \quad\quad 1) \\
\hline
= \quad (\tfrac{1}{2})(-\mathbf{3} \quad 16 \quad -\mathbf{35} \quad 40 \quad -25 \quad 8 \quad -1) = h^5 f^{\mathbf{v}}.
\end{array}
\tag{3.2.31}
$$

The error in an m-point formula for the nth derivative is of order $m - n$, except in *centered even*-derivative formulas for which the error is of order $m - n + 1$, as is also apparent from Table 3.2.1.

The differentiation formulas obtained in this section may also be derived by passing $(m - 1)$st-degree parabolas through m pivotal points and approximating the derivatives of $f(x)$ by the derivatives of the parabolas. This method offers a geometric interpretation of the approximation, but does not allow an estimate of the error. Approximations to derivatives of various orders at a point, and to each derivative at several points, may be obtained from a single parabola. For example, let

$$
p_2(x) = A_2(x - x_i)^2 + A_1(x - x_i) + A_0
\tag{3.2.32}
$$

be a quadratic parabola passing through the points f_{i-1}, f_i, and f_{i+1}. A_2, A_1, and A_0 are determined by the three equations

$$
f_{i-1} = p_2(x_i - h) = A_2 h^2 - A_1 h + A_0,
\tag{3.2.33a}
$$

$$
f_i = p_2(x_i) = A_0,
\tag{3.2.33b}
$$

$$
f_{i+1} = p_2(x_i + h) = A_2 h^2 + A_1 h + A_0,
\tag{3.2.33c}
$$

to be

$$
A_2 = \frac{1}{2h^2}(f_{i+1} - 2f_i + f_{i-1}),
\tag{3.2.34a}
$$

$$
A_1 = \frac{1}{2h}(f_{i+1} - f_{i-1}),
\tag{3.2.34b}
$$

$$
A_0 = f_i.
\tag{3.2.34c}
$$

The first and second derivatives of the parabola (3.2.32) are

$$
p_2'(x) = 2A_2(x - x_i) + A_1,
$$

and

$$
p_2''(x) = 2A_2.
$$

Hence, with the coefficients (3.2.34), the first derivative at x_{i-1}, x_i, and x_{i+1} is approximated by

$$f'_{i-1} = p'_2(x_i - h) = \frac{-f_{i+1} + 4f_i - 3f_{i-1}}{2h}, \qquad \text{(3.2.35a)}$$

$$f'_i = p'_2(x_i) = \frac{f_{i+1} - f_{i-1}}{2h}, \qquad \text{(3.2.35b)}$$

$$f'_{i+1} = p'_2(x_i + h) = \frac{3f_{i+1} - 4f_i + f_{i-1}}{2h}, \qquad \text{(3.2.35c)}$$

while the second derivative at all three points is approximated by

$$f''_{i-1} = f''_i = f''_{i+1} = \frac{f_{i+1} - 2f_i + f_{i-1}}{h^2}. \qquad \text{(3.2.36)}$$

The expressions (3.2.35), (3.2.36) for f'_i and f''_i are seen to be identical with those [(3.2.5), (3.2.6)] derived from Taylor series. Remembering (2.5.2), we may notice from (3.2.2) that

$$hf'_i \doteq f_{i+1} - f_i = \delta f_{i+1/2},$$

and from (3.2.6) that

$$h^2 f''_i \doteq f_{i+1} - 2f_i + f_{i-1} = \delta^2 f_i.$$

It may similarly be shown, in general, that

$$h^n f^{(n)} \doteq \alpha \delta^n f, \qquad \text{(3.2.37)}$$

thus demonstrating the basic property of central differences used in the error detection of Section 2.5.

For differentiation formulas with unevenly spaced pivotal points, see N.M.*, Section 2.3.

Example 3.2.1. Given the following values of e^x:

i	0	1	2	3	4	5
x	0.	.1	.2	.3	.4	.5
$f(x) = e^x$	1.000000	1.105171	1.221403	1.349859	1.491825	1.648721

evaluate the indicated derivatives of $f(x)$ by the indicated formulas of Table 3.2.1 with the given h, compute the predicted error, and compare with the actual error.

---

* N.M. refers throughout to *Numerical Methods in Engineering*, Second Edition, by M. G. Salvadori and M. L. Baron, published by Prentice-Hall, Inc., Englewood Cliffs, N. J., 1961.

$f'(x)$ at $x = 0$, with $h = .1$, by (3.2.7):

$$f_0' = \frac{1.105171 - 1.000000}{.1} = 1.05171 \quad [1.].$$

Predicted error $= -\dfrac{h}{2} f_i'' = -\dfrac{.1}{2} (1.) = -.05 \quad [-0.05171].$

x	$f^{(n)}$	h	Formula	Value	Error e	Pred. e	Row
			(3.2.7)	1.05171	$-.05256$	$-.05171$	1
0.	f'	.1	(3.2.8)	.99640	$+.00368$	$+.00360$	2
			(3.2.9)	1.00028	$-.00029$	$-.00028$	3
			(3.2.10)	.99998	$+.00002$	$+.00002$	4
	f''	.2	(3.2.19)	1.225475	$-.004071$	$-.004072$	5
.2		.1	(3.2.19)	1.222400	$-.001018$	$-.000997$	6
	f^{iv}	.1	(3.2.29)	1.230000	$-.002036$	$-.008597$	7

3.3 Integration Formulas [Program 3.2]

The integral of a function $f(x)$ may be obtained by integrating its Taylor series expansion term by term. Approximate formulas, together with the corresponding errors, may then be determined from the integrated series.

Let $I_n(i)$ indicate the integral of $f(x)$ from $x = x_i$ to $x = x_{i+n}$, i.e., over n strips of width h starting at x_i (Figure 3.3.1):

$$I_n(i) = \int_{x_i}^{x_i + nh} f(x) \, dx = \int_0^{nh} f(x_i + z) \, dz. \qquad \textbf{(3.3.1)}$$

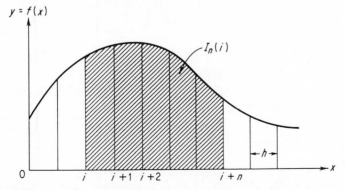

Figure 3.3.1

Upon substitution of the Taylor series for $f(x_i + z)$ about x_i,

$$f(x_i + z) = f_i + zf_i' + \frac{z^2}{2}f_i'' + \cdots, \tag{3.3.2}$$

and upon integration with respect to z, (3.3.1) becomes

$$I_n(i) = (nh)f_i + \frac{(nh)^2}{2}f_i' + \frac{(nh)^3}{6}f_i'' + \cdots. \tag{3.3.3}$$

If the derivatives in (3.3.3) are replaced by m-point differentiation formulas of the type given in Table 3.2.1, approximate expressions $I_{nm}(i)$ for $I_n(i)$ are obtained in terms of the pivotal values of $f(x)$. For example, when the 2-point formula (3.2.7) for f_i',

$$f_i' = \frac{-f_i + f_{i+1}}{h} - \frac{h}{2}f_i'' + \cdots,$$

is used, (3.3.3) becomes

$$I_{n2}(i) = \frac{h}{2}[(2n - n^2)f_i + n^2 f_{i+1}] - \frac{n^2 h^3}{12}(3 - 2n)f_i'' + \cdots, \tag{3.3.4}$$

from which the approximate integration formulas

$$I_{n2}(i) = \frac{h}{2}[(2n - n^2)f_i + n^2 f_{i+1}] \tag{3.3.5}$$

are found. The corresponding errors are

$$e_i = -\frac{n^2 h^3}{12}(3 - 2n)f_i''. \tag{3.3.6}$$

In particular, for $n = 1$, (3.3.5) becomes the familiar *trapezoidal rule*,

$$I_{12}(i) = \frac{h}{2}(f_i + f_{i+1}),$$

which, by (3.3.6), has an error $-h^3 f''/12$. Some of the other formulas which can be derived from (3.3.5) are given in Table 3.3.1.

When n is *even* (Figure 3.3.2), it is often more convenient to integrate $f(x)$ over n strips symmetrically located about $x_{i+(n/2)}$:

$$I_n(i) = \int_{x_i}^{x_i+nh} f(x)\, dx = \int_{-nh/2}^{nh/2} f\left(x_i + \frac{nh}{2} + z\right) dz$$

$$= \int_{-nh/2}^{nh/2} f(x_{i+(n/2)} + z)\, dz. \tag{3.3.7}$$

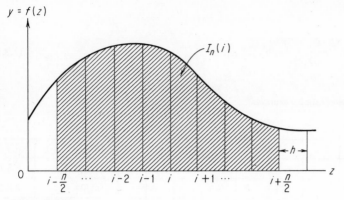

Figure 3.3.2

Thus, by the Taylor series for $f(x_{i+(n/2)} + z)$ about $x_{i+(n/2)}$,

$$f(x_{i+(n/2)} + z) = f_{i+(n/2)} + z f'_{i+(n/2)} + \frac{z^2}{2} f''_{i+(n/2)} + \frac{z^3}{6} f'''_{i+(n/2)}$$
$$+ \frac{z^4}{24} f^{iv}_{i+(n/2)} + \cdots, \tag{3.3.8}$$

we find that, since the integrals of the odd powers of z between $-nh/2$ and $+nh/2$ vanish, (3.3.7) becomes

$$I_n(i) = nh f_{i+(n/2)} + \frac{(nh)^3}{24} f''_{i+(n/2)} + \frac{(nh)^5}{1920} f^{iv}_{i+(n/2)} + \cdots. \tag{3.3.9}$$

Again, approximate values $I_{nm}(i)$ of $I_n(i)$ are derived from (3.3.9) by means of m-point differentiation formulas. For example, using the 3-point formula (3.2.18) for f'',

$$f''_{i+(n/2)} = \frac{f_{i+(n/2)-1} - 2 f_{i+(n/2)} + f_{i+(n/2)+1}}{h^2} - \frac{h^2}{12} f^{iv}_{i+(n/2)} + \cdots, \tag{3.3.10}$$

(3.3.9) becomes

$$I_{n3}(i) = \frac{h}{24} \left[n^3 f_{i+(n/2)-1} + (24n - 2n^3) f_{i+(n/2)} + n^3 f_{i+(n/2)+1} \right]$$
$$- \frac{20n^3 - 3n^5}{5760} h^5 f^{iv}_{i+(n/2)}, \tag{3.3.11}$$

and gives the approximate formulas

$$I_{n3}(i) = \frac{h}{24} \left[n^3 f_{i+(n/2)-1} + (24n - 2n^3) f_{i+(n/2)} + n^3 f_{i+(n/2)+1} \right], \tag{3.3.12}$$

with errors

$$e_i = -\frac{20n^3 - 3n^5}{5760}\, h^5 f^{\mathrm{iv}}_{i+(n/2)}. \tag{3.3.13}$$

Table 3.3.1. Integration Formulas[*]

$I_{nm}(i)$	Mult.	f_{i-1}	f_i	f_{i+1}	f_{i+2}	f_{i+3}	f_{i+4}	f_{i+5}	Error	Equation
$I_{11}(i)$	h		1	0					$(h^2/2)f'$	3.3.14
$I_{12}(i)$	$h/2$		1	1					$-(h^3/12)f''$	3.3.15
$I_{13}(i)$	$h/12$		5	8	-1				$(h^4/24)f'''$	3.3.16
$I_{14}(i)$	$h/24$		9	19	-5	1			$-(19/720)h^5 f^{\mathrm{iv}}$	3.3.17
$I_{15}(i)$	$h/720$		251	646	-264	106	-19		$(27/1440)h^6 f^{\mathrm{v}}$	3.3.18
$I_{14}(i)$	$h/24$	-1	13	13	-1				$(11/720)h^5 f^{\mathrm{iv}}$	3.3.19
$I_{15}(i)$	$h/720$	-19	346	456	-74	11			$-(11/1440)h^6 f^{\mathrm{v}}$	3.3.20
$I_{13}(i)$	$h/12$	-1	8	5					$-(h^4/24)f'''$	3.3.21
$I_{21}(i)$	$2h$		0	1	0				$(h^3/3)f''$	3.3.22
$I_{21}(i)$	$2h$		1	0	0				$2h^2 f'$	3.3.23
$I_{23}(i)$	$h/3$		1	4	1				$-(h^5/90)f^{\mathrm{iv}}$	3.3.24
$I_{24}(i)$	$h/3$		1	4	1	0			$-(h^5/90)f^{\mathrm{iv}}$	3.3.25
$I_{34}(i)$	$3h/8$		1	3	3	1			$-(3/80)h^5 f^{\mathrm{iv}}$	3.3.26
$I_{43}(i)$	$4h/3$		0	2	-1	2	0		$(14/15)h^5 f^{\mathrm{iv}}$	3.3.27
$I_{23}(i)$	$h/12$	4	-8	28	0				$(h^4/3)f'''$	3.3.28
$I_{22}(i)$	$h/2$		0	4	0				$(h^3/3)f''$	3.3.29
$I_{32}(i)$	$h/2$		-3	9	0	0			$(27/12)h^3 f''$	3.3.30
$I_{42}(i)$	$h/2$		-8	16	0	0	0		$(80/12)h^3 f''$	3.3.31
$I_{52}(i)$	$h/2$		-15	25	0	0	0	0	$(175/12)h^3 f''$	3.3.32
$I_{31}(i)$	h		3	0	0	0			$(9/2)h^2 f'$	3.3.33
$I_{41}(i)$	h		4	0	0	0	0		$8h^2 f'$	3.3.34
$I_{51}(i)$	h		5	0	0	0	0	0	$(25/2)h^2 f'$	3.3.35
$I_{33}(i)$	$h/12$		9	0	27	0			$(9/24)h^4 f'''$	3.3.36
$I_{43}(i)$	$h/12$		32	-64	80	0	0		$(64/24)h^4 f'''$	3.3.37
$I_{33}(i)$	$h/12$	27	-72	81	0	0			$(63/24)h^4 f'''$	3.3.38
$I_{43}(i)$	$h/12$	80	-208	176	0	0	0		$(28/3)h^4 f'''$	3.3.39

[*] Some of these formulas are of theoretical interest only, and are included as potential exercises for the interested student.

Two frequently used formulas are special cases of (3.3.12). For $n = 2$, (3.3.12) reduces to

$$I_{23}(i) = \frac{h}{3}(f_i + 4f_{i+1} + f_{i+2}),$$

the well known *Simpson's 1/3 rule*, with an error $-h^5 f^{iv}/90$. For $n = 4$, (3.3.12) becomes

$$I_{43}(i) = \frac{4h}{3}(2f_{i+1} - f_{i+2} + 2f_{i+3}),$$

with an error $\frac{14}{45}h^5 f_{i+2}^{iv}$.

Integration formulas for any n and any m may be derived in a similar manner. Some of them are presented in Table 3.3.1, *where the interval of integration is indicated by the* **boldface** *coefficients.* To illustrate, the 4-point integration formula for the strip from i to $i + 1$, (3.3.17), reads

$$I_{14}(i) = \frac{h}{24}(9f_i + 19f_{i+1} - 5f_{i+2} + f_{i+3})$$

with an error $-19h^5 f_i^{iv}/720$.

The reader may observe that, for any formula in Table 3.3.1, the product of the multiplier and the sum of the coefficients must equal the integration interval, nh, since, for $f(x) = 1$, all the f_i are equal to 1 and the integral equals nh. For instance, the sum of the coefficients of (3.3.17) is 24, the multiplier is $h/24$, and the product equals the integration interval h.

Integration formulas may also be obtained by integrating the approximating parabolas introduced in Section 3.2. This approach offers, again, a geometric interpretation of the approximation but does not allow an estimate of the error. In this case, $I_{nm}(i)$ will denote the integral from x_i to $x_i + nh$ obtained using an $(m - 1)$st degree approximating parabola, i.e.,

$$I_{nm}(i) = \int_{x_i}^{x_i+nh} p_{m-1}(x)\,dx, \tag{3.3.40}$$

where

$$p_{m-1}(x) = \sum_{k=0}^{m-1} A_k(x - x_i)^k. \tag{3.3.41}$$

In particular, if a straight line (a first-degree parabola, $m - 1 = 1$) is used,

$$I_{n2}(i) = \int_{x_i}^{x_i+nh} p_1(x)\,dx, \tag{3.3.42}$$

where

$$p_1(x) = A_1(x - x_i) + A_0, \tag{3.3.43}$$

with

$$A_1 = \frac{f_{i+1} - f_i}{h}, \qquad A_0 = f_i. \tag{3.3.44}$$

The integral (3.3.42) thus becomes

$$I_{n2}(i) = \frac{(nh)^2}{2} A_1 + nhA_0 \tag{3.3.45}$$

or, by (3.3.44),

$$I_{n2}(i) = \frac{h}{2} [(2n - n^2)f_i + n^2 f_{i+1}], \tag{3.3.46}$$

which is identical with (3.3.5).

The formulas in Table 3.3.1 slanted to the right give rise to formulas slanted to the left if we invert the order of the coefficients. For example, from (3.3.16),

$$I_{13}(i) = \frac{h}{12} (-f_{i-1} + 8f_i + 5f_{i+1}). \tag{3.3.21}$$

Integration formulas are usually applied successively to a multiple of the basic number of strips n. For example, applying Simpson's 1/3 rule to an *even* number N of strips of width h, we find

$$I_S = \frac{h}{3} [(f_0 + 4f_1 + f_2) + (f_2 + 4f_3 + f_4) + \cdots + (f_{N-2} + 4f_{N-1} + f_N)]$$
$$+ \frac{N}{2} \left(-\frac{h^5}{90} \right) f^{\mathrm{iv}}(\bar{x}), \tag{3.3.47}$$

where $x_0 \le \bar{x} \le x_N$ (a result which follows from the theorem of the mean). Combining like terms and noting that $Nh = x_N - x_0$, (3.3.47) takes the form

$$I_S = \frac{h}{3} [f_0 + 4f_i + 2f_2 + 4f_3 + \cdots + 2f_{N-2} + 4f_{N-1} + f_N]$$
$$- \frac{x_N - x_0}{180} h^4 f^{\mathrm{iv}}(\bar{x}). \tag{3.3.48}$$

Thus, the error in Simpson's 1/3 rule applied to multiples of $n = 2$ strips is of order h^4.

Simpson's 3/8 rule (3.3.26) may be conveniently used with Simpson's 1/3 rule to integrate with an error of order h^4 over an *odd* number of intervals.

The reader may deduce that the error in an integration formula used over a range of integration $x_N - x_0 \gg nh$ is of order one less than the error associated with the basic interval nh. Thus, for the *trapezoidal rule* (3.3.15),

$$I_T = h \left(\frac{1}{2}f_0 + f_1 + f_2 + \cdots + f_{N-1} + \frac{1}{2}f_N \right) - \frac{x_N - x_0}{12} h^2 f''. \tag{3.3.49}$$

For integration formulas with unevenly spaced pivotal points, see N.M., Section 2.12.

Example 3.3.1. Given the values of e^x in Example 3.2.1, calculate $I_{nm}(i)$ by the method indicated, compute the predicted error, and compare with the actual error.

Trapezoidal rule:

$$I_{12}(1) = I_T = \frac{.1}{2}(1.105171 + 1.221403) = .116329 \quad [.116232].$$

Predicted error:

$$-\frac{h^3}{12}f'' = -\frac{(.1)^3}{12}(1.105171) = -.000092 \quad [-.000097].$$

$I_{nm}(i)$	Integral	Error e	Pred. e
$I_{12}(0)$	.105259	−.000088	−.000088
$I_{13}(0)$	.105166	+.000005	+.000005
$I_{14}(0)$	.105171	.000000	.000000
$I_{12}(1)$	.116329	−.000097	−.000092
$I_{23}(0)$	.221403	.000000	.000000

Example 3.3.2. Evaluate the integral of e^x from 0. to .4 by the trapezoidal rule with $h = .2$ and $h = .1$, and by Simpson's 1/3 rule with $h = .1$, using the values of e^x in Example 3.2.1.

$$h = .2; \quad I_T = .2\left(\frac{1}{2}1. + 1.221403 + \frac{1}{2}1.491825\right) = .493463;$$

$$e = -.001638.$$

$$h = .1;$$

$$I_T = .1\left(\frac{1}{2}1. + 1.105171 + 1.221403 + 1.349859 + \frac{1}{2}1.491825\right)$$

$$= .492235;$$

$$e = -.000410.$$

$$I_S = \frac{.1}{3}[1. + 4(1.105171) + 2(1.221403) + 4(1.349859) + 1.491825]$$

$$= .491825;$$

$$e = .000000.$$

3.4 Parabolic Interpolation and Extrapolation [Program 3.4]

The evaluation of $f(x)$ at a point x located between two pivotal points, i.e., such that $x_i < x < x_{i+1}$, is called *interpolation*. The evaluation of $f(x)$ at a point located outside the range of the pivotal points is called *extrapolation*. Parabolic interpolations and extrapolations are obtained by approximating $f(x)$ by truncated Taylor series, i.e., by parabolas. The coefficients of the approximating parabolas may be taken directly from Table 3.2.1. For example, truncating the Taylor series

$$f(x) = f_i + f_i'(x - x_i) + \frac{1}{2}f_i''(x - x_i)^2 + \cdots \tag{a}$$

after two terms, and approximating f_i' by (3.2.7), which has an error of order h consistent with the error in the truncated series, one obtains the *linear interpolation or 2-point formula*,

$$f(x) = f_i + (f_{i+1} - f_i)\frac{x - x_i}{h}, \tag{b}$$

which, letting

$$p = \frac{x - x_i}{h} \quad \therefore \quad x = x_i + ph, \tag{3.4.1}$$

becomes

$$f^{(1)}(x) \doteq f(x_i + ph) = \frac{1}{p + (1 - p)}[pf_{i+1} + (1 - p)f_i]$$
$$= pf_{i+1} + (1 - p)f_i. \tag{3.4.2}$$

By means of the first three terms of (a), and approximating f_i' by (3.2.11) and f_i'' by (3.2.18), the *quadratic interpolation formula* becomes

$$f^{(2)}(x) \doteq f(x_i + ph) = \frac{-p(1 - p)}{2}f_{i-1} + (1 - p)(1 + p)f_i$$
$$+ \frac{p(1 + p)}{2}f_{i+1} \tag{3.4.3}$$

$$= f_i + \frac{p}{2}(f_{i+1} - f_{i-1}) + \frac{p^2}{2}(f_{i+1} - 2f_i + f_{i-1}).$$

The operators of (3.4.2) and (3.4.3) are represented in the mathematical molecules of Figure 3.4.1(a) and (b), respectively.

The quadratic interpolation formula (3.4.3) may also be derived by the Aitken-Neville method of *successive linear interpolations and extrapolations*. Let $f_{i+1}^{(1)}(x)$ be the value of $f(x) = f(x_i + ph)$ linearly interpolated in the interval (x_i, x_{i+1}) by (3.4.2):

$$f_{i+1}^{(1)}(x) = pf_{i+1} + (1 - p)f_i; \tag{c}$$

and $f_{i-1}^{(1)}(x)$ the value of $f(x)$ linearly extrapolated from the interval (x_{i-1}, x_i) by (3.4.2) [with p changed into $(1 + p)$ and $(1 - p)$ changed into $-p$] (Figure 3.4.2):

$$f_{i-1}^{(1)}(x) = (1 + p)f_i - pf_{i-1}. \tag{d}$$

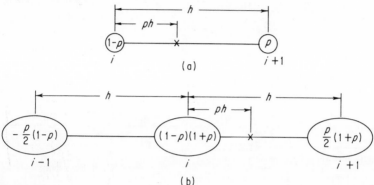

Figure 3.4.1

The quadratic interpolation $f_i^{(2)}(x)$ is then obtained by linear interpolation from $f_{i-1}^{(1)}$ and $f_{i+1}^{(1)}$ in the interval (x_{i-1}, x_{i+1}), i.e., using (3.4.2) with p changed into $(1 + p)$ and $(1 - p)$ unchanged (Fig. 3.4.2):

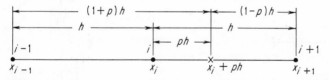

Figure 3.4.2

$$f_i^{(2)}(x) = \frac{1}{(1 + p) + (1 - p)} [(1 + p)f_{i+1}^{(1)}(x) + (1 - p)f_{i-1}^{(1)}(x)]$$

$$= \frac{1}{2} [-p(1 - p)f_{i-1} + 2(1 - p)(1 + p)f_i + p(1 + p)f_{i+1}],$$

which is seen to be identical with (3.4.3).

The Aitken-Neville interpolation method may be extended to obtain higher-degree interpolated (or extrapolated) values by noticing that the divisor in front of the bracketed terms equals 1 for linear interpolation; $(1 + p) + (1 - p)$ or $p + (2 - p)$, i.e., 2 for quadratic interpolation; $(1 + p) + (2 - p)$ or $(2 + p) + (1 - p)$ or $p + (3 - p)$, i.e., 3 for cubic interpolation; and n for nth-degree interpolation.

Example 3.4.1. Given $f(x) = e^x$ for $x = 0(.1).5$ (see Example 3.2.1), evaluate $f(.24)$ by (a) linear interpolation, (b) quadratic interpolation, (c) cubic interpolation using the Aitken-Neville method. (d) Evaluate $f(-.06)$ by quadratic extrapolation using the Aitken-Neville method.

(a) $x = .24$, $x_i = .20$, $h = .1$, $p = (.24 - .20)/.1 = .4$.

$$f^{(1)}(.24) = .4(1.349859) + (1 - .4)(1.221403)$$
$$= 1.272785 \quad [1.271249].$$

(b) $f^{(2)}(.24) = \frac{1}{2}[-(.4)(.6)(1.105171) + 2(.6)(1.4)(1.221403)$
$$+ (.4)(1.4)(1.349859)] = 1.271318 \quad [1.271249].$$

(c)

i	x_i	f_i	p	$1-p$	$f^{(1)}(.24)$	$1+p$	$1-p$	$f^{(2)}(.24)$	$2+p$	$1-p$	$f^{(3)}(.24)$
0	0.	1.		-1.4				1.270993		.6	
					1.252410		$-.4$				1.271253
1	.1	1.105171	2.4	$-.4$				1.271318	2.4		
					1.267896	2.4	.6				[1.271249]
2	.2	1.221403	1.4	.6							
					1.272785	1.4					
3	.3	1.349859	.4								
Divisor			1.			2.			3.		

(d)

i	x_i	f_i	p	$1-p$	$f^{(1)}(-.06)$	p	$2-p$	$f^{(2)}(-.06)$
0	0.	1.		$-.6$				
					.936897	$-.6$		
1	.1	1.105171	-1.6	1.6				.942206
					.919200		2.6	
2	.2	1.221403		2.6				[.941765]
Divisor			1.			2.		

3.5 Lagrangian Interpolation [Program 3.3]

When the pivotal points x_i are not evenly spaced, interpolating polynomials may be obtained by the following method due to Lagrange.

The mth-degree polynomial

$$P_j(x) = A_j(x - x_0)(x - x_1)\cdots(x - x_{j-1})(x - x_{j+1})\cdots(x - x_m) \quad \textbf{(3.5.1)}$$

is zero at all x_i except x_j, and equals 1 at x_j if the constant A_j is chosen equal to

$$A_j = \frac{1}{(x_j - x_0)(x_j - x_1)\cdots(x_j - x_{j-1})(x_j - x_{j+1})\cdots(x_j - x_m)} \cdot \quad \textbf{(3.5.2)}$$

Hence, with this value of A_j,

$$P_j(x_i) = \begin{cases} 0, & \text{for } i \neq j, \\ 1, & \text{for } i = j. \end{cases}$$ (a)

The linear combination of $P_j(x)$,

$$p_m(x) = f_0 P_0(x) + f_1 P_1(x) + \cdots + f_m P_m(x) = \sum_{i=0}^{m} f_i P_i(x),$$ (3.5.3)

is an mth-degree polynomial and by (a) has at $x = x_i$ the value

$$p_m(x_i) = f_0 P_0(x_i) + f_1 P_1(x_i) + \cdots + f_i P_i(x_i) \cdots + f_m P_m(x_i)$$

$$= f_0 \cdot 0 + f_1 \cdot 0 + \cdots + f_i \cdot 1 + \cdots f_m \cdot 0$$

$$= f_i \qquad (i = 0, 1, \ldots, m).$$

Hence, $p_m(x)$ is the mth-degree polynomial passing through the $m + 1$ unevenly spaced pivotal points x_i $(i = 0, 1, 2, \ldots, m)$.

Example 3.5.1. Given

i	0	1	2	3
x_i	1	2	5	9
f_i	1	3	6	10

interpolate $f(6)$ by Lagrangian polynomials.

$$P_0(x) = \frac{(x-2)(x-5)(x-9)}{(1-2)(1-5)(1-9)} ; \qquad P_0(6) = \frac{3}{8} ;$$

$$P_1(x) = \frac{(x-1)(x-5)(x-9)}{(2-1)(2-5)(2-9)} ; \qquad P_1(6) = -\frac{5}{7} ;$$

$$P_2(x) = \frac{(x-1)(x-2)(x-9)}{(5-1)(5-2)(5-9)} ; \qquad P_2(6) = \frac{5}{4} ;$$

$$P_3(x) = \frac{(x-1)(x-2)(x-5)}{(9-1)(9-2)(9-5)} ; \qquad P_3(6) = \frac{5}{56} ;$$

$$p_3(6) = 1\left(\frac{3}{8}\right) + 3\left(-\frac{5}{7}\right) + 6\left(\frac{5}{4}\right) + 10\left(\frac{5}{56}\right) = \frac{371}{56} = 6.625.$$

When the pivotal points are evenly spaced by h, letting

$$p = \frac{x - x_0}{h},$$ (3.5.4)

(3.5.1) and (3.5.2) reduce to

$$P_j(x) = A_j h^m p(p-1)(p-2)\cdots(p-j+1)(p-j-1)\cdots(p-m),$$

$$A_j = \frac{1}{h^m j(j-1)(j-2)\cdots(1)(-1)\cdots(j-m)}$$

$$= \frac{(-1)^{m-i}}{h^m j!(m-j)!},$$

and (3.5.3) becomes the *mth-degree interpolation formula*

$$p_m(x) = \sum_{i=0}^{m}\left[\frac{(-1)^{m-i}}{i!(m-i)!}p(p-1)(p-2)\cdots \right.$$

$$\left. \cdots(p-i+1)(p-i-1)\cdots(p-m)\right]f_i. \qquad \textbf{(3.5.5)}$$

For $m = 1$, (3.5.5) is identical with (3.4.2). For $m = 2$ it differs from (3.4.3) because of the different definitions of p [see (3.4.1) and (3.5.4)].

Example 3.5.2. Evaluate by Lagrangian interpolation $f(x) = e^x$ at $x = .24$ given e^x at $x = 0.(.1).3$ (see Example 3.2.1).

$$h = .1, \quad p = \frac{.24 - 0.}{0.1} = 2.4, \quad m = 3;$$

$$P_0(.24) = \frac{(-1)^3}{0!\,3!}(1.4)(.4)(-.6) = .056; \quad f_0 = 1;$$

$$P_1(.24) = \frac{(-1)^2}{1!\,2!}(2.4)(.4)(-.6) = -.288; \quad f_1 = 1.105171;$$

$$P_2(.24) = \frac{(-1)^1}{2!\,1!}(2.4)(1.4)(-.6) = 1.008; \quad f_2 = 1.221403;$$

$$P_3(.24) = \frac{(-1)^0}{3!\,0!}(2.4)(1.4)(.4) = .224; \quad f_3 = 1.349859;$$

$$p_3(.24) = \sum_{i=0}^{3} P_i(.24)f_i = 1.271253 \quad [1.271249].$$

$p_3(.24)$ is identical with the Aitken-Neville interpolation of Example 3.4.1(c).

3.6   Richardson's Extrapolations [Programs 3.2-A, 9.9-A]

The use of Taylor series allows the evaluation of the order of error in differentiation and integration formulas. The knowledge of the order of error permits, in turn, fairly accurate estimates of the true value, Q, of the approximated quantities (derivatives or integrals) as soon as two approximate values Q_1, Q_2 of Q have been obtained by means of two different spacings, say, h_1, h_2.

If the order of the error is n, truncating the error series after its first term, we obtain, approximately,

$$Q - Q_1 \doteq ch_1^n, \qquad Q - Q_2 \doteq ch_2^n, \qquad \text{(a)}$$

where in differentiation formulas the constant c depends on the pivotal point at which the derivative is evaluated.

Dividing equations (a) by h_1^n, h_2^n, respectively, and solving them for Q, one obtains the approximate value Q_{12} of Q by the so-called h^n-*extrapolation formula of Richardson:*

$$Q_{12} = \frac{(h_1/h_2)^n Q_2 - Q_1}{(h_1/h_2)^n - 1}. \qquad \text{(3.6.1)}$$

For the commonly encountered cases in which $h_1/h_2 = 2$ and the error is of order h^2 ($n = 2$), (3.6.1) becomes the $\frac{1}{3} h^2$-*extrapolation formula:*

$$Q_{12} = \frac{4}{3} Q_2 - \frac{1}{3} Q_1 \qquad \left[e = 0(h^2); \quad \frac{h_1}{h_2} = 2 \right]. \qquad \text{(3.6.2)}$$

For $h_1/h_2 = 2$ and $n = 4$, (3.6.1) becomes the $\frac{1}{15} h^4$-*extrapolation formula:*

$$Q_{12} = \frac{16}{15} Q_2 - \frac{1}{15} Q_1 \qquad \left[e = 0(h^4); \quad \frac{h_1}{h_2} = 2 \right]. \qquad \text{(3.6.3)}$$

For more powerful Richardson extrapolations see N.M. Section 2.13.

Example 3.6.1. Evaluate by h^2-extrapolation an estimate of $f''(.2)$ by means of the results of rows 5 and 6 of Example 3.2.1, which have errors $-.004072$ and $-.000997$, respectively.

$$\frac{h_1}{h_2} = \frac{.2}{.1} = 2; \quad e = 0(h^2);$$

$$f''_{12}(.2) = \frac{4}{3} 1.222400 - \frac{1}{3} 1.225475 = 1.221375; \quad e = +.000028.$$

Example 3.6.2. Evaluate by h^2-extrapolation [see (3.3.49)] an estimate of the integral I of Example 3.3.2 by means of the two approximate values obtained by the trapezoidal rule with $h = .2$ and $h = .1$, which have errors $-.001638$ and $-.000410$, respectively.

$$I_{12} = \frac{4}{3} .492235 - \frac{1}{3} .493463 = .491826; \quad e = -.000001.$$

PROBLEMS

3.1 Given the following tabular values of $f(x)$, evaluate the following derivatives at the given points by the indicated formulas.

i	0	1	2	3	4	5	6
x_i	0.	.1	.2	.3	.4	.5	.6
f_i	1.	.90484	.81873	.74082	.67032	.60653	.54881

(a) f_0' by 2-, 3-, and 4-point formulas.

(b) f_2'' by 3- and 5-point centered formulas.

(c) f_0''' by 5-point formula.

(d) f_6''' by 5-point formula.

(e) f_1''', f_2''' by 4-point formulas starting at $i = 0$.

(f) f_1^{iv} by 5-point formula.

3.2 Evaluate the derivatives of Problem 3.1(a) to (d) for the following tabular values.

i	0	1	2	3	4	5	6
x_i	.8	.9	1.0	1.1	1.2	1.3	1.4
f_i	.71736	.78333	.84147	.89121	.93204	.96356	.98545

3.3 Evaluate the following derivatives for the function of Problem 3.1, using $h_1 = .02$, $h_2 = .01$ and h^n-extrapolations. Use formulas with the minimum number of points in all cases.

(a) f_0', f_2' (b) f_0'', f_2'' (c) f_4', f_4''

3.4 Solve Problem 3.3 for the tabular values of Problem 3.2, with $h_1 = .2$, $h_2 = .1$.

3.5 Derive finite-difference operators for the following derivatives by shifting lower-order operators.

(a) f_i''', centered 5-point formula.

(b) f_i'', lateral 3-point formula, starting at i.

(c) f_i^{iv}, lateral 5-point formula, starting at i.

(d) f_i''', lateral 5-point formula, starting at $i - 1$.

3.6 Derive f_i'' by interpolating parabolas going through

(a) $i, i + 1, i + 2, i + 3$.

(b) $i - 1, i, i + 1, i + 2$.

(c) $i - 2, i - 1, i + 1, i + 2$.

3.7 Evaluate the integral of the function in Problem 3.1 by the trapezoidal rule with $h_1 = .02$, $h_2 = .01$ and h^2-extrapolation.

3.8 Evaluate the integral of the function in Problem 3.1

(a) from $i = 0$ to $i = 4$ by Simpson's 1/3 rule with $h_1 = .02$, $h_2 = .01$.

(b) from $i = 0$ to $i = 2$ by Simpson's 1/3 rule and from $i = 2$ to $i = 5$ by Simpson's 3/8 rule.

3.9 Evaluate by parabolic interpolations the following values of $f(x)$ for the function tabulated in Problem 3.1.

(a) $f(.525)$ by linear and quadratic interpolations.

(b) $f(.120)$ by linear and quadratic interpolations.

(c) $f(.252)$ by Aitken-Neville interpolation, using the points $i = 1$ to 4.

3.10 Evaluate $f(1.06)$ for the function tabulated in Problem 3.2 by linear, quadratic, and cubic Aitken-Neville interpolations, using the points $i = 1$ to 4.

3.11 (a) Evaluate $f_1 = f(.1)$ in Problem 3.1 by Lagrangian interpolation, using f_0, f_2, f_3, f_5.

(b) Evaluate $f_6 = f(1.4)$ in Problem 3.2 by Lagrangian interpolation, using f_0, f_1, f_3, f_5, and f_0, f_2, f_4, f_5.

Solution
of Algebraic and
Transcendental
Equations

Chapter Four

4.1 Solution of Algebraic Equations by Formula [Programs 4.1, 4.3, 4.5]

The nth-degree algebraic equation with real coefficients

$$p_n(x) \equiv a_n x^n + a_{n-1} x^{n-1} + \cdots + a_1 x + a_0 = 0 \tag{4.1.1}$$

has n roots, which may be (a) real and separate, (b) real and repeated, (c) complex conjugate and separate, (d) complex conjugate and repeated.

For equations of degree four or less all the roots may be obtained by formula, even though it is often more efficient to evaluate them by the approximate methods of the following sections.

(a) The two roots x_1, x_2 of the *quadratic equation*

$$p_2(x) = a_2 x^2 + a_1 x + a_0 = 0 \tag{4.1.2}$$

are given by

$$x_{1,2} = -\frac{a_1}{2a_2} \pm \sqrt{\left(\frac{a_1}{2a_2}\right)^2 - \frac{a_0}{a_2}}.^* \tag{4.1.3}$$

---

* When the roots of (4.1.2) are real and one is much larger than the other in absolute value, the smaller root may be more accurately evaluated by dividing the larger root from (4.1.3) into a_0/a_2.

(b) The *cubic equation*

$$p_3(x) \equiv a_3 x^3 + a_2 x^2 + a_1 x + a_0 = 0 \tag{4.1.4}$$

has always at least one real root, say, x_1. As shown by direct substitution in (4.1.4), x_1 is given (see p. 180 for signs in front of roots) by

$$x_1 = -\frac{a_2}{3a_3} + (\sqrt{P^3 + Q^2} - Q)^{1/3} - (\sqrt{P^3 + Q^2} + Q)^{1/3}, \tag{4.1.5a}$$

where

$$P = \frac{a_1}{3a_3} - \left(\frac{a_2}{a_3}\right)^2, \tag{4.1.5b}$$

$$Q = \frac{1}{2a_3}\left(a_0 - \frac{a_2^3}{27a_3^2} - a_2 P\right). \tag{4.1.5c}$$

Factoring the root x_1 from (4.1.4) by synthetic substitution (Sec. 2.4) one obtains the quadratic equation for x_2, x_3:

$$a_3 x^2 + (a_2 + a_3 x_1)x + (a_2 + a_3 x_1)x_1 + a_1 = 0. \tag{4.1.6}$$

(c) The four roots of the *quartic equation*

$$p_4(x) \equiv x^4 + a_3 x^3 + a_2 x^2 + a_1 x + a_0 = 0, \tag{4.1.7}$$

in which the coefficient of x^4 is made equal to 1 by dividing through by a_4, are conveniently obtained by *Brown's method*. Writing (4.1.7) as the difference of two squares,

$$(x^2 + Ax + B)^2 - (Cx + D)^2 = 0, \tag{4.1.8}$$

and equating the coefficients of each power of x in (4.1.7) and (4.1.8), one finds that

$$\begin{aligned} 2A &= a_3, \\ A^2 + 2B - C^2 &= a_2, \\ 2AB - 2CD &= a_1, \\ B^2 - D^2 &= a_0. \end{aligned} \tag{a}$$

Elimination of A, C, and D shows that $2B$ is a root of the cubic equation

$$z^3 - a_2 z^2 + b_1 z + b_0 = 0, \tag{4.1.9}$$

where

$$\begin{aligned} b_1 &= a_3 a_1 - 4a_0, \\ b_0 &= a_0(4a_2 - a_3^2) - a_1^2. \end{aligned} \tag{4.1.10}$$

Choosing as $2B$ the *algebraically largest* (real) root z_1 of (4.1.9) (in order to obtain real coefficients throughout) one finds, by (a),

$$A = \frac{a_3}{2}; \quad B = \frac{z_1}{2}; \quad D = \sqrt{B^2 - a_0};$$

$$C = \frac{(a_1/2) - AB}{D} \qquad \text{for } D \neq 0,$$

(4.1.11)

$$C = \sqrt{A^2 - a_2 + z_1} \qquad \text{for } D = 0.$$

With these values of A, B, C, and D, (4.1.8), and hence (4.1.7), is equivalent to the two quadratic equations

$$x^2 + (A - C)x + (B - D) = 0,$$
$$x^2 + (A + C)x + (B + D) = 0.$$

(4.1.12)

Example 4.1.1. Determine the roots of the quartic equation

$$p_4(x) = x^4 + 4x^3 + 7x^2 + 6x + 3 = 0$$

by Brown's method.

$$b_1 = 4 \cdot 6 - 4 \cdot 3 = 12; \quad b_0 = 3(4 \cdot 7 - 4^2) - 6^2 = 0;$$
$$z^3 - 7z^2 + 12z + 0 = z(z - 3)(z - 4) = 0; \quad z_1 = 4;$$
$$A = 2; \quad B = 2; \quad D = \sqrt{4 - 3} = 1; \quad C = (3 - 2)/1 = 1.$$
$$x^2 + x + 1 = 0; \quad x^2 + 3x + 3 = 0;$$
$$x_{1,2} = -\frac{1}{2} \pm \frac{\sqrt{3}}{2} i; \quad x_{3,4} = -\frac{3}{2} \pm \frac{\sqrt{3}}{2} i.$$

4.2 Real Roots of Algebraic Equations by Iteration [Program 4.7-A]

The roots of algebraic equations of degree higher than four may be evaluated by successive approximations. It is often convenient to apply the same methods to obtain the roots of third- and fourth-degree equations.

Real separate roots of algebraic equations are conveniently evaluated by the *Newton-Raphson method of tangents*. Let $x^{(k)}$ be an approximate value of a real separate root x of (4.1.1), and approximate $p_n(x)$ by the Taylor series (2.3.1) with $x_0 = x^{(k)}$ up to the linear term in x,

$$p_n(x) \doteq p_n(x^{(k)}) + p_n'(x^{(k)})(x - x^{(k)}) = 0.$$

(a)

Solving (a) for x we obtain the approximation $x^{(k+1)}$ of x as

$$x^{(k+1)} = x^{(k)} - \frac{p_n(x^{(k)})}{p_n'(x^{(k)})}.$$

(4.2.1)

The iteration equation (4.2.1) allows successive improvements of the root to any required accuracy by evaluation of the intersection $x^{(k+1)}$ of the tangent to $p_n(x)$ at $x = x^{(k)}$ with the x-axis (Figure 4.2.1). The values of $p_n(x^{(k)})$ and $p_n'(x^{(k)})$ are conveniently computed by two successive synthetic substitutions (Sec. 2.4).

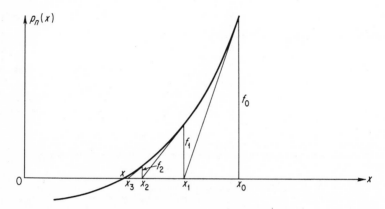

Figure 4.2.1 Newton-Raphson's method.

The roots of $p_n(x) = 0$ are usually evaluated starting with the algebraically largest root x_1; its initial value may be approximated by

$$x_1^{(0)} = - \frac{a_{n-1}}{a_n} \tag{4.2.2}$$

when no other value is suggested by a knowledge of the problem at hand.

When $p_n(x^{(k)})$ is evaluated by synthetic substitution, the first n numbers on the row of the scheme for which $p_n(x^{(k)}) = 0$ are the coefficients of the $(n - 1)$st-degree *reduced equation*, containing the remaining $n - 1$ roots of $p_n(x) = 0$. Hence, the Newton-Raphson iterative procedure can be applied directly to the reduced equation to obtain the second largest real root of $p_n(x) = 0$, and can be continued until all the real roots are evaluated. At this point the last reduced equation contains only conjugate complex roots: if the reduced equation is a quadratic, it is solved by (4.1.3); if a quartic, by Brown's method [Sec. 4.1(c)]. Higher-degree equations with complex conjugate roots are solved by Graeffe's root-squaring method (N.M., Sec. 1.4), the Lin-Barstow successive approximations method (N.M., Sec. 1.5), or by the Newton-Raphson method for complex roots (see Program 4.7-A).

The Newton-Raphson method fails if $p_n(x^{(k)}) \neq 0$ and $p_n'(x^{(k)}) = 0$; in this case a new $x^{(k)}$ must be chosen to continue the procedure.

When $p_n(x) = p_n'(x) = \cdots = p_n^{(m)}(x) = 0$, x is a root of $p_n(x) = 0$ repeated $m + 1$ times.

The values of the roots of $p_n(x) = 0$ may be checked by Newton's relations:

$$\sum_{i=1}^{n} x_i = -\frac{a_{n-1}}{a_n}; \quad x_1 \cdot x_2 \cdot x_3 \cdot \cdots \cdot x_{n-1} \cdot x_n = (-1)^n \frac{a_0}{a_n}. \tag{4.2.3}$$

Example 4.2.1. Determine the roots of the cubic equation

$$p_3(x) = x^3 - 12.1x^2 + 7.2x + 41.5 = 0$$

to two decimal figures by the Newton-Raphson method.

Initial guess: $x_1^{(0)} = -(-12.1)/1 \doteq 12$.

		1	-12.10	7.20	41.50	
$x_1^{(0)} = 12.$			12.00	-1.20	72.00	
		1	$-.10$	6.00	$113.50 = p_3(12.)$	
12.			12.00	142.80		
		1	11.90	$148.80 = p_3'(12.);$	$x_1^{(1)} = 12. - \dfrac{113.50}{148.80} = 11.24$	
$x_1^{(1)} = 11.24$			11.24	-9.67	-27.76	
		1	$-.86$	-2.47	$13.74 = p_3(11.24)$	
11.24			11.24	116.67		
		1	10.38	$114.20 = p_3'(11.24);$	$x_1^{(2)} = 11.24 - \dfrac{13.74}{114.20} = 11.12$	
$x_1^{(2)} = 11.12$			11.12	-10.90	-41.14	
		1	$-.98$	-3.70	$.36 = p_3(11.12)$	
11.12			11.12	112.76		
		1	10.14	$109.06 = p_3'(11.12);$	$x_1^{(3)} = 11.12 - \dfrac{.36}{109.06} = 11.12$	

Reduced equation: $x^2 - .98x - 3.70 = 0$.

$$x_1 = 11.12; \quad x_{2,3} = .49 \pm \sqrt{(.49)^2 + 3.70} = \begin{cases} 2.48, \\ -1.50. \end{cases}$$

$$\sum_{i=1}^{3} x_i = 11.12 + 2.48 - 1.50 = 12.10,$$

$$x_1 \cdot x_2 \cdot x_3 = (11.12)(2.48)(-1.50) = -41.37.$$

The iterative equation (4.2.1) applied to the quadratic equation, which defines $x = \sqrt{N}$,

$$p_2(x) = x^2 - N = 0; \qquad p_2'(x) = 2x,$$

gives the iteration equation for the square root:

$$x^{(k+1)} = x^{(k)} - \frac{(x^{(k)})^2 - N}{2x^{(k)}} = \frac{1}{2}\left(x^{(k)} + \frac{N}{x^{(k)}}\right), \qquad \text{(4.2.4)}$$

which allows the extraction of square roots by successive divisions and averaging.

Example 4.2.2. Evaluate $\sqrt{28}$ to two decimal figures.

$$x^{(0)} = 5; \quad x^{(1)} = \frac{1}{2}\left(5 + \frac{28}{5}\right) = 5.3; \quad x^{(2)} = \frac{1}{2}\left(5.3 + \frac{28}{5.3}\right) = 5.292;$$

$$x^{(3)} = \frac{1}{2}\left(5.292 + \frac{28}{5.292}\right) = 5.2915.$$

4.3 Real Roots of Transcendental Equations [Programs 4.7, 4.8]

The Newton-Raphson iteration formula (4.2.1) can be applied to the evaluation of the real roots (if any) of the transcendental equation

$$f(x) = 0 \qquad \text{(4.3.1)}$$

by substituting $f(x)$ for $p_n(x)$,

$$x^{(k+1)} = x^{(k)} - \frac{f_k}{f_k'}, \qquad \text{(4.3.2)}$$

where $f_k = f(x^{(k)})$ and $f_k' = f'(x^{(k)})$.

The values of $f(x)$ and $f'(x)$, of course, cannot be computed by synthetic substitutions. The initial value $x^{(0)}$ of the root is sometimes determined graphically.

Example 4.3.1. Using the Newton-Raphson method, evaluate to two decimal figures the root of the transcendental equation

$$f(x) \equiv e^{3x} - 3x = 0$$

lying between 0 and 1.

$$f(x) = e^x - 3x; \qquad f'(x) = e^x - 3.$$

k	$x^{(k)}$	$e^{x^{(k)}}$	f_k	f_k'
0	0.	1.	1.	$-2.$
1	.50	1.65	.15	-1.35
2	.61	1.84	.01	-1.16
3	.62	1.86	.00	

When the evaluation of $f'(x)$ is burdensome, one may more conveniently apply *von Mises' iteration formula,*

$$x^{(k+1)} = x^{(k)} - \frac{f_k}{f_0'}, \qquad\qquad (4.3.3)$$

which uses the initial value of the slope, f_0' (Figure 4.2.2), at each step, but often does not converge as rapidly as the Newton-Raphson formula.

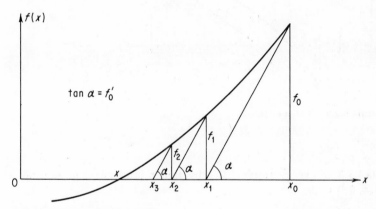

Figure 4.2.2.   von Mises' method.

Example 4.3.2. Solve Example 4.3.1 by von Mises' formula.

$$f_0' = f'(0) = -2.$$

k	$x^{(k)}$	$e^{x^{(k)}}$	f_k
0	0.	1.	1.
1	.50	1.65	.15
2	.58	1.79	.05
3	.60	1.82	.02
4	.61	1.84	.01
5	.62	1.86	.00

The evaluation of $f'(x)$ is also avoided by the *chords method* or *linear interpolation iterative formula.* Given two approximations $x^{(0)}$ and $x^{(k)}$ on *either* side of the root x, the $x^{(k+1)}$ approximation is obtained as the intersection $f(x) = 0$ of the straight line,

$$f(x) - f_k = \frac{f_0 - f_k}{x^{(0)} - x^{(k)}} (x - x^{(k)}),$$

connecting the points $(x^{(0)}, f_0)$, $(x^{(k)}, f_k)$ with the x-axis (Figure 4.2.3):

$$x^{(k+1)} = x^{(k)} - f_k \frac{x^{(0)} - x^{(k)}}{f_0 - f_k} = \frac{x^{(k)}f_0 - x^{(0)}f_k}{f_0 - f_k}. \qquad (4.3.4)$$

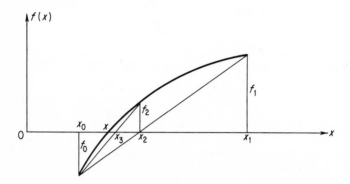

Figure 4.2.3 Chords method.

Example 4.3.3. Solve Example 4.3.1 by linear interpolation starting with $x^{(0)} = .4$, $x^{(1)} = .9$

k	$x^{(k)}$	f_k
0	.4	.29
1	.9	−.24
2	.67	−.06
3	.624	−.006
4	.620	−.001
5	.6192	−.0002

The *Bolzano* or *bisection method* is an exceptionally simple procedure for the determination of the real roots of an algebraic or transcendental equation $f(x) = 0$. The method does not usually converge as rapidly as Newton's method, but avoids the evaluation of $f'(x)$ and is well adapted to computer usage.

Starting at a point x to the *left* of the root, the method increments x successively by h until a "separation interval" of width h is found such that $f(x)$ and $f(x + h)$ have opposite signs $[f(x) \cdot f(x + h) < 0]$. A root is then known to fall between x and $x + h$. The increment h is then cut in half at every step, with the new interval $(x, x + h/4)$ used when $f(x)$ and $f(x + h/2)$ are of opposite signs, and the new interval $(x + h/2, x + 3h/4)$ used when $f(x + h/2)$ has the same sign as $f(x)$. The root is thus always approached from the left, and at any stage the width of the interval at the previous stage gives an upper bound of the error. Since $2^{10} \doteq 1000$, the width of the interval is reduced to $1/1000$ in ten steps.

Once a root is found, one may start to the right of it to locate the next root.

Example 4.3.4. Evaluate the root of Example 4.3.1 within .0001 by the bisection method, starting at $x = 0$ with $h = .5$.

x	h	$x + h$	$f(x)$	$f(x + h)$	Sign
0.	.5	.5	1.00000	.14872	+
.5	.5	1.	.14872	−.28171	−
.5	.25	.75	.14872	−.13300	−
.5	.125	.625	.14872	−.00675	−
.5	.0625	.5625	.14872	.06755	+
.5625	.03125	.59375	.06755	.02951	+
.59375	.01562	.60937	.02951	.01115	+
.60937	.00781	.61718	.01115	.00214	+
.61718	.00390	.62108	.00214	−.00231	−
.61718	.00195	.61913	.00214	−.00009	−
.61718	.00098	.61815	.00214	.00102	+
.61815	.00049	.61864	.00102	.00046	+
.61864	.00024	.61888	.00046	.00018	+
.61888	.00012	.61900	.00018	.00004	+
.61900	.00006	.61906	.00004	−.00002	−

PROBLEMS

4.1 Evaluate the roots of the following cubic equations by formula.

(a) $x^3 - .8x^2 + .2x - 3.6 = 0$

(b) $x^3 - x^2 + x - 1 = 0$

(c) $x^3 + x^2 + x + 1 = 0$

(d) $2x^3 - 3x + 4 = 0$

4.2 Evaluate the roots of the following quartic equations by Brown's method.

(a) $x^4 - 5x^2 + 4 = 0$

(b) $x^4 + x^3 - 7x^2 - x + 6 = 0$

(c) $x^4 - x^3 + 3x^2 - 4x + 12 = 0$

(d) $x^4 + 2x^3 + 5x^2 + 4x + 3 = 0$

(e) $x^4 - x^2 - 2x + 2 = 0$

(f) $x^4 + 2x^3 + 5x^2 + 4x + 4 = 0$

4.3 Evaluate the real roots of the following algebraic equations by the Newton-Raphson method, and their complex roots by the quadratic equation formula. Check the results by Newton's formulas.

(a) $x^3 - .8x^2 + .2x - 3.6 = 0$

(b) $x^3 + 2x^2 + 2.2x + .4 = 0$

(c) $x^3 + 12.1x^2 + 13.1x + 22.2 = 0$

(d) $x^4 + .5x^3 + .84x^2 - 1.66x - 1.32 = 0$

(e) $x^4 + x^3 + .56x^2 - 1.44x - 2.88 = 0$

(f) $x^4 - 3.2x^3 + 3.21x^2 - 8.19x + 13.23 = 0$

(g) $x^5 + 1.3x^4 + .86x^3 - 1.14x^2 - 2.58x + .3 = 0$

4.4 Evaluate the real roots of the equations of Problem 4.3 by the linear interpolation method.

4.5 Derive the iterative formulas for the evaluation of cubic and fourth roots by means of (4.2.1), and evaluate the following roots by iteration.

(a) $x^3 = 30$ (b) $x^3 = 7$

(c) $x^3 = .8$ (d) $x^4 = 15$

(e) $x^4 = 600$ (f) $x^4 = 1.30$

4.6 Evaluate the real root of the following transcendental equations lying within the given interval by the Newton-Raphson method.

(a) $\tan x = 4x$; $(0, \pi/2)$ (b) $4 \sin x = e^x$; $(0, .5)$

(c) $3 \cos x = \cosh x$; $(0, \pi/2)$ (d) $e^x \sin x = \frac{1}{2}x$; $(0, \pi)$

(e) $e^{2x} - e^x = 2x$; $(0, 1)$ (f) $2 \sinh x = \cosh x$; $(0, 1)$

4.7 Evaluate the roots of Problem 4.6 by von Mises' method.

4.8 Evaluate the roots of Problem 4.6 by linear interpolation.

4.9 Evaluate the roots of Problem 4.6 by the bisection method, starting from the given separation intervals.

Simultaneous Linear Algebraic Equations

Chapter Five

5.1 Pivotal Condensation of Determinants [Program 5.1]

The formal solution of the system of linear algebraic equations,

$$a_{11}x_1 + a_{12}x_2 + \cdots + a_{1j}x_j + \cdots + a_{1n}x_n = c_1$$
$$a_{21}x_1 + a_{22}x_2 + \cdots + a_{2j}x_j + \cdots + a_{2n}x_n = c_2$$
$$\cdots\cdots\cdots\cdots\cdots\cdots\cdots\cdots\cdots\cdots\cdots\cdots\cdots\cdots\cdots\cdots$$
$$a_{n1}x_1 + a_{n2}x_2 + \cdots + a_{nj}x_j + \cdots + a_{nn}x_n = c_n$$

(5.1.1)

is obtained by expressing the roots x_j as ratios of nth-order determinants,

$$x_j = \frac{D_{n,j}}{D_n},$$

(5.1.2)

where

$$D_n = \begin{vmatrix} a_{11} & a_{12} & \cdots & a_{1j} & \cdots & a_{1n} \\ a_{21} & a_{22} & \cdots & a_{2j} & \cdots & a_{2n} \\ \cdots & \cdots & \cdots & \cdots & \cdots & \cdots \\ a_{n1} & a_{n2} & \cdots & a_{nj} & \cdots & a_{nn} \end{vmatrix}$$

(5.1.3)

is the determinant of the coefficients, and $D_{n,j}$ is obtained from D_n by substituting the c_i for the a_{ij}:

$$D_{n,j} = \begin{vmatrix} a_{11} & a_{12} & \cdots & c_1 & \cdots & a_{1n} \\ a_{21} & a_{22} & \cdots & c_2 & \cdots & a_{2n} \\ \cdots\cdots\cdots\cdots\cdots\cdots\cdots\cdots\cdots \\ a_{n1} & a_{n2} & \cdots & c_n & \cdots & a_{nn} \end{vmatrix}. \tag{5.1.4}$$

Determinants are seldom used to solve systems with more than a few unknowns, but their numerical evaluation is needed in many applications of linear algebra.

The most efficient procedure for evaluating determinants, *pivotal condensation* (first given by Chiò in 1853), is based on the following two properties of determinants: (a) If all the elements of one row of a determinant D_n are multiplied by a constant, the value of D_n is multiplied by that constant; (b) the value of D_n is unchanged if the elements of one row multiplied by a constant are added to the corresponding elements of another row.

By these two rules, multiplying the $n - 1$ rows $i = 2, 3, \ldots, n$ by a_{11} and subtracting from them the first row multiplied respectively by a_{i1}, one obtains:

$$a_{11}^{n-1} D_n = \begin{vmatrix} a_{11} & a_{12} & a_{13} & & a_{1n} \\ 0 & a_{11}a_{22} - a_{21}a_{12} & a_{11}a_{23} - a_{21}a_{13} & \cdots & a_{11}a_{2n} - a_{21}a_{1n} \\ 0 & a_{11}a_{32} - a_{31}a_{12} & a_{11}a_{33} - a_{31}a_{13} & \cdots & a_{11}a_{3n} - a_{31}a_{1n} \\ \cdots\cdots\cdots\cdots\cdots\cdots\cdots\cdots\cdots\cdots\cdots \\ 0 & a_{11}a_{n2} - a_{n1}a_{12} & a_{11}a_{n3} - a_{n1}a_{13} & \cdots & a_{11}a_{nn} - a_{n1}a_{1n} \end{vmatrix}.$$

Expanding the last determinant by minors in terms of the elements of the first column and dividing by a_{11}^{n-1}, D_n becomes

$$D_n = \frac{1}{a_{11}^{n-2}} \begin{vmatrix} a_{11}a_{22} - a_{21}a_{12} & a_{11}a_{23} - a_{21}a_{13} & \cdots & a_{11}a_{2n} - a_{21}a_{1n} \\ a_{11}a_{32} - a_{31}a_{12} & a_{11}a_{33} - a_{31}a_{13} & \cdots & a_{11}a_{3n} - a_{31}a_{1n} \\ \cdots\cdots\cdots\cdots\cdots\cdots\cdots\cdots\cdots\cdots\cdots \\ a_{11}a_{n2} - a_{n1}a_{12} & a_{11}a_{n3} - a_{n1}a_{13} & \cdots & a_{11}a_{nn} - a_{n1}a_{1n} \end{vmatrix} \equiv D_{n-1}. \tag{a}$$

The elements of the $(n - 1)$st-order determinant of (a) are the second-order determinants obtained from (5.1.3) having the first-column elements a_{11}, a_{i1}. Any element a_{ij} may be brought to the *pivotal position* a_{11} by interchanging rows and/or columns, and remembering that each interchange is equivalent to multiplication of D_n by -1. Theoretically, the a_{ij} with largest absolute value should be used as pivot, but this is not always practical. Condensation is applied to D_{n-1} to obtain D_{n-2} and continued until the order of the determinant is reduced to 2.

The condensation of D_n to D_{n-1} by (a) requires $[2(n-1)^2 + (n-3)]$ multiplications, $(n-1)^2$ subtractions, and one division, or for large n a number of operations of the order of $3n^2$. Dividing the $n-1$ rows of D_{n-1} in (a) by a_{11}, and multiplying outside by a_{11}^{n-1}, the equivalent expression for D_{n-1} becomes

$$D_{n-1} \equiv D_n = a_{11} \begin{vmatrix} a_{22} - a_{21}\dfrac{a_{12}}{a_{11}} & a_{23} - a_{21}\dfrac{a_{13}}{a_{11}} & \cdots & a_{2n} - a_{21}\dfrac{a_{1n}}{a_{11}} \\ a_{32} - a_{31}\dfrac{a_{12}}{a_{11}} & a_{33} - a_{31}\dfrac{a_{13}}{a_{11}} & \cdots & a_{3n} - a_{31}\dfrac{a_{1n}}{a_{11}} \\ \cdots\cdots\cdots\cdots\cdots\cdots\cdots\cdots\cdots\cdots\cdots \\ a_{n2} - a_{n1}\dfrac{a_{12}}{a_{11}} & a_{n3} - a_{n1}\dfrac{a_{13}}{a_{11}} & \cdots & a_{nn} - a_{n1}\dfrac{a_{1n}}{a_{11}} \end{vmatrix}, \quad \textbf{(5.1.5)}$$

which requires $(n-1)^2 + 1$ multiplications, $(n-1)^2$ subtractions, and $n-1$ divisions, or for large n a number of operations of the order of $2(n-1)^2 \doteq 2n^2$. The evaluation of D_n by condensation thus requires $\sum\limits_{n=1}^{n} 2n^2 \doteq \frac{2}{3}n^3$ operations.

The solution of a system of n linear equations by determinants requires the evaluation of n $D_{n,j}$ and one D_n; hence, of $\frac{2}{3}n^3(n+1) \doteq \frac{2}{3}n^4$ operations.

Example 5.5.1. Evaluate D_4 by pivotal condensation (see Program 5.1).

$$D_4 = \begin{vmatrix} 2 & 4 & 6 & 8 \\ 3 & 1 & 2 & 1 \\ 1 & 2 & -2 & 2 \\ 2 & 3 & 4 & 1 \end{vmatrix} = 2\begin{vmatrix} 1 & 2 & 3 & 4 \\ 3 & 1 & 2 & 1 \\ 1 & 2 & -2 & 2 \\ 2 & 3 & 4 & 1 \end{vmatrix}$$

$$= 2\begin{vmatrix} 1 - 3\left(\frac{2}{1}\right) & 2 - 3\left(\frac{3}{1}\right) & 1 - 3\left(\frac{4}{1}\right) \\ 2 - 1\left(\frac{2}{1}\right) & -2 - 1\left(\frac{3}{1}\right) & 2 - 1\left(\frac{4}{1}\right) \\ 3 - 2\left(\frac{2}{1}\right) & 4 - 2\left(\frac{3}{1}\right) & 1 - 2\left(\frac{4}{1}\right) \end{vmatrix} = 2\begin{vmatrix} -5 & -7 & -11 \\ 0 & -5 & -2 \\ -1 & -2 & -7 \end{vmatrix}$$

$$= 2(-5)\begin{vmatrix} 1 & \frac{7}{5} & \frac{11}{5} \\ 0 & -5 & -2 \\ -1 & -2 & -7 \end{vmatrix} = 2(-5)\begin{vmatrix} -5 - 0\left(\frac{7}{5}\right) & -2 - 0\left(\frac{11}{5}\right) \\ -2 + 1\left(\frac{7}{5}\right) & -7 + 1\left(\frac{11}{5}\right) \end{vmatrix}$$

$$= -10\begin{vmatrix} -5 & -2 \\ -\frac{3}{5} & -\frac{24}{5} \end{vmatrix} = \frac{-10}{-5}\begin{vmatrix} -5 & -2 \\ 3 & 24 \end{vmatrix} = 2(-120 + 6) = -228.$$

5.2 Gauss's Elimination Methods [Programs 5.2, 9.7]

The system of linear equations of (5.1.1) is often written in *matrix* form as

$$
\begin{bmatrix}
a_{11} & a_{12} & \dots & a_{1n} \\
a_{21} & a_{22} & \dots & a_{2n} \\
& \cdots \cdots \cdots \cdots \cdots & \\
a_{n1} & a_{n2} & \dots & a_{nn}
\end{bmatrix}
\begin{bmatrix}
x_1 \\ x_2 \\ \cdots \\ x_n
\end{bmatrix}
=
\begin{bmatrix}
c_1 \\ c_2 \\ \cdots \\ c_n
\end{bmatrix},
\tag{5.2.1}
$$

or

$$
AX = C,
\tag{5.2.2}
$$

where the $n \times n$ array A of the a_{ij} is called the *matrix of the coefficients*, X is called the *column* of the unknowns x_i, and C the column of the constants c_i. The linear equations of the system are obtained by so-called *row-into-column multiplication* of the rows of A by the column X. For example, the second equation is obtained by multiplying the elements of the second row of A by the elements of the column X, adding these n products and equating the sum to the second element of C:

$$
a_{21}x_1 + a_{22}x_2 + \cdots + a_{2n}x_n = c_2.
$$

A linear system of equations may also be concisely written in *tabular form* as shown in Table 5.2.1.

Table 5.2.1

x_1	x_2	x_3	$\dots$	x_n	c_i
a_{11}	a_{12}	a_{13}	$\dots$	a_{1n}	c_1
a_{21}	a_{22}	a_{23}	$\dots$	a_{2n}	c_2
$\dots$	$\dots$	$\dots$	$\dots$	$\dots$	$\dots$
a_{n1}	a_{n2}	a_{n3}	$\dots$	a_{nn}	c_n

Most *elimination methods*, including the popular method of Gauss, first reduce the system of Table 5.2.1 to *triangular form* by eliminating one of the unknowns at a time. The unknown x_1 is first eliminated from $n-1$ equations by dividing the first equation by a_{11} and by subtracting this equation multiplied by a_{i1} $(i = 2, 3, \ldots, n)$ from the remaining $n-1$ equations. (The elimination process is thus seen to be identical with pivotal condensation.) The unknown x_2 is then eliminated from $n-2$ of the $n-1$ equations not containing x_1, and the process is continued until x_n appears only in the last equation, x_{n-1} and x_n in the next to the last, etc., and the system appears as in Table 5.2.2.

Table 5.2.2

x_1	x_2	x_3	...	x_n	c_i
1	t_{12}	t_{13}	...	t_{1n}	k_1
...	1	t_{23}	...	t_{2n}	k_2
...	...	...	...	...	...
...	...	...	...	1	k_n

The unknowns are then evaluated by *backward substitution:* x_n is obtained from the nth equation and substituted in the $(n-1)$st, which is solved for x_{n-1}; x_{n-1} and x_n are substituted in the $(n-2)$nd equation, which is solved for x_{n-2}, etc.

When an electric desk computer, or a slide rule, is used, the computations *should* be checked at each row by means of an additional column S of *sum checks* in the elimination table, which contains the sum of all the numbers appearing on each row and is operated upon as any other number of that row.*

Example 5.2.1. Solve the following system by Gauss's method.

No. of row	x_1	x_2	x_3	C	S	Explanations
[1]	2	2	4	18	26	Eq. I
[2]	1	3	2	13	19	Eq. II
[3]	3	1	3	14	21	Eq. III
[4]	1	1	2	9	13	$[1]/a_{11} = [1]/2$
[5]	0	2	0	4	6	$[2] -1\cdot[4]$
[6]	0	-2	-3	-13	-18	$[3] -3\cdot[4]$
[7]		1	0	2	3	$[5]/a_{22} = [5]/2$
[8]			0	-3	-9	$[6] + 2\cdot[7]$
[9]			1	3	4	$[8]/a_{33} = [8]/(-3)$

From [9]:

$$x_3 = 3;$$

from [7]:

$$x_2 = 2 - 0\cdot x_3 = 2;$$

from [4]:

$$x_1 = 9 - 2x_3 - x_2 = 1.$$

---

* See Program 6.2 for an example of solution by elimination of *band matrix* systems, i.e., systems with only a few neighboring unknowns in each equation.

Alternatively, by the Gauss-Jordan method,* after eliminating x_1 from each equation but the first, one eliminates x_2 from each equation but the second, etc.

Example 5.2.2. Solve the following system by the Gauss-Jordan method.

Row	x_1	x_2	x_3	C	S	Explanation
[1]	2	2	4	18	26	Eq. I
[2]	1	3	2	13	19	Eq. II
[3]	3	1	3	14	21	Eq. III
[4]	1	1	2	9	13	$[1]/a_{11} = [1]/2$
[5]	0	2	0	4	6	$[2] - 1 \cdot [4]$
[6]	0	−2	−3	−13	−18	$[3] - 3 \cdot [4]$
[7]		1	0	2	3	$[5]/a_{22} = [5]/2$
[8]	1	0	2	7	10	$[4] - 1 \cdot [7]$
[9]			−3	−9	−12	$[6] + 2 \cdot [7]$
[10]			1	3	4	$[9]/a_{33} = [9]/(-3)$
[11]		1	0	2	3	$[7] - 0 \cdot [10]$
[12]	1	0	0	1	2	$[8] - 2 \cdot [10]$

From [12]: $x_1 = 1$; from [11]: $x_2 = 2$; from [10]: $x_3 = 3$.

The Gauss elimination schemes require, for large n, a number of operations of the order of $2n^3/3$.

For the commonly used Cholewsky-Crout elimination method see N.M. Sec. 1.10.

5.3 Matrix Inversion by Elimination [Program 9.7]

It is often required in practice to solve m systems of n linear equations each, which have the same matrix of coefficients a_{ij}, but different columns of constants c_i, say columns $c_i^{(1)}$, $c_i^{(2)}$, ..., $c_i^{(m)}$, where m may be *larger* than n. In this case, instead of solving m separate systems, it is advantageous to solve n separate systems with columns of constants $\boldsymbol{C}^{(i)}$ equal to

system 1: $\quad c_1^{(1)} = 1, \ c_2^{(1)} = 0, \ c_3^{(1)} = 0, \ \ldots, \ c_n^{(1)} = 0,$

system 2: $\quad c_1^{(2)} = 0, \ c_2^{(2)} = 1, \ c_3^{(2)} = 0, \ \ldots, \ c_n^{(2)} = 0,$

. . . .

system n: $\quad c_1^{(n)} = 0, \ c_2^{(n)} = 0, \ c_3^{(n)} = 0, \ \ldots, \ c_n^{(n)} = 1.$

---

* At each stage of the Gauss-Jordan method the largest absolute value a_{ij} is usually chosen as pivot for greater accuracy (see Program 9.7). This is unnecessary in simple systems like the system of Example 5.2.2.

Calling the roots of these systems, respectively,

system 1: b_{11}, b_{21}, b_{31}, ..., b_{n1},

system 2: b_{12}, b_{22}, b_{32}, ..., b_{n2},

....

system n: b_{1n}, b_{2n}, b_{3n}, ..., b_{nn},

the root x_i of the system having a column of constants c_1, c_2, ..., c_n is obtained by row-into-column multiplication of the ith row of the matrix b_{ij}

$$B = \begin{bmatrix} b_{11} & b_{12} & b_{13} & \dots & b_{1n} \\ b_{21} & b_{22} & b_{23} & \dots & b_{2n} \\ \multicolumn{5}{c}{\dotfill} \\ b_{n1} & b_{n2} & b_{n3} & \dots & b_{nn} \end{bmatrix} \equiv A^{-1} \qquad \textbf{(5.3.1)}$$

by the column c_1, c_2, ..., c_n. The matrix B of the b_{ij} is called the *inverse* of the matrix A of the coefficients and is indicated by A^{-1}. Thus

$$x_i = b_{i1}c_1 + b_{i2}c_2 + \cdots + b_{in}c_n. \qquad \textbf{(5.3.2)}$$

The validity of (5.3.2) is immediately apparent if we notice that when the column C equals $C^{(j)}$, $x_i = b_{ij}$, and that the roots of a linear system of equations are proportional to the column of the constants.

The roots of the n separate systems

$$AX = C^{(i)} \qquad (i = 1, 2, \dots, n)$$

can be obtained simultaneously by elimination. The n columns $C^{(i)}$ are written one next to the other in the elimination table and, using the Gauss-Jordan elimination scheme, the unknowns b_{ij} are obtained directly in a single matrix. Inversion by elimination requires a number of operations of the order of $2n^3$.

Example 5.3.1. Evaluate by Gauss-Jordan elimination the inverse of the following matrix.

Row	x_1	x_2	x_3	$c^{(1)}$	$c^{(2)}$	$c^{(3)}$	Explanations
[1]	2	2	4	1	0	0	Eqs. I$^{(i)}$
[2]	1	3	2	0	1	0	Eqs. II$^{(i)}$
[3]	3	1	3	0	0	1	Eqs. III$^{(i)}$
[4]	1	1	2	1/2	0	0	$[1]/a_{11} = [1]/2$
[5]		2	0	$-1/2$	1	0	$[2] - 1 \cdot [4]$
[6]		-2	-3	$-3/2$	0	1	$[3] - 3 \cdot [4]$
[7]		1	0	$-1/4$	1/2	0	$[5]/a_{22} = [5]/2$
[8]	1	0	2	3/4	$-1/2$	0	$[4] - 1 \cdot [7]$
[9]			-3	-2	1	1	$[6] + 2 \cdot [7]$
[10]			1	2/3	$-1/3$	$-1/3$	$[9]/a_{33} = [9]/(-3)$
[11]		1	0	$-1/4$	1/2	0	$[7] - 0 \cdot [10]$
[12]	1	0	0	$-7/12$	1/6	2/3	$[8] - 2 \cdot [10]$

$$A^{-1} = \begin{bmatrix} -\dfrac{7}{12} & \dfrac{1}{6} & \dfrac{2}{3} \\[2ex] -\dfrac{1}{4} & \dfrac{1}{2} & 0 \\[2ex] \dfrac{2}{3} & -\dfrac{1}{3} & -\dfrac{1}{3} \end{bmatrix} \qquad \begin{matrix} \text{Row [12]} \\[2ex] \text{Row [11]} \\[2ex] \text{Row [10]} \end{matrix}$$

The scheme starts with a matrix

$$C = \begin{bmatrix} 1 & 0 & 0 \\ 0 & 1 & 0 \\ 0 & 0 & 1 \end{bmatrix} \equiv I$$

called a *unit matrix* I on the right half of the scheme, and ends with a unit matrix on the left half of the scheme. The rows of A^{-1} appear opposite the rows [12], [11], [10], rearranged to form the rows of a unit matrix I on the left half of the scheme. The value of x_3 for the constants column $c_1 = 18$, $c_2 = 13$, $c_3 = 14$ of Example 5.2.2 is, by (5.3.2), the product of the third row of A^{-1} into the column of the c_i's:

$$x_3 = \tfrac{2}{3}(18) - \tfrac{1}{3}(13) - \tfrac{1}{3}(14) = 3.$$

The value of x_1 for $c_1 = 2$, $c_2 = 2$, $c_3 = -2$ is the product of the first row of A^{-1} into the column of the c_i's:

$$x_1 = -\tfrac{7}{12}(2) + \tfrac{1}{6}(2) + \tfrac{2}{3}(-2) = -\tfrac{13}{6}.$$

5.4 Gauss-Seidel Iteration Method [Program 5.3]

Whenever the coefficient of a different root in each equation is large compared to the others, the equations may be solved for the large coefficient roots, which may always be put in the position a_{ii} by rearranging the rows and columns of the system. Thus, letting $b_{ij} = a_{ij}/a_{ii}$ and $k_i = c_i/a_{ii}$,

$$\begin{aligned}
x_1 &= k_1 - b_{12}x_2 - b_{13}x_3 - \cdots - b_{1n}x_n, \\
x_2 &= k_2 - b_{21}x_1 - b_{23}x_3 - \cdots - b_{2n}x_n, \\
&\cdots\cdots\cdots\cdots\cdots\cdots\cdots\cdots\cdots\cdots\cdots\cdots\cdots \\
x_n &= k_n - b_{n1}x_1 - b_{n2}x_2 - \cdots - b_{n,n-1}x_{n-1},
\end{aligned} \qquad (5.4.1)$$

initial values $x_j^{(0)}$ may be substituted in the right-hand members of (5.4.1) to determine improved values $x_j^{(1)}$. Substitution of the values $x_j^{(1)}$ in the right-hand members of (5.4.1) leads to the second approximations $x_j^{(2)}$, and so forth. The iteration process is continued until $x_j^{(k)} = x_j^{(k+1)}$ within the required accuracy.

It is seen from (5.4.1) that, letting

$$B = - \begin{bmatrix} 0 & b_{12} & b_{13} & \ldots & b_{1n} \\ b_{21} & 0 & b_{23} & \ldots & b_{2n} \\ \multicolumn{5}{c}{\dotfill} \\ b_{n1} & b_{n2} & b_{n3} & \ldots & 0 \end{bmatrix}, \qquad (5.4.2)$$

this iteration process (which is due to Gauss) is represented by the *matrix iteration equation*

$$X^{(k+1)} = K + BX^{(k)}. \qquad (5.4.3)$$

In the *Gauss-Seidel iteration method* $x_j^{(0)}$ is usually set equal to zero for $j = 2, 3, \ldots, n$, so that $x_1^{(1)} = k_1$. In the second of the equations (5.4.1) $x_j^{(0)}$ is set equal to zero for $j = 3, 4, \ldots, n$, but x_1 is taken equal to $x_1^{(1)}$; the equation is then solved for $x_2^{(1)}$. Similarly, in all other equations the last available value of the x_j is used at each step.

Splitting the iteration matrix B into the *upper* and *lower triangular* matrices,

$$U = - \begin{bmatrix} 0 & b_{12} & b_{13} & \ldots & b_{1n} \\ 0 & 0 & b_{23} & \ldots & b_{2n} \\ \multicolumn{5}{c}{\dotfill} \\ 0 & 0 & 0 & \ldots & 0 \end{bmatrix}, \qquad (5.4.4)$$

$$L = - \begin{bmatrix} 0 & 0 & 0 & \ldots & 0 \\ b_{21} & 0 & 0 & \ldots & 0 \\ b_{31} & b_{32} & 0 & \ldots & 0 \\ \multicolumn{5}{c}{\dotfill} \\ b_{n1} & b_{n2} & b_{n3} & \ldots & 0 \end{bmatrix}, \qquad (5.4.5)$$

the Gauss-Seidel iteration method is represented by the matrix equation

$$X^{(k+1)} = K + UX^{(k)} + LX^{(k+1)}. \qquad (5.4.6)$$

The Gauss and Gauss-Seidel iteration methods converge, whatever the initial values $x_j^{(0)}$, if in *each* of the equations (5.4.1) the sum of the *absolute* values of the coefficients b_{ij} is at most equal to, and in at least one equation less than one,[*] i.e., provided

$$\sum_{\substack{j=1 \\ j \neq i}}^{n} |b_{ij}| \leq 1 \qquad (i = 1, 2, \ldots, n), \qquad (5.4.7)$$

with the $<$ sign valid for at least one i. Usually, the smaller the sums in (5.4.7), the faster the convergence.

[*]This condition assumes that the coefficient matrix is irreducible.

Example 5.4.1. Solve the following system by Gauss-Seidel iteration.

$$10x_1 + 2x_2 + x_3 = 9,$$
$$2x_1 + 20x_2 - 2x_3 = -44,$$
$$-2x_1 + 3x_2 + 10x_3 = 22,$$

or

$$x_1 = .9 - .2x_2 - .1x_3, \qquad \Sigma |b_{1j}| = .3 < 1;$$
$$x_2 = -2.2 - .1x_1 + .1x_3, \qquad \Sigma |b_{2j}| = .2 < 1;$$
$$x_3 = 2.2 + .2x_1 - .3x_2, \qquad \Sigma |b_{3j}| = .5 < 1.$$

Solution to two decimal places:

$$x_2^{(0)} = x_3^{(0)} = 0; \quad x_1^{(1)} = .90;$$
$$x_1^{(1)} = .90; \quad x_3^{(0)} = 0; \quad x_2^{(1)} = -2.20 - .09 = -2.29;$$
$$x_1^{(1)} = .90; \quad x_2^{(1)} = -2.29; \quad x_3^{(1)} = 2.20 + .18 + .69 = 3.07;$$
$$x_2^{(1)} = -2.29; \quad x_3^{(1)} = 3.07; \quad x_1^{(2)} = .90 + .46 - .31 = 1.05, \text{ etc.}$$

k	1	2	3	4
x_1	.90	1.05	1.00	1.00
x_2	-2.29	-2.00	-2.00	-2.00
x_3	3.07	3.01	3.00	3.00

5.5 Homogeneous Equations and Eigenvalues [Programs 5.4, 5.5]

When all the constants c_i of the system (5.1.1) are equal to zero the system is called *homogeneous*. A homogeneous system always has a trivial solution $x_j = 0 (j = 1, 2, \ldots, n)$. Since the x_j are given by the ratios $D_{n,j}/D_n$ [see (5.1.2)], and since the $D_{n,j}$ are all equal to zero because of their zero jth column [see (5.1.4)], a necessary condition for the existence of roots $x_j \neq 0$ is that the determinant D_n of the coefficients be equal to zero. This condition is also sufficient.

Homogeneous equations of the following type are often encountered in certain kinds of physical problems:

$$a_{11}x_1 + a_{12}x_2 + \cdots + a_{1n}x_n = \lambda x_1,$$
$$a_{21}x_1 + a_{22}x_2 + \cdots + a_{2n}x_n = \lambda x_2,$$
$$\cdots\cdots\cdots\cdots\cdots\cdots\cdots\cdots\cdots\cdots\cdots \qquad \textbf{(5.5.1)}$$
$$a_{n1}x_1 + a_{n2}x_2 + \cdots + a_{nn}x_n = \lambda x_n,$$

where λ is an undetermined parameter. The n values of λ for which non-zero roots of the homogeneous equations (5.5.1) exist, that is, for which $D_n = 0$, are called the *eigenvalues* or the *characteristic values* of the parameter λ. When the n eigenvalues are distinct, to each eigenvalue corresponds a set of n roots, called an *eigenvector*, which may always be determined, within an arbitrary multiplying constant, by solving $n - 1$ of the equations (5.5.1) for $n - 1$ unknowns in terms of the remaining unknown.

Example 5.5.1. Determine the eigenvalues and the corresponding eigenvectors of the following system.

$$10x_1 + 2x_2 + x_3 = \lambda x_1,$$
$$2x_1 + 10x_2 + x_3 = \lambda x_2,$$
$$2x_1 + x_2 + 10x_3 = \lambda x_3.$$

$$D_n(\lambda) = \begin{vmatrix} 10 - \lambda & 2 & 1 \\ 2 & 10 - \lambda & 1 \\ 2 & 1 & 10 - \lambda \end{vmatrix}$$

$$= (10 - \lambda)^3 - 7(10 - \lambda) + 6 = 0.$$

$$10 - \lambda = \begin{cases} -3 \\ +1 \\ +2 \end{cases} \quad \lambda_1 = 13; \quad \lambda_2 = 9; \quad \lambda_3 = 8.$$

$\lambda_1 = 13$:

$$-3x_1 + 2x_2 + x_3 = 0,$$
$$2x_1 - 3x_2 + x_3 = 0,$$
$$2x_1 + x_2 - 3x_3 = 0.$$

Solution of the first two equations for x_1, x_2 with $x_3 = 1$, gives the eigenvector

$$x_1^{(1)} = 1, \quad x_2^{(1)} = 1, \quad x_3^{(1)} = 1,$$

which satisfies all three equations.

$\lambda_2 = 9$:

$$x_1 + 2x_2 + x_3 = 0,$$
$$2x_1 + x_2 + x_3 = 0,$$
$$2x_1 + x_2 + x_3 = 0.$$

With $x_3^{(2)} = 1$, the second eigenvector becomes

$$x_1^{(2)} = -\tfrac{1}{3}, \quad x_2^{(2)} = -\tfrac{1}{3}, \quad x_3^{(2)} = 1.$$

$\lambda_3 = 8$:

$$2x_1 + 2x_2 + x_3 = 0,$$
$$2x_1 + 2x_2 + x_3 = 0,$$
$$2x_1 + x_2 + 2x_3 = 0.$$

With $x_3^{(3)} = 1$, the third eigenvector becomes

$$x_1^{(3)} = -\tfrac{3}{2}, \quad x_2^{(3)} = 1, \quad x_3^{(3)} = 1.$$

The largest eigenvalue and the corresponding eigenvector may also be obtained by iteration. Starting with an initial eigenvector $x_i^{(0)}$ one operates on it repeatedly with the matrix of the coefficients of the system (5.5.1), using row-into-column multiplication, and dividing the column at each step by the x_i one chooses equal to unity. This method is well adapted to machine calculations. (See Program 5.5 for exceptions.)

Example 5.5.2. Solve Example 5.5.1 by iteration for $\lambda = \lambda_1$.

Initial eigenvector:

$$x_1^{(0)} = 1, \quad x_2^{(0)} = 1, \quad x_3^{(0)} = 0.$$

$$\begin{bmatrix} 10 & 2 & 1 \\ 2 & 10 & 1 \\ 2 & 1 & 10 \end{bmatrix} \begin{bmatrix} 1 \\ 1 \\ 0 \end{bmatrix} = \begin{bmatrix} 12 \\ 12 \\ 3 \end{bmatrix} \doteq 12 \begin{bmatrix} 1 \\ 1 \\ .25 \end{bmatrix};$$

$$\begin{bmatrix} 10 & 2 & 1 \\ 2 & 10 & 1 \\ 2 & 1 & 10 \end{bmatrix} \begin{bmatrix} 1 \\ 1 \\ .25 \end{bmatrix} = \begin{bmatrix} 12.25 \\ 12.25 \\ 5.50 \end{bmatrix} = 12.25 \begin{bmatrix} 1 \\ 1 \\ .45 \end{bmatrix}.$$

Repeating the row-into-column multiplication with $x_1^{(0)} = 1$, the successive approximations become

$$12.45 \begin{bmatrix} 1 \\ 1 \\ .6 \end{bmatrix}; \quad 12.6 \begin{bmatrix} 1 \\ 1 \\ .7 \end{bmatrix}; \quad 12.7 \begin{bmatrix} 1 \\ 1 \\ .8 \end{bmatrix};$$

$$12.8 \begin{bmatrix} 1 \\ 1 \\ .9 \end{bmatrix}; \quad 12.9 \begin{bmatrix} 1 \\ 1 \\ .93 \end{bmatrix}; \quad 12.93 \begin{bmatrix} 1 \\ 1 \\ .95 \end{bmatrix};$$

$$13 \begin{bmatrix} 1 \\ 1 \\ 1 \end{bmatrix}; \quad 13 \begin{bmatrix} 1 \\ 1 \\ 1 \end{bmatrix},$$

or

$$\lambda_1 = 13; \quad x_1 = x_2 = x_3 = 1.$$

PROBLEMS

5.1 Evaluate the following determinants by pivotal condensation.

(a) $\begin{vmatrix} 1 & 1 & 1 \\ 1 & 2 & 1 \\ 1 & 3 & 2 \end{vmatrix}$

(b) $\begin{vmatrix} 2 & 1 & 2 & 1 \\ 1 & 1 & 1 & 1 \\ 1 & 2 & 1 & -2 \\ 3 & 1 & 2 & 2 \end{vmatrix}$

(c) $\begin{vmatrix} 1.2 & -2.1 & 3.2 & 4.3 \\ -1.4 & -2.6 & 3.0 & 4.1 \\ -2.2 & 1.7 & .4 & 1.2 \\ 1.1 & 3.6 & .5 & 4.6 \end{vmatrix}$

(d) $\begin{vmatrix} 1 & 1 & 0 & 0 & 0 \\ 0 & 1 & 1 & 0 & 0 \\ -2 & 0 & 0 & 0 & 1 \\ -2 & 1 & 0 & 0 & 1 \\ -3 & 1 & 0 & 1 & 0 \end{vmatrix}$

5.2 Solve the following systems by Gauss's elimination.

(a) $\begin{bmatrix} 1 & 2 & 1 \\ 2 & 2 & 1 \\ 1 & 2 & 2 \end{bmatrix} \begin{bmatrix} x_1 \\ x_2 \\ x_3 \end{bmatrix} = \begin{bmatrix} 5 \\ 6 \\ 7 \end{bmatrix}$

(b) $\begin{bmatrix} 2 & 2 & 1 & 2 \\ -1 & 2 & 0 & 1 \\ -3 & 1 & 2 & 1 \\ -1 & 0 & 0 & 2 \end{bmatrix} \begin{bmatrix} x_1 \\ x_2 \\ x_3 \\ x_4 \end{bmatrix} = \begin{bmatrix} 7 \\ -2 \\ -3 \\ 0 \end{bmatrix}$

(c) $\begin{bmatrix} 2 & 1 & 0 & 0 & 0 & 0 \\ 1 & 2 & 1 & 0 & 0 & 0 \\ 0 & 1 & 2 & 1 & 0 & 0 \\ 0 & 0 & 1 & 2 & 1 & 0 \\ 0 & 0 & 0 & 1 & 2 & 1 \\ 0 & 0 & 0 & 0 & 1 & 2 \end{bmatrix} \begin{bmatrix} x_1 \\ x_2 \\ x_3 \\ x_4 \\ x_5 \\ x_6 \end{bmatrix} = \begin{bmatrix} 4 \\ 8 \\ 10 \\ 16 \\ 20 \\ 17 \end{bmatrix}$

(d) $\begin{bmatrix} 1.2 & 2.1 & -1.1 & 4.0 \\ -1.1 & 2.0 & 3.1 & 3.9 \\ -2.1 & -2.2 & 3.7 & 16.0 \\ -1.0 & -2.3 & 4.7 & 12.0 \end{bmatrix} \begin{bmatrix} x_1 \\ x_2 \\ x_3 \\ x_4 \end{bmatrix} = \begin{bmatrix} 6.0 \\ 3.9 \\ 12.2 \\ 4.0 \end{bmatrix}$

5.3 Evaluate the inverse of each matrix of coefficients in Problem 5.2.

5.4 Evaluate the unknowns in the equations of Problem 5.2 for the following columns of constants:

(a) $\begin{bmatrix} 2 \\ -1 \\ 4 \end{bmatrix}$, $\begin{bmatrix} -1 \\ 2 \\ 3 \end{bmatrix}$

(b) $\begin{bmatrix} 1 \\ 1 \\ -1 \\ -1 \end{bmatrix}$, $\begin{bmatrix} 3 \\ -1 \\ -2 \\ -3 \end{bmatrix}$

(c) $\begin{bmatrix} 10 \\ 9 \\ 8 \\ 7 \\ 6 \\ 5 \end{bmatrix}$, $\begin{bmatrix} 1 \\ -1 \\ 1 \\ -1 \\ 1 \\ -1 \end{bmatrix}$

(d) $\begin{bmatrix} 2.1 \\ 4.2 \\ -3.9 \\ 6.2 \end{bmatrix}$, $\begin{bmatrix} -1.2 \\ 1.3 \\ -1.4 \\ 2.6 \end{bmatrix}$

5.5 Solve the following systems by the Gauss-Seidel iteration method:

(a) $\begin{bmatrix} 10 & -5 & -2 \\ -4 & 10 & -3 \\ -1 & -6 & 10 \end{bmatrix} \begin{bmatrix} x_1 \\ x_2 \\ x_3 \end{bmatrix} = \begin{bmatrix} 3 \\ 3 \\ 3 \end{bmatrix}$

(b) $\begin{bmatrix} 10 & -2 & -1 & -1 \\ -2 & 10 & -1 & -1 \\ -1 & -1 & 10 & -2 \\ -1 & -1 & -2 & 10 \end{bmatrix} \begin{bmatrix} x_1 \\ x_2 \\ x_3 \\ x_4 \end{bmatrix} = \begin{bmatrix} 3 \\ 15 \\ 27 \\ -9 \end{bmatrix}$

(c) $\begin{bmatrix} 2 & 1 & 0 & 0 & 0 & 0 \\ 1 & 2 & 1 & 0 & 0 & 0 \\ 0 & 1 & 2 & 1 & 0 & 0 \\ 0 & 0 & 1 & 2 & 1 & 0 \\ 0 & 0 & 0 & 1 & 2 & 1 \\ 0 & 0 & 0 & 0 & 1 & 2 \end{bmatrix} \begin{bmatrix} x_1 \\ x_2 \\ x_3 \\ x_4 \\ x_5 \\ x_6 \end{bmatrix} = \begin{bmatrix} 2 \\ 2 \\ 2 \\ 2 \\ 2 \\ 1 \end{bmatrix}$

(d) $\begin{bmatrix} 4 & 1 & 0 & 0 & 1 & 0 & 0 \\ 1 & 4 & 1 & 0 & 0 & 1 & 0 \\ 0 & 1 & 4 & 1 & 0 & 0 & 1 \\ 0 & 0 & 1 & 4 & 1 & 0 & 0 \\ 1 & 0 & 0 & 1 & 4 & 1 & 0 \\ 0 & 1 & 0 & 0 & 1 & 4 & 1 \\ 0 & 0 & 1 & 0 & 0 & 1 & 4 \end{bmatrix} \begin{bmatrix} x_1 \\ x_2 \\ x_3 \\ x_4 \\ x_5 \\ x_6 \\ x_7 \end{bmatrix} = \begin{bmatrix} 8 \\ 4 \\ 8 \\ 9 \\ 5 \\ 6 \\ 10 \end{bmatrix}$

5.6 Determine the eigenvalues of the following matrices and the corresponding eigenvectors:

(a) $\begin{bmatrix} 2 & 1 \\ 1 & 2 \end{bmatrix}$

(b) $\begin{bmatrix} 0 & 1 & 1 \\ 1 & 0 & 1 \\ 1 & 1 & 0 \end{bmatrix}$

(c) $\begin{bmatrix} 2 & -1 & -1 \\ -1 & 2 & -1 \\ -1 & -1 & 2 \end{bmatrix}$

(d) $\begin{bmatrix} 2 & 1 & 3 \\ 1 & 3 & 4 \\ 3 & 4 & 5 \end{bmatrix}$

(e) $\begin{bmatrix} 2 & 1 & 0 & 0 \\ 1 & 2 & 1 & 0 \\ 0 & 1 & 2 & 1 \\ 0 & 0 & 1 & 2 \end{bmatrix}$

5.7 Determine the largest eigenvalue and the corresponding eigenvector of the following matrices by iteration, starting with a vector of the form $\begin{bmatrix} 1 \\ 0 \\ \cdot \\ \cdot \\ 0 \end{bmatrix}$:

(a) $\begin{bmatrix} 2 & 1 \\ 1 & 2 \end{bmatrix}$

(b) $\begin{bmatrix} 4 & -1 \\ -1 & 4 \end{bmatrix}$

(c) $\begin{bmatrix} 10 & -2 & 1 \\ -2 & 10 & -2 \\ 1 & -2 & 10 \end{bmatrix}$

(d) $\begin{bmatrix} 10 & 1 & 1 & 0 & 0 \\ 1 & 10 & 1 & 1 & 0 \\ 1 & 1 & 10 & 1 & 1 \\ 0 & 1 & 1 & 10 & 1 \\ 0 & 0 & 1 & 1 & 10 \end{bmatrix}$

**Ordinary
Boundary-value
Problems**

Chapter Six

6.1 Second-order Boundary-value Problems [Programs 6.1, 6.2]

The numerical solution of the *linear*, second-order, boundary-value problem

$$y'' + f(x)y' + g(x)y = F(x),$$
$$y(a) = y_0, \quad y(b) = y_n,$$

(6.1.1)

consists in

(a) substituting approximate expressions with the same order of error for the derivatives of y,

(b) applying the linear difference operators thus obtained at the $n - 1$ pivotal points $(i = 1, 2, \ldots, n - 1)$ where the y_i are unknown, and

(c) solving the system of $n - 1$ linear algebraic equations in the unknowns y_i.

The differentiation formulas most commonly used for this purpose are 3-point, centered formulas, with errors of order h^2.

Multiplying (6.1.1) by h^2 and substituting (3.2.18) and (3.2.11) for $h^2 y''$ and hy', respectively, we obtain the finite difference equation

$$y_{i+1} - 2y_i + y_{i-1} + \frac{h}{2}f_i(y_{i+1} - y_{i-1}) + h^2 g_i y_i = h^2 F_i,$$

or

$$\left(1 - \frac{h}{2}f_i\right)y_{i-1} - (2 - h^2 g_i)y_i + \left(1 + \frac{h}{2}f_i\right)y_{i+1} = h^2 F_i. \qquad \textbf{(6.1.2)}$$

Equation (6.1.2), applied at $i = 1, 2, \ldots, n - 1$, gives the set of $n - 1$ equations to be solved for the $n - 1$ unknowns y_i.

Example 6.1.1. Integrate the following problem using $h_1 = \frac{1}{4}$ and $h_2 = \frac{1}{8}$.

$$y'' - y = 0; \quad y(0) = 0, \quad y(1) = 1.$$

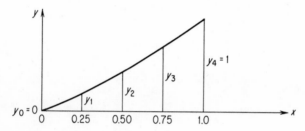

Figure 6.1.1

With $f(x) = 0, g(x) = -1, F(x) = 0$, and $h_1 = \frac{1}{4}$ (Fig. 6.1.1),

$$(1 - 0)y_{i-1} - (2 + \tfrac{1}{16})y_i + (1 + 0)y_{i+1} = 0 \qquad \text{[by (6.1.2)]}$$

or

$$y_{i-1} - 2.0625y_i + y_{i+1} = 0; \quad y_0 = 0, \quad y_4 = 1.$$

$i = 1:$ $0 - 2.0625y_1 + y_2 = 0;$

$i = 2:$ $y_1 - 2.0625y_2 + y_3 = 0;$

$i = 3:$ $y_2 - 2.0625y_3 + 1 = 0;$

from which, by elimination,

$$y_1 = .2151, \quad y_2 = .4437, \quad y_3 = .7000.$$

With $h_2 = \frac{1}{8}$, and with coefficients rounded off to four decimal figures, the system of seven equations,

$$y_{i-1} - (2 + \tfrac{1}{64})y_i + y_{i+1} = 0; \quad y_0 = 0, \quad y_8 = 1 \quad (i = 1, 2, \ldots, 7),$$

gives (see Program 6.1)

$y_1 = .1067;$ $y_2 = .2150;$ $y_3 = .3267;$ $y_4 = .4435;$

$y_5 = .5672;$ $y_6 = .6998;$ $y_7 = .8433.$

From the values of y at $x = .25, .50, .75$ obtained with $h_1 = .25$ and $h_2 = .125$ the following h^2-extrapolated values are obtained which may be compared with the exact solution $y = \sinh x/\sinh 1$.

$y_{1,2}(.25) = \frac{4}{3}(.2150) - \frac{1}{3}(.2151) = .21497$ [.21495],

$y_{1,2}(.50) = \frac{4}{3}(.4435) - \frac{1}{3}(.4437) = .44343$ [.44341],

$y_{1,2}(.75) = \frac{4}{3}(.6998) - \frac{1}{3}(.7000) = .69973$ [.69973].

Example 6.1.2. Integrate the following problem with $h = \frac{1}{3}$.

$$y'' - \frac{14}{x} y' + x^3 y = 2x^3; \quad y(0) = 2; \quad y(1) = 0.$$

With $f(x) = -14/x$, $g(x) = x^3$, $F(x) = 2x^3$, $h = \frac{1}{3}$, (6.1.2) gives

$$\left(1 + \frac{1}{6}\frac{14}{x_i}\right) y_{i-1} - \left(2 - \frac{1}{9}x_i^3\right) y_i + \left(1 - \frac{1}{6}\frac{14}{x_i}\right) y_{i+1} = \frac{2}{9} x_i^3;$$

$i = 1$:

$$\left(1 + \frac{1}{6}\frac{14}{\frac{1}{3}}\right) 2 - \left(2 - \frac{1}{9}\frac{1}{27}\right) y_1 + \left(1 - \frac{1}{6}\frac{14}{\frac{1}{3}}\right) y_2 = \frac{2}{9}\frac{1}{27},$$

$i = 2$:

$$\left(1 + \frac{1}{6}\frac{14}{\frac{2}{3}}\right) y_1 - \left(2 - \frac{1}{9}\frac{8}{27}\right) y_2 + \left(1 - \frac{1}{6}\frac{14}{\frac{2}{3}}\right) \cdot 0 = \frac{2}{9}\frac{8}{27},$$

from which

$y_1 = 1.03\ [2.00], \quad y_2 = 2.32\ [2.00].$*

The solution of nonlinear second-order boundary-value problems by forward integration is illustrated in Section 7.7.

6.2 Higher-order Boundary-value Problems [Program 6.3]

Ordinary, linear boundary-value problems are usually governed by even-order equations and have the same number of conditions at both ends of the range of integration. Fictitious pivotal points, outside the range of integration, must be used at times to express the boundary conditions in terms of finite differences.

---

* For the solutions with 5, 11, and 23 pivotal values see Program 6.2.

Example 6.2.1. Solve the following problem using $h = \frac{1}{4}$.

$$y^{iv} - 16y = x; \quad y(0) = y''(0) = 0, \quad y(1) = y'(1) = 0.$$

By (3.2.29), the differential equation becomes

$$y_{i-2} - 4y_{i-1} + (6 - 16h^4)y_i - 4y_{i+1} + y_{i+2} = h^4 x_i. \tag{a}$$

Using (3.2.11) and (3.2.18) to approximate y' and y'', the boundary conditions become

$$y_0 = 0; \quad y_{-1} + y_1 = 0 \quad \text{or} \quad y_{-1} = -y_1; \tag{b}$$
$$y_n = 0; \quad y_{n-1} - y_{n+1} = 0 \quad \text{or} \quad y_{n+1} = y_{n-1}.$$

With $h = \frac{1}{4}$, (a) and (b) give,

$$i = 1: \quad -y_1 - 4 \cdot 0 + (6 - \tfrac{1}{16})y_1 - 4y_2 + y_3 = .25/256,$$
$$i = 2: \quad 0 - 4y_1 + (6 - \tfrac{1}{16})y_2 - 4y_3 + 0 = .50/256,$$
$$i = 3: \quad y_1 - 4y_2 + (6 - \tfrac{1}{16})y_3 + 0 + y_3 = .75/256,$$

from which (see Program 6.3)

$$y_1 = .00255 \,[.00197], \quad y_2 = .00340 \,[.00251], \quad y_3 = .00202 \,[.00127].$$

6.3 Characteristic-value Problems [Program 5.4]

A homogeneous differential equation with homogeneous boundary conditions may have a solution $y(x)$ not identically zero for certain values of a parameter appearing in the equation, called *characteristic values* or *eigenvalues*.

Approximations to the *lowest* characteristic values of *linear* equations are easily obtained by transforming the differential equation into the corresponding difference equation, and solving the eigenvalue problem for the set of linear algebraic equations thus derived (Sec. 5.5).

Example 6.3.1. Determine the lowest eigenvalue k of the following problem:

$$y'' + ky = 0, \quad y(0) = 0, \quad y(1) = 0. \tag{a}$$

By Eq. (6.1.2), with $f(x) = 0, g(x) = k$, and $F(x) = 0$,

$$y_{i-1} - (2 - kh^2)y_i + y_{i+1} = 0, \quad y_0 = y_n = 0.$$

With $h = \frac{1}{2}$:

$$0 - (2 - k/4)y_1 + 0 = 0,$$

$$y_1 \neq 0 \quad \therefore \quad 2 - \frac{k}{4} = 0, \quad k^{(1)} = 8.$$

With $h = \frac{1}{3}$ and assuming y to be symmetrical about $x = \frac{1}{2}$ so that $y_2 = y_1$:

$$0 - \left(2 - \frac{k}{9}\right) y_1 + y_1 = -\left(1 - \frac{k}{9}\right) y_1 = 0,$$

$$y_1 \neq 0 \quad \therefore \quad 1 - \frac{k}{9} = 0, \quad k^{(2)} = 9.$$

With $h = \frac{1}{4}$ and $y_1 = y_3$:

$$0 - \left(2 - \frac{k}{16}\right) y_1 + y_2 = 0,$$

$$y_1 - \left(2 - \frac{k}{16}\right) y_2 + y_1 = 0.$$

For y_1 and y_2 to be different from zero, the determinant of this set of equations must be equal to zero (Sec. 5.1):

$$\begin{vmatrix} (2 - k/16) & -1 \\ -2 & (2 - k/16) \end{vmatrix} = \left(2 - \frac{k}{16}\right)^2 - 2 = 0,$$

$$2 - \frac{k}{16} = \mp\sqrt{2}, \quad k^{(3)} = 16(2 \mp \sqrt{2}) = \begin{cases} 9.38, \\ 54.62. \end{cases}$$

[The value $k = 54.62$ is the first approximation to the third eigenvalue of problem (a), and corresponds to deflections $y_1 = y_3$ of sign opposite to the sign of y_2.] The h^2-extrapolations of (3.6.1) may be used to estimate the true value of $k(= \pi^2 = 9.87)$:

$$h_1 = \frac{1}{2}, \quad h_2 = \frac{1}{3}, \quad \frac{h_1}{h_2} = \frac{3}{2}, \quad k_{1,2} = \frac{(\frac{3}{2})^2 \cdot 9 - 8}{(\frac{3}{2})^2 - 1} = 9.8;$$

$$h_1 = \frac{1}{3}, \quad h_2 = \frac{1}{4}, \quad \frac{h_1}{h_2} = \frac{4}{3}, \quad k_{2,3} = \frac{(\frac{4}{3})^2 \cdot 9.38 - 9}{(\frac{4}{3})^2 - 1} = 9.87.$$

The solution of nonlinear second-order characteristic-value problems by forward integration is illustrated in Section 7.7.

PROBLEMS

6.1 Evaluate the pivotal values of the solutions of the following boundary-value problems by finite difference equations with the given spacings h. Use h^2-extrapolations to improve the values at the points common to two spacings.

(a) $y'' + 4y = 0$; $y(0) = 0$, $y(1) = 1$; $h_1 = .5$, $h_2 = .25$

(b) $y'' - y = x^2$; $y(0) = 0$, $y(1) = 0$; $h = .2$

(c) $y'' + 2y' + y = 30x$; $y(0) = 0$, $y(1) = 0$; $h_1 = .5$, $h_2 = .25$

(d) $y'' + 50xy = 50$; $y(0) = 0$, $y(1) = 0$; $h = .2$

(e) $y'' + (1 - x)y' + xy = x$; $y(0) = 0$, $y(1) = 0$; $h = .25$

(f) $y'' + (\sin x)y = \cos x$; $y(0) = 0$, $y(\pi) = 0$; $h_1 = \pi/5$, $h_2 = \pi/10$

(g) $y'' + 200e^{-x}y = 100x^2$; $y(0) = 0$, $y(1) = 0$; $h = .1$

(h) $y^{iv} + 256y = 0$; $y(0) = 0$, $y'(0) = 0$, $y(1) = 1$, $y'(1) = 0$; $h_1 = .5$, $h_2 = .25$

(i) $y^{iv} + 125x^2y = 125x$; $y(0) = y'(0) = 0$, $y(1) = 2$, $y''(1) = 0$; $h = .2$

(j) $y^{iv} + 256(1 - x^2)y = 256x(1 - x)$; $y(0) = y'(0) = 0$, $y(1) = y'(1) = 0$; $h_1 = .5$, $h_2 = .25$

(k) $y^{iv} + 625(x^2 - 1)y = 625x$; $y(0) = y''(0) = 0$, $y(1) = y''(1) = 0$; $h = .2$

(l) $y^{iv} + 25xy'' + 625x^2y = 0$; $y(0) = 1$, $y'(0) = 0$, $y(1) = 0$, $y'(1) = 0$; $h = .2$

(m) $y^{iv} + 15y''' + 50y'' + 125y' + 625y = 1250$; $y(0) = 1$, $y'(0) = 0$, $y(1) = 0$, $y''(1) = 0$; $h_1 = .2$, $h_2 = .1$

6.2 Determine the lowest eigenvalue k of the following problems, using the given spacings h, and h^2-extrapolation.

(a) $y'' + kxy = 0$; $y(0) = y(1) = 0$; $h_1 = .5$, $h_2 = .25$

(b) $y'' + k(1 - x^2)y = 0$; $y(0) = y(1) = 0$; $h_1 = .5$, $h_2 = .25$

(c) $y'' + kx(1 - x)y = 0$; $y(0) = y(1) = 0$; $h_1 = .5$, $h_2 = .25$

(d) $y^{iv} + ky'' = 0$; $y(0) = y'(0) = y(1) = y'(1) = 0$; $h_1 = .5$, $h_2 = .25$

(e) $y^{iv} + ky'' = 0$; $y(0) = y''(0) = y(1) = y''(1) = 0$; $h_1 = .5$, $h_2 = .25$

(f) $y^{iv} + kx(1 - x)y'' = 0$; $y(0) = y'(0) = y(1) = y'(1) = 0$; $h_1 = .5$, $h_2 = .25$

Ordinary
Initial-value
Problems

Chapter Seven

7.1 Starting the Solution [Programs 2.1, 2.3]

An ordinary *initial-value* problem is governed by an ordinary differential equation and a set of conditions *all* valid at the same "starting" point, $x = x_0$. The solution $y(x)$ of such a problem can be formally evaluated in the immediate neighborhood of $x = x_0$ in terms of a Taylor series expansion (Sec. 2.3) by obtaining the derivatives of $y(x)$ at $x = x_0$ through successive differentiation of the differential equation itself.

Example 7.1.1. Evaluate the solution of the following problem by the first four terms of its Maclaurin series for $x = 0(.1).6$.

$$y' = \frac{1}{2}(1 + x)y^2, \quad y(0) = 1. \tag{a}$$

From the differential equation and its successive derivatives,

$$y' = \frac{1}{2}(1 + x)y^2; \quad y'(0) = \frac{1}{2}y_0^2 = \frac{1}{2};$$

$$y'' = \tfrac{1}{2}y^2 + (1+x)y \cdot y'; \quad y''(0) = \tfrac{1}{2} \cdot 1 + 1 \cdot 1 \cdot \tfrac{1}{2} = 1;$$

$$y''' = 2y \cdot y' + (1+x)(y'^2 + y \cdot y''); \quad y'''(0) = 1 + 1 \cdot (\tfrac{1}{4} + 1) = \tfrac{9}{4}.$$

$$y(x) \doteq y_0 + y_0'x + \frac{y_0''x^2}{2} + \frac{y_0'''x^3}{6} \doteq 1 + \frac{x}{2} + \frac{x^2}{2} + \frac{3x^3}{8}.$$

The approximate values of y appearing in the following table may be compared with the values $[y]$ of the exact solution, $y = 4/(4 - 2x - x^2)$, which approaches infinity as x approaches $-1 \pm \sqrt{5} = 1.236, -3.236$.

x	y	$[y]$
0.	1.	1.
.1	1.055375	1.055409
.2	1.123	1.123596
.3	1.205125	1.208459
.4	1.304	1.315789
.5	1.421875	1.454545
.6	1.561	1.639344

Example 7.1.2. Evaluate the solution y of the following problem at $x = .2$, .3, 1 by the first four nonzero terms of its Maclaurin series.

$$y'' + y' + y = e^x; \qquad\qquad y(0) = y'(0) = 0; \qquad\qquad \textbf{(b)}$$

$$y'' = e^x - y - y'; \qquad\qquad y''(0) = 1;$$

$$y''' = e^x - y' - y''; \qquad\qquad y'''(0) = 0;$$

$$y^{iv} = e^x - y'' - y'''; \qquad\qquad y^{iv}(0) = 0;$$

$$y^{v} = e^x - y''' - y^{iv}; \qquad\qquad y^{v}(0) = 1;$$

$$y = \frac{x^2}{2} + \frac{x^5}{120},$$

$y(.2) = .0200027$ $[.0200033]$, $\quad y(.3) = .0450202$ $[.0450203]$,

$y(1.) = .508333$ $[.508358]$.

The exact values of y are given by

$$y = \frac{1}{3}\left[e^x - e^{-x/2}\left(\cos \frac{\sqrt{3}}{2}x + \sqrt{3} \sin \frac{\sqrt{3}}{2}x \right) \right].$$

7.2 Euler's Methods [Program 7.1]

The solution of an initial-value problem is usually obtained step-by-step by *forward integration methods* which give y_{i+1} as soon as one or more preceding pivotal values $y_i, y_{i-1}, \ldots$ of y are known. The simplest of these methods, due to Euler, is applicable to first-order equations and does not require the knowledge of preceding pivotal values.

Given the first-order problem

$$y' = f(x, y), \qquad y(x_0) = y_0, \tag{7.2.1}$$

the derivative of y at i, $f(x_i, y_i) \equiv f_i$, can be evaluated by means of (7.2.1) as soon as y_i is known. Once f_i is known, the approximate integration formula (3.3.14) gives

$$\Delta y_i = y_{i+1} - y_i = \int_{x_i}^{x_{i+1}} f(x, y) \, dx \doteq (x_{i+1} - x_i) f_i,$$

and, solving for y_{i+1},

$$y_{i+1} = y_i + (x_{i+1} - x_i) f_i. \tag{7.2.2}$$

Equation (7.2.2) is known as *Euler's formula*. As shown by (3.3.14), it has a truncation error of order h^2. It does not require even spacing of the pivotal points.

Example 7.2.1. Evaluate the solution of Example 7.1.1 by Euler's formula at $x = .1$ and $x = .3$.

x_i	y_i	f_i	$(x_{i+1} - x_i) f_i$	$[y]$
0.	1.	.5	.05	1.
.1	1.05	.606	.1212	1.055409
.3	1.1712			1.208459

The table shows how the accumulation of error (see Sec. 7.8) in Euler's method leads rapidly to a severe loss in accuracy.

The *Euler-Richardson method* is an improved Euler procedure in which y_{i+1} is first evaluated by Euler's formula (7.2.2) with spacings h and $h/2$, and then improved by h^2-extrapolation (Sec. 3.6). Since the extrapolation takes into account the first term of the error series, the truncation error in the Euler-Richardson method is of order h^3.

With

$$x_{i+1} - x_i = h_i, \tag{7.2.3}$$

one computes successively

$$f(x_i, y_i) = f_i, \tag{7.2.4}$$

$$y_{i+1}^{(1)} = y_i + h_i f_i,$$

$$y_{i+1/2} = y_i + \frac{h_i}{2} f_i,$$

$$f_{i+1/2} = f(x_{i+1/2},\, y_{i+1/2}), \tag{7.2.5}$$

$$y_{i+1}^{(2)} = y_{i+1/2} + \frac{h_i}{2} f_{i+1/2} = y_i + \frac{h_i}{2}(f_i + f_{i+1/2}),$$

and extrapolates from $y_{i+1}^{(1)}$ and $y_{i+1}^{(2)}$ by (3.6.2) to obtain the *Euler-Richardson formula*:

$$y_{i+1} = \frac{4}{3} y_{i+1}^{(2)} - \frac{1}{3} y_{i+1}^{(1)} = y_i + \frac{h_i}{3}(f_i + 2f_{i+1/2}). \tag{7.2.6}$$

Example 7.2.2. Solve Example 7.2.1 by the Euler-Richardson method.

x_i	$x_{i+1/2}$	y_i	f_i	$y_{i+1/2}$	$f_{i+1/2}$	$\frac{h_i}{3}(f_i + 2f_{i+1/2})$	$[y]$
0.		1.	.5				1.
	.05			1.025	.552	.0535	
.1		1.0535	.6104				1.0554
	.20			1.1145	.7453	.1407	
.3		1.1942					1.2085

Another improvement of Euler's method, the *Euler-Gauss method*, is obtained by first computing $y_{i+1}^{(1)}$ by Euler's formula (7.2.2) and then evaluating Δy by the trapezoidal rule of Eq. (3.3.15):

$$\Delta y_i = y_{i+1} - y_i = \frac{1}{2}(f_i + f_{i+1})(x_{i+1} - x_i), \tag{7.2.7}$$

with a truncation error of order h^3.

Example 7.2.3. Solve Example 7.2.1 by the Euler-Gauss method.

x_i	y_i	f_i	$y_{i+1}^{(1)}$	f_{i+1}	$\frac{1}{2}(f_i + f_{i+1})$	Δy_i	$[y]$
0.	1.	.5	1.05	.606	.553	.0553	1.
.1	1.0553	.5569	1.1667	.8848	.7208	.1442	1.0554
.3	1.1995						1.2085

The accuracy of all the Euler methods may be increased by using iteration to improve the values of $f(x, y)$ and hence of y_{i+1}. For example, the *Euler-Gauss predictor-corrector method* uses Euler's formula (7.2.2) to obtain a predicted value $y_{i+1,p}$ of y_{i+1} and then iterates Euler-Gauss's formula (7.2.7) to obtain corrected values $y_{i+1,c}$:

$$y_{i+1,c}^{(k+1)} = y_i + \frac{1}{2}\left[f(x_i, y_i) + f(x_{i+1}, y_{i+1}^{(k)})\right](x_{i+1} - x_i). \tag{7.2.8}$$

The iterative process is stopped as soon as $y_{i+1}^{(k+1)} = y_{i+1}^{(k)}$ to the required degree of accuracy. The truncation error is of order h^3, as indicated in (3.3.15).

Example 7.2.4. Solve Example 7.2.1 by the Euler-Gauss predictor-corrector method.

$$f_0 = \frac{1}{2}(1. + 0.)(1.)^2 = 0.5,$$

$$y_{1,p} = 1. + (0.1)(.5) = 1.05 \qquad\qquad \text{[by (7.2.2)]},$$

$$f_1 = \frac{1}{2}(1. + .1)(1.05)^2 = .606,$$

$$\Delta y_{1,c}^{(0)} = \frac{1}{2}(f_0 + f_1)(x_1 - x_0)$$

$$= \frac{1}{2}(.5 + .606)(.1) = .055 \qquad\qquad \text{[by (7.2.7)]},$$

$$y_{1,c}^{(0)} = 1. + .055 = 1.055 \qquad\qquad \text{[by (7.2.8)]},$$

$$f_1^{(0)} = \frac{1}{2}(1. + .1)(1.055)^2 = .612,$$

$$\frac{1}{2}(f_0 + f_1^{(0)}) = .556,$$

$$y_{1,c}^{(1)} = 1. + .0556 = 1.0556.$$

k	i	x_i	$y_i^{(k)}$	$f_i^{(k)}$	$\frac{1}{2}(f_i + f_{i+1}^{(k)})$	$\Delta y_i^{(k)}$	$[y_i]$
0	0	0.	1.	.5		.05	1.
p			1.05	.606	.553	.055	
0	1	.1	1.055	.612	.556	.0556	1.0554
1			1.0556	.613	.556	.0556	
0			1.0556	.613		.123	
p			1.18	.905	.759	.152	
0			1.208	.949	.781	.156	
1	2	.3	1.213	.956	.785	.157	1.2085
2			1.2136	.957	.785	.157	
3			1.2136				

7.3 Runge-Kutta Methods [Programs 7.2, 7.3]

Given the equation

$$y' = f(x, y), \tag{a}$$

the *Runge-Kutta forward integration formulas* are obtained by determining a point

$$\bar{x} = x_i + \alpha h, \quad \bar{y} = y_i + \beta h \qquad (h = x_{i+1} - x_i) \tag{b}$$

such that the increment $\overline{\Delta} y_i$ computed by the one-term formula

$$\overline{\Delta} y_i \equiv y_{i+1} - y_i = f(\bar{x}, \bar{y}) h \tag{c}$$

is identical with the increment Δy_i,

$$\Delta y_i = y_i' h + y_i'' \frac{h^2}{2} + y_i''' \frac{h^3}{6} + \cdots, \tag{d}$$

computed by means of a predetermined number of terms of the Taylor expansion (d). The point $\bar{x}$, $\bar{y}$ is computed in a finite number of steps, starting with $\alpha = \beta = 0$, i.e., from $\bar{x} = x_i$, $\bar{y} = y_i$.

For example, the *second-order* Runge-Kutta formula is derived by setting $\overline{\Delta} y$ equal to the first two terms of (d), that is, by letting

$$f(\bar{x}, \bar{y}) \equiv f(x_i + \alpha h, y_i + \beta h) = y_i' + \frac{h}{2} y_i''. \tag{e}$$

By (2.3.8), $f(\bar{x}, \bar{y})$, when expanded into a double Taylor series about (x_i, y_i) truncated after the first-derivative terms, equals

$$f(x_i + \alpha h, y_i + \beta h) = f_i + \alpha h f_{x,i} + \beta h f_{y,i}. \tag{f}$$

By (a), the right-hand member of (e) becomes

$$y_i' + \frac{h}{2} y_i'' = \left[f + \frac{h}{2} \frac{df}{dx} \right]_{x=x_i}, \tag{g}$$

where $f(x, y)$ is to be considered a function of x only, through substitution of $y(x)$ for y. Hence

$$\frac{df(x, y)}{dx} = \frac{\partial f}{\partial x} + \frac{\partial f}{\partial y} \frac{dy}{dx} = f_x + f_y f, \tag{h}$$

by means of which (g) becomes

$$y_i' + \frac{h}{2} y_i'' = f_i + \frac{h}{2} (f_{x,i} + f_{y,i} f_i). \tag{i}$$

Substitution of (f) and (i) in (e) shows that

$$f_i + \alpha h f_{x,i} + \beta h f_{y,i} \equiv f_i + \frac{h}{2} f_{x,i} + \frac{h}{2} f_{y,i} f_i,$$

from which

$$\alpha = \frac{1}{2}, \quad \beta = \frac{1}{2} f_i, \quad \bar{x} = x_i + \frac{h}{2}, \quad y = y_i + \frac{h}{2} f_i. \tag{i}$$

The evaluation of $\overline{\Delta} y_i$ by the second-order Runge-Kutta formula thus requires the following two steps:

$$\Delta' y_i = h f_i = h f(x_i, y_i),$$

$$\overline{\Delta} y_i = h f(\bar{x}, \bar{y}) = h f\left(x_i + \frac{h}{2}, y_i + \frac{1}{2} \Delta' y_i\right). \tag{7.3.1}$$

The truncation error in $\overline{\Delta} y_i$ is of order h^3.

Example 7.3.1. Solve Example 7.2.1 by the second-order Runge-Kutta method.

x	y_i	$f(x_i, y_i)$	$\frac{1}{2}\Delta' y_i$	$x_i + \frac{h}{2}$	$y_i + \frac{1}{2}\Delta' y_i$	$f(\bar{x}, \bar{y})$	$\overline{\Delta} y_i$	$[y]$
0.	1.	.5	.025	.05	1.025	.5516	.0552	1.
.1	1.0552	.6124	.0612	.20	1.1164	.7478	.1496	1.0554
.3	1.2048							1.2085

To obtain a third-order Runge-Kutta formula with error of order h^4, the following successive values of Δy must be evaluated:

$$\Delta' y_i = h f(x_i, y_i),$$

$$\Delta'' y_i = h f\left(x_i + \frac{h}{2}, y_i + \frac{1}{2} \Delta' y_i\right),$$

$$\Delta''' y_i = h f(x_i + h, y_i + 2\Delta'' y_i - \Delta' y_i), \tag{7.3.2}$$

$$\overline{\Delta} y_i = \tfrac{1}{6}\left(\Delta' y_i + 4\Delta'' y_i + \Delta''' y_i\right).$$

Similarly, a fourth-order Runge-Kutta formula with error of order h^5 is given by

$$\Delta' y_i = h f(x_i, y_i),$$

$$\Delta'' y_i = h f\left(x_i + \frac{h}{2}, y_i + \frac{1}{2} \Delta' y_i\right), \tag{7.3.3}$$

$$\Delta''' y_i = h f\left(x_i + \frac{h}{2}, y_i + \frac{1}{2} \Delta'' y_i\right),$$

$$\Delta^{iv}y_i = hf(x_i + h, y_i + \Delta'''y_i), \tag{7.3.3}$$
$$\overline{\Delta}y_i = \tfrac{1}{6}(\Delta'y_i + 2\,\Delta''y_i + 2\,\Delta'''y_i + \Delta^{iv}y_i).$$

While the second-order formula is uniquely determined, it can be shown that a variety of higher-order formulas may be derived.* Those given above are among the most commonly employed.

Example 7.3.2. Evaluate $y(.1)$ in Example 7.2.1: (a) by (7.3.2); (b) by (7.3.3).

By (7.3.2) and Example 7.3.1:

$$\Delta'''y_0 = (.1)(\tfrac{1}{2})(1 + .1)[1. + 2(.055158) - .050]^2 = 0.061835,$$
$$\overline{\Delta}y_0 = \tfrac{1}{6}[0.050 + 4(.055158) + .061835] = .055411,$$
$$y_1 = 1.055411 \quad [1.055409].$$

By (7.3.3) and Example 7.3.1:

$$\Delta'''y_0 = (.1)(\tfrac{1}{2})(1. + .05)(1. + (\tfrac{1}{2})\,.055158)^2 = .055436,$$
$$\Delta^{iv}y_0 = (.1)(\tfrac{1}{2})(1. + .1)(1. + .055436)^2 = .061267,$$
$$\overline{\Delta}y_0 = \tfrac{1}{6}[.05 + 2(.055158) + 2(.055436) + .061267] = .055409,$$
$$y_1 = 1.055409 \quad [1.055409].$$

7.4   Milne's Predictor-corrector Method [Program 7.4]

Predictor-corrector formulas with higher-order errors than the Euler-Gauss formula are easily derived, but require the previous evaluation of y and $y' = f(x, y)$ at a certain number of evenly spaced pivotal points in the neighborhood of x_0. These values of y are obtained by a self-starting method, e.g., Runge-Kutta or Taylor series.

For example, given

$$y' = f(x, y); \quad y_0, y_1, y_2, y_3; \quad f_1, f_2, f_3, \tag{7.4.1}$$

Milne's *predictor* is obtained by the integration formula (3.3.27) applied at $i - 1$:

$$y_{i+1,p} = y_{i-3} + \int_{x_{i-3}}^{x_{i+1}} y'\,dx = y_{i-3} + \frac{4h}{3}(2f_{i-2} - f_{i-1} + 2f_i), \tag{7.4.2}$$

which allows the evaluation of f_{i+1}. Milne's *corrector* is then obtained by Simpson's 1/3 rule (3.3.24):

$$y_{i+1,c} = y_{i-1} + \frac{h}{3}(f_{i-1} + 4f_i + f_{i+1}) \tag{7.4.3}$$

* See K. S. Kunz, *Numerical Analysis* (New York: McGraw-Hill Book Company, N. Y., 1957).

with an error of order h^5. Equation (7.4.3) may be iterated by using $y_{i+1,c}$ to obtain improved values of f_{i+1}, but this is seldom necessary if h is chosen appropriately small.*

Example 7.4.1. Given the correct solution of Example 7.1.1,

$$y' = \tfrac{1}{2}(1 + x)y^2, \qquad y(0) = 1,$$

for the first four values of y and y',

x_i	0.	.1	.2	.3
y_i	1.	1.055409	1.123596	1.208459
f_i	.5	.61264	.75748	.94924

evaluate $y(.4)$ by Milne's predictor-corrector method.

By (7.4.2):

$$y_{4,p} = 1. + \frac{4(.1)}{3}\,[2(.61264) - .75748 + 2(.94924)] = 1.315504;$$

by (7.4.1):

$$f_4 = \tfrac{1}{2}(1 + .4)(1.315504)^2 = 1.21139;$$

by (7.4.3):

$$y_{4,c} = 1.123596 + \frac{.1}{3}\,[.75748 + 4(.94924) + 1.21139]$$

$$= 1.315790 \quad [1.315789].$$

7.5 Simultaneous and Higher-order Equations [Programs 7.5, 7.6]

Any method for the forward integration of first-order equations may be extended to integrate systems of simultaneous first-order equations, or higher-order equations.

For example, the second-order Runge-Kutta method of Section 7.3, applied to the system

$$y' = f(x, y, z), \qquad z' = g(x, y, z),$$
$$y(x_0) = y_0, \qquad z(x_0) = z_0,$$

(7.5.1)

results in the following set of formulas:

---

* Milne's method is likely to be unstable (see Sec. 7.8).

$$\Delta' y_i = hf(x_i, y_i, z_i); \quad \Delta' z_i = hg(x_i, y_i, z_i),$$

$$\overline{\Delta} y_i = hf\left(x_i + \frac{h}{2}, y_i + \frac{1}{2}\Delta' y_i, z_i + \frac{1}{2}\Delta' z_i\right),$$

$$\overline{\Delta} z_i = hg\left(x_i + \frac{h}{2}, y_i + \frac{1}{2}\Delta' y_i, z_i + \frac{1}{2}\Delta' z_i\right), \qquad (7.5.2)$$

$$y_{i+1} = y_i + \overline{\Delta} y_i; \quad z_{i+1} = z_i + \overline{\Delta} z_i.$$

Example 7.5.1. Given

$$y' = xyz, \quad z' = \frac{xy}{z}; \qquad y(1) = \frac{1}{3}, \quad z(1) = 1,$$

evaluate $y(1.1)$, $z(1.1)$ by (7.5.2).

$$f(x_0, y_0, z_0) = (1)(\tfrac{1}{3})(1) = \frac{1}{3},$$

$$g(x_0, y_0, z_0) = \frac{(1)(\tfrac{1}{3})}{(1)} = \frac{1}{3},$$

$$\Delta' y_0 = (.1)(\tfrac{1}{3}) = 0.0333; \quad \Delta' z_0 = (.1)(\tfrac{1}{3}) = .0333,$$

$$\overline{\Delta} y_0 = (.1)(1. + .05)(.3333 + (\tfrac{1}{2}).0333)(1. + (\tfrac{1}{2}).0333) = .0374,$$

$$\overline{\Delta} z_0 = \frac{(.1)(1. + .05)(.3333 + (\tfrac{1}{2}).0333)}{(1. + (\tfrac{1}{2}).0333)} = .0361,$$

$$y_1 = .3707; \quad z_1 = 1.0361.$$

From the exact solution of the equations,

$$y = \frac{72}{(7 - x^2)^3}, \quad z = \frac{6}{7 - x^2}; \qquad y(1.1) = .3709, \quad z(1.1) = 1.0363.$$

A higher-order equation can always be written as a set of simultaneous first-order equations. For example, the third-order equation

$$y''' = f(x, y, y', y'')$$

is equivalent to the system

$$y' = z, \quad (y'' =) z' = w, \quad (y''' = z'' =) w' = f(x, y, z, w).$$

Hence, higher-order equations may be solved by any of the methods developed for simultaneous first-order equations.

Example 7.5.2. Given

$$y'' = e^x - y - y'; \qquad y(0) = 0, \quad y'(0) = 0,$$

evaluate $y(.1)$ and $y'(.1)$ by the Runge-Kutta second-order method.

$$y' = z; \quad z' = e^x - y - z; \quad y_0 = 0, \quad z_0 = 0.$$
$$\Delta' y_0 = (.1)(0.) = 0.; \quad \Delta' z_0 = (.1)(e^{0 \cdot} + 0. + 0.) = .1;$$
$$y_1 = \overline{\Delta} y_0 = (.1)(\tfrac{1}{2})(.1) = .005;$$
$$z_1 = \overline{\Delta} z_0 = (.1)(e^{.05} - 0. - .05) = .10013.$$

7.6 The Direct Integration Forward of Higher-order Equations [Programs 7.7, 7.8]

Higher-order equations may also be solved directly, without transforming them into systems of simultaneous equations.

For example, Milne's method of Section 7.4 can be extended to the second-order problem,

$$y'' = f(x, y, y'); \qquad y(x_0) = y_0, \quad y'(x_0) = y_0', \tag{7.6.1}$$

provided the values of

$$y_0, y_1, y_2, y_3; \quad y_0', y_1', y_2', y_3'; \quad f_1, f_2, f_3, \tag{a}$$

are known. Thus, if the integration formula (3.3.27), applied at $i - 1$, is used to predict the value of y_{i+1}',

$$y_{i+1,p}' = y_{i-3}' + \frac{4h}{3}(2f_i - f_{i-1} + 2f_{i-2}), \tag{7.6.2}$$

Simpson's 1/3 rule (3.3.24) applied at i allows the evaluation of the predicted value of y_{i+1}:

$$y_{i+1,p} = y_{i-1} + \frac{h}{3}(y_{i-1}' + 4y_i' + y_{i+1,p}'). \tag{7.6.3}$$

The value of f_{i+1} is then obtained by (7.6.1):

$$f_{i+1} = f(x_{i+1}, y_{i+1,p}, y_{i+1,p}'). \tag{7.6.4}$$

The corrected value of y_{i+1}' is evaluated by Simpson's 1/3 rule (3.3.24) applied at i:

$$y_{i+1,c}' = y_{i-1}' + \frac{h}{3}(f_{i-1} + 4f_i + f_{i+1}), \tag{7.6.5}$$

and the corrected value of y_{i+1}, again, by (3.3.24) applied at i:

$$y_{i+1,c} = y_{i-1} + \frac{h}{3}(y_{i-1}' + 4y_i' + y_{i+1,c}'). \tag{7.6.6}$$

The procedure may be iterated, if necessary, to improve the value of f_{i+1} by means of $y_{i+1,c}'$ and $y_{i+1,c}$.

Example 7.6.1. Given

$$y'' + y = 0; \qquad y(0) = 1, \quad y'(0) = 0 \qquad \text{(a)}$$

and the correct values of y at $x = 0.(.2).6$, evaluate $y(.8)$ by Milne's predictor-corrector method.

i	0	1	2	3
x_i	0.	.2	.4	.6
y_i	1.	.980067	.921061	.825336
y_i'	0.	$-.198669$	$-.389418$	$-.564642$
f_i	$-1.$	$-.980067$	$-.921061$	$-.825336$

By (7.6.2):

$$y_{4,p}' = 0. + \frac{4(.2)}{3} [2(-.825336) - (-.921061) + 2(-.980067)]$$

$$= -.717265,$$

by (7.6.3):

$$y_{4,p} = .921061 + \frac{.2}{3} [-.389418 + 4(-.564642) + (-.717265)]$$

$$= .696711,$$

by (7.6.4) and (a):

$$f_4 = -.696711,$$

by (7.6.5):

$$y_{4,c}' = -.389418 + \frac{.2}{3} [-.921061 + 4(-.825336) - .696711]$$

$$= -.717359,$$

by (7.6.6):

$$y_{4,c} = .921061 + \frac{.2}{3} [-.389418 + 4(-.564642) - .717359]$$

$$= .696705 \quad [.696706].$$

Integration forward of a higher-order equation may also be conveniently performed by substitution in the equation of consistent *finite difference* differentiation formulas from Table 3.2.1. The finite difference equation thus obtained, solved for the highest subscript y_i in terms of a number of the preceding pivotal values of y, is known as a *recurrence equation*. This procedure may often be used without starting the solution by Taylor series.

Example 7.6.2. Evaluate $y(.4)$, $y(.6)$, and $y(.8)$ in Example 7.6.1, using finite differences with error of order h^2.

Multiplying the differential equation by h^2 and substituting (3.2.18) for $h^2 y''$, the recurrence equation for y_{i+1} becomes

$$y_{i+1} = -y_{i-1} + (2 - h^2)y_i$$

or, with $h = .2$,

$$y_{i+1} = -y_{i-1} + 1.96y_i. \tag{a}$$

By (3.2.11) the initial conditions give

$$y_0 = 1.; \quad \frac{1}{2h}(y_1 - y_{-1}) = 0 \quad \text{or} \quad y_{-1} = y_1. \tag{b}$$

Making use of the value $y_1 = .980067$ obtained by the first three terms of the Taylor series for y, $y = 1 - (x^2/2) + (x^4/24) - \cdots$, (a) gives

$$y_2 = -1. + 1.96(.980067) = .920931 \qquad [.921061],$$
$$y_3 = -.980067 + 1.96(.920931) = .824958 \quad [.825336],$$
$$y_4 = -.920931 + 1.96(.824958) = .695987 \quad [.696706].$$

Alternatively, to avoid the use of a Taylor series one may apply (a) at $i = 0$,

$$y_1 = -y_{-1} + 1.96y_0 = -y_{-1} + 1.96, \tag{c}$$

and, solving (b) and (c) simultaneously for y_1, obtain $y_1 = .98$, by means of which $y_2 = .9208$; $y_3 = .8248$; $y_4 = .6958$.

7.7   Solution of Boundary-value and Characteristic-value Problems by Forward Integration

The integration of a boundary-value or a characteristic-value problem by the numerical methods of Chapter 6 requires the solution of simultaneous algebraic equations. When the problem is linear, this solution is always obtainable by standard procedures. When the equation is nonlinear, its solution may often present exceptional difficulties.

Second-order boundary-value or characteristic-value problems may be conveniently solved, at times, by forward integration methods. The gist of the procedure consists in considering the unknown first pivotal value y_1 of y as a parameter of the problem, and in repeatedly integrating forward the differential equation with assumed values of y_1 until the corresponding solution satisfies the boundary condition at the far end of the interval of integration. Starting with initial guesses $y_1^{(0)}$, $y_1^{(1)}$ for y_1, linear or quadratic interpolation can be used to improve y_1 successively, thus transforming the method into an iterative procedure. (A knowledge of the nature of the problem is most helpful in choosing initial guesses.)

Example 7.7.1. Integrate the nonlinear boundary-value problem

$$y'' + y^2 = 0; \quad y(0) = 0; \quad y(1) = 1 \tag{a}$$

by forward integration, using finite differences of order h^2 and $h = .2$.

Multiplication of (a) by h^2 and substitution of (3.2.18) for $h^2 y''$ lead to the recurrence equation,

$$y_{i+1} = -y_{i-1} + y_i(2 - .04y_i). \tag{b}$$

With $y_1^{(0)} = .3$ and $y_1^{(1)} = .25$, (b) leads to the $y_i^{(0)}$ and $y_i^{(1)}$ of the following table:

k	i	0	1	2	3	4	5	$\epsilon^{(k)}$
	x_i	0.	.2	.4	.6	.8	1.	
0	$y_i^{(0)}$	0.	.3	.5964	.8785	1.1298	1.3300	.3300
1	$y_i^{(1)}$	0.	.25	.4975	.7351	.9511	1.1310	.1310
2	$y_i^{(2)}$	0.	.22	.4381	.6485	.8421	1.0073	.0073
	$[y]$	0.	.2361	.4628	.6710	.8525	1.0000	

The errors in $y_5^{(0)}$ and $y_5^{(1)}$ are $\epsilon^{(0)} = 1.3300 - 1. = .3300$, $\epsilon^{(1)} = 1.1310 - 1. = .1310$. We obtain $y_1^{(2)} = .22$ by linear extrapolation from (3.4.2):

$$y_1^{(2)} = \frac{\epsilon^{(1)} y_1^{(0)} - \epsilon^{(0)} y_1^{(1)}}{\epsilon^{(1)} - \epsilon^{(0)}} = \frac{(.1310)(.3) - (.3300)(.25)}{.1310 - .3300} = .22.$$

The correct solution is $y = \sin x/\sin 1. = 1.1884 \sin x$.

In the forward integration of the homogeneous equations governing second-order characteristic-value problems, y_1 may be given any convenient value, say 1., since the solution is determined within a multiplying constant, i.e., within a scale factor in y. The eigenvalue parameter λ is then given successive values $\lambda^{(0)}, \lambda^{(1)}, \ldots$, until the boundary condition at the far end of the interval of integration is satisfied. λ is usually improved by interpolation.

Example 7.7.2. Determine the smallest eigenvalue of λ in the following problem by forward integration of the corresponding finite difference problem and interpolation, using $h = .2$.

$$y'' + \lambda y = 0; \quad y(0) = 0, \quad y(1) = 0. \tag{a}$$

With $h = .2$, (3.2.18) gives the recurrence equation

$$y_{i+1} = -y_{i-1} + (2 - .04\lambda)y_i. \tag{b}$$

y_1 is chosen equal to 1. The initial values $\lambda^{(0)} = 12$, $\lambda^{(1)} = 8$ are guessed.

k	$\lambda^{(k)}$	i	0	1	2	3	4	5	$\epsilon^{(k)}$
		x_i	0.	.2	.4	.6	.8	1.	
0	12	$y_i^{(0)}$	0.	1.	1.52	1.3104	.4718	$-.5933$	$-.5933$
1	8	$y_i^{(1)}$	0.	1.	1.68	1.8224	1.3816	$+.4987$	$+.4987$
2	9.83	$y_i^{(2)}$	0.	1.	1.61	1.5921	.9533	$-.0573$	$-.0573$

The value $\lambda^{(2)} = 9.83$ is obtained by linear interpolation from (3.4.2):

$$\lambda^{(2)} = \frac{(.4987) \cdot 12 - (-.5933) \cdot 8}{.4987 - (-.5933)} = 9.83 \quad [9.87].$$

A smaller spacing eventually improves the accuracy of the solution.

The solution by forward integration of fourth- or higher-order boundary-value and characteristic-value problems is cumbersome because it requires accurate guesses of the initial values of two or more parameters and their improvement by multiple interpolation.

7.8 Accumulation of Error

The errors considered in the preceding sections of this chapter are the *truncation errors* involved in *one* step of the forward integration process. Given a differential equation and its initial conditions, the truncation error is uniquely determined by the chosen integration procedure. The error due to rounding off of decimal figures also appears at each step, but it is of the same nature as the truncation error, and may be formally incorporated with it.

Thus, if y_i were known exactly, one step of the integration procedure would lead to an approximate value $\bar{y}_{i+1}$ of y_{i+1} affected by a truncation and round-off error $\epsilon_{i+1,t}$:

$$y_{i+1} = \bar{y}_{i+1} + \epsilon_{i+1,t}. \tag{a}$$

If, instead, y_i is affected by an error ϵ_i, the value of y_{i+1} is affected by two errors: the *propagated error* $\epsilon_{i+1,p}$ due to the error ϵ_i in the starting value $\bar{y}_i$, and the truncation error $\epsilon_{i+1,t}$. It is obvious that the errors due to these two causes may accumulate from step to step and that, if they are all of the same sign, they may well lead to meaningless results after a number of steps.

For example, in the integration by Euler's formula (7.2.2) of the equation $y' = f(x, y)$, if y_i were known exactly, the exact value of y_{i+1} would be

$$y_{i+1} = \bar{y}_{i+1} + \epsilon_{i+1,t} = y_i + f(x_i, y_i)h + \epsilon_{i+1,t}, \tag{7.8.1}$$

where

$$\epsilon_{i+1,t} = \tfrac{1}{2} y''(\bar{x}_i)h^2, \qquad x_i \le \bar{x}_i \le x_{i+1}. \tag{7.8.2}$$

If, instead, y_i is affected by a total error ϵ_i, the *exact* value of y_{i+1} is given by

$$y_{i+1} = (\bar{y}_i + \epsilon_i) + f(x_i, \bar{y}_i + \epsilon_i)h + \epsilon_{i+1,t}. \tag{7.8.3}$$

Expanding $f(x_i, \bar{y}_i + \epsilon_i)$ into a Taylor series in y about $\bar{y}_i$, and assuming ϵ_i small enough to allow the dropping of higher-order terms, it is seen that

$$f(x_i, \bar{y}_i + \epsilon_i) \doteq f(x_i, \bar{y}_i) + f_y(x_i, \bar{y}_i)\epsilon_i. \tag{7.8.4}$$

Substitution of (7.8.4) in (7.8.3) gives, by (7.8.1),

$$y_{i+1} = \bar{y}_i + f(x_i, \bar{y}_i)h + [1 + f_y(x_i, \bar{y}_i)h]\epsilon_i + \epsilon_{i+1,t} \tag{7.8.5}$$
$$= \bar{y}_{i+1} + \epsilon_{i+1,p} + \epsilon_{i+1,t},$$

where

$$\epsilon_{i+1,p} = (1 + f_{y,i}h)\epsilon_i \text{ with } f_{y,i} = f_y(x_i, \bar{y}_i) \tag{7.8.6}$$

is the *propagated error* in y_{i+1} due to the error ϵ_i in y_i. Equation (7.8.6) shows ϵ_i to be propagated to y_{i+1} with a *propagation factor* $(1 + f_{y,i}h)$. Hence, it will be propagated to y_{i+2} with a factor $(1 + f_{y,i}h)(1 + f_{y,i+1}h)$, and to y_{i+n} after n steps, with a factor

$$(1 + f_{y,i}h)(1 + f_{y,i+1}h)(1 + f_{y,i+2}h) \cdots (1 + f_{y,i+n-1}h). \tag{7.8.7}$$

If f_y is always *negative* in the range from i to $i + n$ and h is *sufficiently small*, the propagation factors will be less than 1 and the influence of the error ϵ_i will die out as the integration proceeds. But if f_y is positive in the range from i to $i + n$, or h is not sufficiently small, the error ϵ_i will eventually "blow up" the solution, i.e., make it meaningless. Similarly, the accumulation of truncation errors in the n steps from i to $i + n$,

$$\sum_{i}^{i+n} \epsilon_{i,t} = \frac{h^2}{2} \sum_{i}^{i+n} y''(\bar{x}_i), \tag{7.8.8}$$

will not blow up the solution if the sign of y'' alternates in this range and h is small enough, but will lead to a meaningless solution if the sign of y'' is constant over the range of integration and h is not sufficiently small.

A complete analysis of the accumulation of error in the integration procedures of this chapter may be obtained, but is beyond the scope of this book. All the same, the following qualitative remarks on the subject should be carefully noted by the reader.

Given an initial-value problem, a numerical integration procedure is said to be *convergent* if, as the spacing h approaches zero, the numerical solution approaches the solution of the differential initial-value problem. A numerical integration procedure is said to be *stable* if the propagated error is bounded. In general, a numerical integration method is stable provided the spacing h is smaller than a given h_{max}, where h_{max} depends on the numerical procedure *and* the equation to be integrated. For example, it may be shown (see N.M. Sec. 3.14) that the finite difference solution $\bar{y}$ of Example 7.7.1 is stable provided $h < 2$. For $h > 2$, $\bar{y}$ has an oscillatory behavior with increasing amplitude and after a few steps diverges from the exact solution $y = \cos x$. For $h \leq 2$, $\bar{y}$ is stable, i.e., its amplitude is constant and equal to one, but its frequency differs from the frequency of y. As h approaches 0, $\bar{y}$ approaches y. Hence, in this case the finite difference procedure is convergent, and stable for $h < 2$.

An empirical test of the influence of the spacing h on the accuracy of the numerical solution may be obtained by integrating the same problem with two spacings h_1 and h_2 ($< h_1$) and noticing the differences between the corresponding solutions at points common to both. In this connection, Richardson's extrapolations (Sec. 3.6) are often useful in estimating the accuracy of the second solution. In any case it must be noticed that not even a reduction in the value of h is a guarantee that the accumulation of error will not blow up the numerical solution. For example, this is the case for Milne's method (Sec. 7.4).

Finally, in electronic calculations a repetition of the same elementary procedure at each step is the most efficient method of performing forward integration, because of both simplicity in programming and shorter calculation time per step. In any problem involving a large amount of computing time, the convergence and stability of the numerical integration procedure, as well as the computing time, must be carefully investigated beforehand.

PROBLEMS

7.1 Derive the first three nonzero terms of the Taylor expansion for the solution of the following problems, and evaluate y at the first three pivotal points by these series terms for $h = .2$.

(a) $y' - y = 0$; $y(0) = 1$.

(b) $y' - 2y = e^x$; $y(0) = 2$.

(c) $y' - x(1 - x)y = 0$; $y(0) = 10$.

(d) $y' - x^2 y = x^2$; $y(0) = 10$.

(e) $y' - y^2 = 0$; $y(0) = -10$.

(f) $y' + x^2 y^2 = 2$; $y(0) = 1$.

(g) $y' + (1 - x^2)y^2 = 0$; $y(0) = 2$.

(h) $y' + (\sin x)y^2 = \cos x; y(0) = 0.$

(i) $y'' - y = 0; y(0) = 1; y'(0) = 0.$

(j) $y'' - xy = x; y(0) = y'(0) = 1.$

(k) $y'' + (1 - x)y = x(1 - x); y(0) = y'(0) = 0.$

(l) $y'' + y^2 = 0; y(0) = 1; y'(0) = 1.$

(m) $y'' - x^2y^2 = 2; y(0) = 1; y'(0) = 1.$

(n) $y'' + xy'^2 + x^2y^2 = x^3; y(0) = 1; y'(0) = -1.$

(o) $y''' + 4y'' - y' + y = 0; y(0) = 0, y'(0) = y''(0) = 1.$

(p) $y^{iv} - 2y'' + x^2y = 0; y(0) = 1, y'(0) = 2, y''(0) = -1,$
$y'''(0) = -1.$

7.2 Evaluate the pivotal values of the solutions of Problem 7.1(a) to (h) by Euler's method, in the given intervals, using four significant figures.

(a) $x = 0(.2).4.$ (b) $x = 0(.2).4.$

(c) $x = 0(.2).4.$ (d) $x = 0(.25).5.$

(e) $x = 0(.1).2.$ (f) $x = 0(.1).2.$

(g) $x = 0(.2).4.$ (h) $x = 0(\pi/5)2\pi/5.$

7.3 Solve Problem 7.2 by the Euler-Richardson method.

7.4 Solve Problem 7.2 by the Euler-Gauss method.

7.5 Solve Problem 7.2 by the Euler-Gauss predictor-corrector iteration method.

7.6 Solve Problem 7.2 by the Runge-Kutta second-order formula.

7.7 Solve Problem 7.2 by the Runge-Kutta fourth-order formula.

7.8 Solve Problem 7.2 by Milne's predictor-corrector method using the answers to Problem 7.1 as starting values.

7.9 Solve the following simultaneous-equation problems in the given intervals by the indicated method.

(a) $y' - z = 0, z' - y = 0; y(0) = 1, z(0) = 0; x = 0(.1).2$ by Euler's method.

(b) Problem (a) by the second-order Runge-Kutta method.

(c) $y' + xz = 0, z' - y^2 = 0; y(0) = 1, z(0) = 1; x = 0(.2).4$ by the second-order Runge-Kutta method.

(d) $y' - z^2 = x, z' - y^2 = x^2; y(0) = 0, z(0) = 0; x = 0(.1).3$ by the second-order Runge-Kutta method.

7.10 Evaluate the solutions of the following problems in the given range by the indicated method, using four significant figures. Transform the problems into simultaneous-equation problems.

(a) $y'' - xy^2 = 0$; $y(0) = 1$, $y'(0) = 0$; $x = 0(.1).2$ by Euler's method.

(b) Problem (a) by the Euler-Gauss predictor-corrector method.

(c) $y'' - y' + x^2y = x^3$; $y(0) = y'(0) = 0$; $x = 0(.1).4$ by the Runge-Kutta second-order method.

(d) $y'' + xy' + x^2y = x^3$; $y(0) = 1$, $y'(0) = 0$; $x = 0(.1).3$ by the Runge-Kutta second-order method.

(e) $y'' - y^3 = 0$; $y(0) = 10$, $y'(0) = 5$; $x = 0(.1).3$ by the Runge-Kutta second-order method.

(f) $y'' + 2y^2 = e^x$; $y(0) = 0$, $y'(0) = 0$; $x = 0(.1).3$ by the Runge-Kutta second-order method.

7.11 Evaluate two more pivotal values in the solutions of Problems 7.10(a), (c), (d), and (f) by Milne's method for second-order equations, using the results of Problem 7.10 for the first four pivotal values.

7.12 Solve by finite differences with errors of order h^2 the following problems in the given intervals, using Taylor series to evaluate starting points where needed.

(a) Problem 7.1(a), 0(.2).4.   (b) Problem 7.1(d), 0(.2).4.

(c) Problem 7.1(i), 0(.2).4.   (d) Problem 7.9(a), 0(.1).2.

(e) Problem 7.9(c), 0(.2).4.   (f) Problem 7.10(a), 0(.1).2.

(g) $y^{iv} - 2y'' + 100y = 0$; $y(0) = 1$, $y'(0) = 0$, $y''(0) = 0$, $y'''(0) = 0$; $x = 0(.2).6$.

(h) $y^{iv} - 10x^2y = 25$; $y_0 = 1.$, $y_1 = 1.1$, $y_2 = 1.3$, $y_3 = 1.6$; $x = 0(.2).4$.

7.13 Solve Problem 6.1(a) to (d) by forward integration using finite differences of order h^2 and interpolation.

7.14 Compute the eigenvalues of Problems 6.2(a) to (c) by forward integration using finite differences of order h^2 and interpolation, with $h = .25$.

7.15 Determine whether the propagation factors for Euler's method of Problem 7.2 are greater or smaller than 1.

7.16 Determine the propagation factor of the Euler-Gauss method.

7.17 Determine the propagation factor of the Runge-Kutta second-order method.

7.18 Determine the propagation factor of the Euler-Richardson method.

Two-dimensional Problems

Chapter Eight

8.1 Pivotal Points, Partial Operators, and Double Interpolation

The pivotal values f_{ij} of a function $z = f(x, y)$ are usually given at the corners of a rectangular mesh with spacing h in the x-direction and k in the y-direction (Figure 8.1.1), with coordinates

$$x_i = x_0 + ih; \quad y_j = y_0 + jk \qquad (i, j = 0, 1, 2, \ldots). \tag{8.1.1}$$

For skew cartesian, triangular, hexagonal, and curvilinear meshes, see N.M., Ch. V.

Since the partial derivatives of $f(x, y)$ with respect to x (or y) are the ordinary derivatives of f with respect to x (or y) when y (or x) does not change, the operators of Section 3.2 may be used in the x-direction to determine derivatives with respect to x, and in the y-direction to determine derivatives with respect to y. For example, by (3.2.11) and (3.2.18),

$$f_{x,ij} = \left. \frac{\partial f}{\partial x} \right]_{\substack{x=x_i \\ y=y_j}} \doteq \frac{1}{2h} (f_{i+1,j} - f_{i-1,j}), \tag{8.1.2a}$$

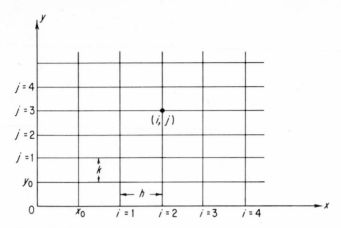

Figure 8.1.1

$$f_{y,ij} = \frac{\partial f}{\partial y}\bigg]_{\substack{x=x_i \\ y=y_j}} \doteq \frac{1}{2k}\,(f_{i,j+1} - f_{i,j-1}), \tag{8.1.2b}$$

$$f_{xx,ij} = \frac{\partial^2 f}{\partial x^2}\bigg]_{\substack{x=x_i \\ y=y_j}} \doteq \frac{1}{h^2}\,(f_{i-1,j} - 2f_{ij} + f_{i+1,j}), \tag{8.1.3a}$$

$$f_{yy,ij} = \frac{\partial^2 f}{\partial y^2}\bigg]_{\substack{x=x_i \\ y=y_j}} \doteq \frac{1}{k^2}\,(f_{i,j-1} - 2f_{ij} + f_{i,j+1}). \tag{8.1.3b}$$

The operator for the mixed derivative $f_{xy,ij}$ is obtained by applying the operator (8.1.2a) to the operator (8.1.2b):

$$f_{xy,ij} \equiv \frac{\partial^2 f}{\partial x\,\partial y}\bigg]_{\substack{x=x_i \\ y=y_j}}$$

$$\doteq \frac{1}{4hk}\,(f_{i+1,j+1} - f_{i+1,j-1} - f_{i-1,j+1} + f_{i-1,j-1}), \tag{8.1.4}$$

i.e., by "shifting" the operator for f_x up to $j + 1$, subtracting the same operator "shifted" down to $j - 1$, and dividing by $2k$.

One of the commonly encountered two-dimensional differential operators is the *Laplacian operator*

$$\nabla^2 f = f_{xx} + f_{yy}. \tag{8.1.5}$$

By means of (8.1.3) the finite difference expression for the Laplacian becomes

$$\nabla^2 f \doteq \frac{1}{h^2}\,(f_{i+1,j} - 2f_{ij} + f_{i-1,j}) + \frac{1}{k^2}\,(f_{i,j+1} - 2f_{ij} + f_{i,j-1}). \tag{8.1.6}$$

With

$$\frac{h}{k} = r,$$ (8.1.7)

the $h^2 \nabla^2 f$ finite difference operator becomes

$$h^2 \nabla^2 f_{ij} \doteq f_{i+1,j} + f_{i-1,j} + r(f_{i,j+1} + f_{i,j-1}) - 2(1 + r^2)f_{ij},$$ (8.1.8)

and, for $h = k$ $(r = 1)$,

$$h^2 \nabla^2 f_{ij} = f_{i+1,j} + f_{i-1,j} + f_{i,j+1} + f_{i,j-1} - 4f_{ij} \qquad (h = k),$$ (8.1.9)

which is represented by the molecule of Figure 8.1.2.

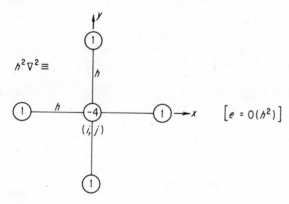

Figure 8.1.2

The error in the operators of (8.1.8) and (8.1.9) for $\nabla^2 f$ is of order h^2, since the operators are the sum of two operators (3.2.18) and k is of the same order of magnitude as h.

Example 8.1.1. Given $f(x, y) = \sqrt{1 + x^2 + 2y^2}$ at the points of Table 8.1.1, evaluate $\nabla^2 f_{0,0}$ for $h = .2$ and for $h = .1$, and find a more accurate estimate of $\nabla^2 f_{0,0}$ by an h^2-extrapolation (Sec. 3.6).

Table 8.1.1

y \ x	$-.2$	$-.1$	$0.$	$.1$	$.2$
$-.2$			1.03923		
$-.1$			1.00995		
$0.$	1.01980	1.00499	1.	1.00499	1.01980
$+.1$			1.00995		
$+.2$			1.03923		

$h = .2$:

$$\nabla^2 f_{0,0} = \frac{1.03923 + 1.03923 + 1.01980 + 1.01980 - 4\cdot1.}{(.2)^2} = 2.951,$$

$h = .1$:

$$\nabla^2 f_{0,0} = \frac{1.00995 + 1.00995 + 1.00499 + 1.00499 - 4\cdot1.}{(.1)^2} = 2.988,$$

$$\nabla^2 f_{0,0}]_{1,2} = \tfrac{4}{3}(2.988) - \tfrac{1}{3}(2.951) = 3.0003 \quad [3.].$$

Two-dimensional interpolation formulas are obtained by application of one-dimensional interpolation formulas operating in the x-direction "shifted" at various y-ordinates, and by application of the same formulas in the y-direction to the interpolated values obtained in the x-direction.

For example, applying the linear interpolation formula (3.4.2) at (i, j) and $(i, j + 1)$ (Figure 8.1.3) one obtains the interpolated values

$$\bar{f}_{i,j} = (1 - p)f_{i,j} + pf_{i+1,j}; \tag{8.1.10a}$$
$$\bar{f}_{i,j+1} = (1 - p)f_{i,j+1} + pf_{i+1,j+1}$$

by means of which the *two-dimensional linear interpolation formula* becomes

$$\begin{aligned}
f(x_i + ph, y_j + qk) &= (1 - q)\bar{f}_{i,j} + q\bar{f}_{i,j+1} \\
&= (1 - p)(1 - q)f_{i,j} + p(1 - q)f_{i+1,j} \\
&\quad + q(1 - p)f_{i,j+1} + pqf_{i+1,j+1}.
\end{aligned} \tag{8.1.10b}$$

Equation (8.1.10b) is conveniently represented by the "mathematical molecule" of Figure 8.1.3.

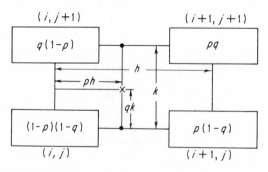

Figure 8.1.3

Similarly, applying the quadratic interpolation formula (3.4.3) at $(i, j - 1)$, (i, j) and $(i, j + 1)$ in the x-direction, and applying (3.4.3) again in the y-direction to the three interpolated values in the x-direction, one obtains the *two-dimensional quadratic interpolation formula*, represented by the "mathematical molecule" of Figure 8.1.4:

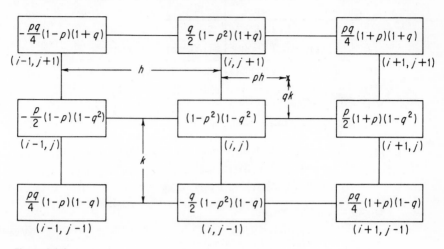

Figure 8.1.4

$$\bar{f}_{i,j-1} = -\frac{p(1-p)}{2}f_{i-1,j-1}$$
$$+ (1-p)(1+p)f_{i,j-1} + \frac{p(1+p)}{2}f_{i+1,j-1},$$

$$\bar{f}_{i,j} = -\frac{p(1-p)}{2}f_{i-1,j} + (1-p)(1+p)f_{i,j}$$
$$+ \frac{p(1+p)}{2}f_{i+1,j}, \tag{8.1.11}$$

$$\bar{f}_{i,j+1} = -\frac{p(1-p)}{2}f_{i-1,j+1}$$
$$+ (1-p)(1+p)f_{i,j+1} + \frac{p(1+p)}{2}f_{i+1,j+1},$$

$$f(x_i + ph,\, y_j + qk) = -\frac{q(1-q)}{2}\bar{f}_{i,j-1}$$
$$+ (1-q)(1+q)\bar{f}_{i,j} + \frac{q(1+q)}{2}\bar{f}_{i,j+1}.$$

Example 8.1.2. Given $f(x, y) = \sqrt{1 + x^2 + 2y^2}$ at the points of Table 8.1.2, evaluate $f(.25, .75)$ by linear and by quadratic interpolations.

Table 8.1.2

x y	−1.	0.	+1.
−1.	. 2.	1.732051	2.
0.	1.414214	1.	1.414214
+1.	2.	1.732051	2.

$p = .25, \ q = .75;$

Linear interpolation:

$$f(.25, .75) = (.75)(.25)(1.) + (.25)(.25)(1.4142)$$
$$+ (.75)(.75)(1.7321)$$
$$+ (.25)(.75)(2.) = 1.6253$$

Quadratic interpolation:

$$\bar{f}_{i,j-1} = - \frac{(.25)(.75)}{2} (2) + (.75)(1.25)(1.7321)$$

$$+ \frac{(.25)(1.25)}{2} (2) = 1.7488,$$

$$\bar{f}_{i,j} = - \frac{(.25)(.75)}{2} (1.4142) + (.75)(1.25)(1)$$

$$+ \frac{(.25)(.75)}{2} (1.4142) = 1.0257,$$

$$\bar{f}_{i,j+1} = \bar{f}_{i,j-1} = 1.7488,$$

$$f(.25, .75) = - \frac{(.75)(.25)}{2} (1.7488) + (.25)(1.75)(1.0257)$$

$$+ \frac{(.75)(1.75)}{2} (1.7488) = 1.4327 \quad [1.4790]$$

8.2 Double Integration [Program 9.9-A]

Double integration formulas are obtained by "shifting" the single integration formulas of Section 3.3. Thus, the *trapezoidal rule* in two dimensions for the integration of $f(x, y)$ over a rectangle of sides h, k is obtained by applying (3.3.15) first in the x-direction between i and $i + 1$, and then in the y-direction between j and $j + 1$:

$$I_T = \int_{x_i}^{x_{i+1}} \int_{y_j}^{y_{j+1}} f(x, y)\, dx\, dy$$

$$= \frac{k}{2}\left[\frac{h}{2}\left(f_{i+1,j+1} + f_{i,j+1}\right) + \frac{h}{2}\left(f_{i+1,j} + f_{ij}\right)\right]$$

$$= \frac{hk}{4}\left(f_{ij} + f_{i+1,j} + f_{i,j+1} + f_{i+1,j+1}\right). \tag{8.2.1}$$

I_T is represented by the molecule of Figure 8.2.1.

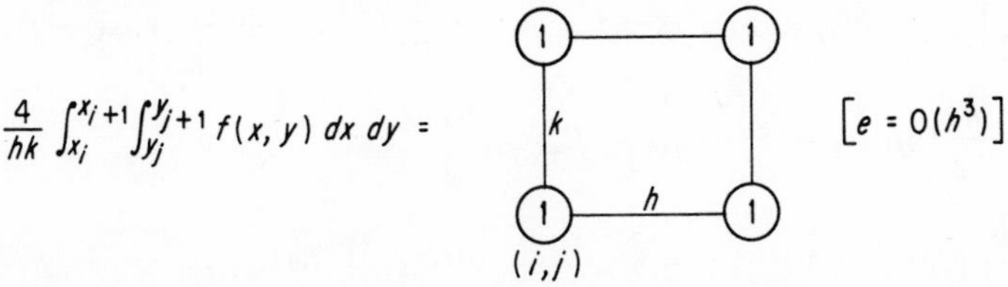

$$\frac{4}{hk}\int_{x_i}^{x_i+1}\int_{y_j}^{y_j+1} f(x, y)\, dx\, dy =$$

Figure 8.2.1

Similarly, shifting (3.3.24) gives *Simpson's 1/3 rule* for the integral over a rectangle $2h$ by $2k$ centered at i, j:

$$I_S = \int_{x_{i-1}}^{x_{i+1}} \int_{y_{j-1}}^{y_{j+1}} f(x, y)\, dx\, dy = \frac{k}{3}\left[\frac{h}{3}\left(f_{i+1,j+1} + 4f_{i,j+1} + f_{i-1,j+1}\right)\right.$$

$$\left. + 4\frac{h}{3}\left(f_{i+1,j} + 4f_{ij} + f_{i-1,j}\right) + \frac{h}{3}\left(f_{i+1,j-1} + 4f_{i,j-1} + f_{i-1,j-1}\right)\right]$$

$$= \frac{hk}{9}\left[\left(f_{i+1,j+1} + f_{i+1,j-1} + f_{i-1,j+1} + f_{i-1,j-1}\right)\right.$$

$$\left. + 4\left(f_{i,j+1} + f_{i,j-1} + f_{i+1,j} + f_{i-1,j}\right) + 16f_{ij}\right], \tag{8.2.2}$$

which is represented in Figure 8.2.2.

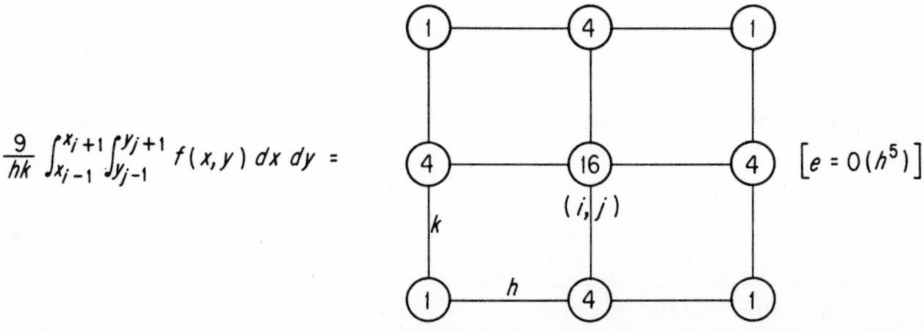

$$\frac{9}{hk}\int_{x_{i-1}}^{x_i+1}\int_{y_{j-1}}^{y_j+1} f(x, y)\, dx\, dy =$$

Figure 8.2.2

When the trapezoidal rule or Simpson's 1/3 rule is applied to a large number of rectangles of sides h, k, the corresponding error is of order h^2 or h^4, respectively (see Sec. 3.3).

"Slanted" double integration formulas may be obtained by shifting slanted simple integration formulas. For example, by (3.3.16) the integral over one rectangle with error of order h^4 is given by

$$
\int_{x_i}^{x_{i+1}} \int_{y_j}^{y_{j+1}} f(x, y)\, dx\, dy
$$

$$
= \frac{k}{12} \left[5\frac{h}{12}(5f_{ij} + 8f_{i+1,j} - f_{i+2,j}) + 8\frac{h}{12}(5f_{i,j+1} + 8f_{i+1,j+1} - f_{i+2,j+1}) \right.
$$

$$
\left. - \frac{h}{12}(5f_{i,j+2} + 8f_{i+1,j+2} - f_{i+2,j+2}) \right]
$$

$$
= \frac{hk}{144} [25f_{ij} + 40f_{i+1,j} - 5f_{i+2,j} + 40f_{i,j+1} + 64f_{i+1,j+1}
$$

$$
- 8f_{i+2,j+1} - 5f_{i,j+2} - 8f_{i+1,j+2} + f_{i+2,j+2}],
$$

(8.2.3)

and is represented by the molecule of Figure 8.2.3.

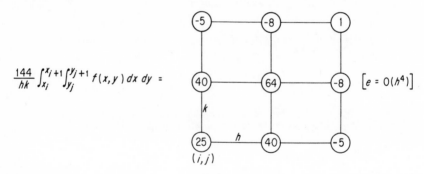

$$
\frac{144}{hk} \int_{x_i}^{x_i+1} \int_{y_j}^{y_j+1} f(x,y)\, dx\, dy =
$$

$[e = O(h^4)]$

Figure 8.2.3

Example 8.2.1. Given Table 8.2.1 for $f(x, y) = e^y \sin x$, evaluate the integral of $f(x, y)$ over the interval $0 \le x \le .2, 0 \le y < .2$, (a) by the trapezoidal rule with $h = .2$ and $h = .1$, and (b) by Simpson's 1/3 rule with $h = .1$.

Table 8.2.1

y \ x	0.	.1	.2
0.	0.	.0998	.1987
.1	0.	.1103	.2196
.2	0.	.1219	.2427

(a) $I_{T,1} = \dfrac{(.2)^2}{4}(0 + 0 + .1987 + .2427) = .004414$ [.004413].

$I_{T,2} = \dfrac{(.1)^2}{4}[0 + 2(.0998) + .1987 + 2 \cdot 0 + 4(.1103) + 2(.2196)$

$\qquad + 0 + (2).1219 + .2427]$

$\qquad = .004413$ [.004413].

(b) $I_S = \dfrac{(.1)^2}{9}[1 \cdot 0 + 4(.0998) + 1(.1987) + 4 \cdot 0 + 16(.1103)$

$\qquad + 4(.2196) + 1 \cdot 0 + 4(.1219) + 1(.2427)]$

$\qquad = .004413$ [.004413].

8.3 Integration of Elliptic Equations [Program 8.1]

Most of the basic partial differential equations of physics and engineering are of the second order, and have the form

$$a_{11}f_{xx} + 2a_{12}f_{xy} + a_{22}f_{yy} = F(x, y, f_x, f_y), \qquad \textbf{(8.3.1)}$$

where the coefficients a_{11}, a_{12}, a_{22} may be functions of x and y and the function F is often linear. Equations of this kind are classified as

elliptic,   if $a_{12}^2 - a_{11}a_{22} < 0$,

parabolic,   if $a_{12}^2 - a_{11}a_{22} = 0$,   **(8.3.2)**

hyperbolic, if $a_{12}^2 - a_{11}a_{22} > 0$.

Elliptic equations are governed by conditions on the boundary of a closed domain. These specify the value of (a) the function $f(x, y)$, or (b) its derivative f_n in a direction perpendicular to the boundary (*normal derivative*), or (c) a linear combination of f and its normal derivative f_n.

Laplace's equation,

$$\nabla^2 f \equiv f_{xx} + f_{yy} = 0, \qquad \textbf{(8.3.3)}$$

and *Poisson's equation,*

$$\nabla^2 f \equiv f_{xx} + f_{yy} = F(x, y), \qquad \textbf{(8.3.4)}$$

where $F(x, y)$ is a given function of x and y, are commonly encountered elliptic equations. Their constant coefficients $a_{11} = 1$, $a_{12} = 0$, $a_{22} = 1$ make $a_{12}^2 - a_{11}a_{22} = -1 < 0$ over the entire x,y-plane.

To evaluate numerically the solution of a Laplacian or a Poissonian equation at the points of a *square* mesh, one applies the operator of Figure 8.1.2 at the points of the mesh where f_{ij} is unknown, thus obtaining a system of linear algebraic equations in the pivotal values f_{ij}.

This system is nonhomogeneous for Laplace's equation because the values of f (or its normal derivative, or a linear combination thereof) are given on the boundary; for Poisson's equation because $F(x, y)$ has given values F_{ij} at the pivotal points i, j.

To obtain the pivotal values of f by iterative methods (Sec. 5.4), one solves for f_{ij} the equations obtained by using the molecule of Figure 8.1.2 in (8.3.3):

$$f_{ij} = \tfrac{1}{4}\,(f_{i+1,j} + f_{i-1,j} + f_{i,j+1} + f_{i,j-1}). \tag{8.3.4}$$

Equation (8.3.4) shows that the value of f at a mesh point is the average of the values of f at the four adjoining points [Figure 8.3.1(a)].

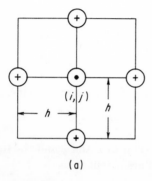
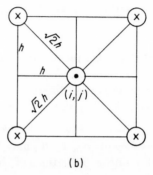

(a)   (b)

Figure 8.3.1

To obtain speedier convergence in the solution of Eqs. (8.3.4) by the *cross-averaging* Liebmann procedure, initial values of the f_{ij} are often obtained by first using a large mesh size, or by considering f_{ij} as the average of the four pivotal values adjoining f_{ij} diagonally [Figure 8.3.1(b)], as shown in the following examples.

Example 8.3.1. Given the values of $f(x, y)$ on the boundary of the square in Figure 8.3.2, evaluate the function $f(x, y)$ satisfying Laplace's equation, $\nabla^2 f = 0$, at the pivotal points of this figure.

By (8.3.4) at 1:

$$1000 + 2000 + f_3 + f_2 - 4f_1 = 0, \ \ldots.$$

Point	f_1	f_2	f_3	f_4	c
1	-4	1	1		-3000
2	1	-4		1	-1500
3	1		-4	1	-2500
4		1	1	-4	0

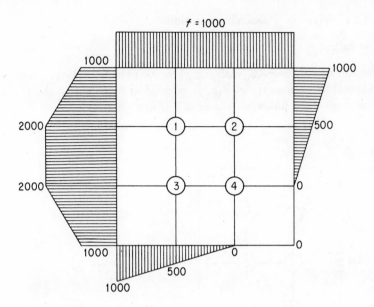

Figure 8.3.2

The roots of this system are

$$f_1 = 1208; \quad f_2 = 792; \quad f_3 = 1042; \quad f_4 = 458.$$

Appropriate initial values for the iterative solution of the system are obtained by diagonal averaging at 1 and cross averaging at 2, 3, and 4, assuming at first $f_4 = 0$.

$$f_1 = \tfrac{1}{4}(1000 + 1000 + 2000 + 0) = 1000,$$
$$f_2 = \tfrac{1}{4}(1000 + 1000 + 0 + 500) \doteq 600,$$
$$f_3 = \tfrac{1}{4}(1000 + 2000 + 500 + 0) \doteq 900,$$
$$f_4 = \tfrac{1}{4}(600 + 900 + 0 + 0) \doteq 400.$$

Equation (8.3.4) gives the iterative system

$$f_1^{(k+1)} = \tfrac{1}{4}(3000 + f_2^{(k)} + f_3^{(k)}),$$
$$f_2^{(k+1)} = \tfrac{1}{4}(1500 + f_1^{(k+1)} + f_4^{(k)}),$$
$$f_3^{(k+1)} = \tfrac{1}{4}(2500 + f_1^{(k+1)} + f_4^{(k)}),$$
$$f_4^{(k+1)} = \tfrac{1}{4}(f_2^{(k+1)} + f_3^{(k+1)}).$$

k	0	1	2	3	4	5
f_1	1000	1125	1191	1204	1208	1208
f_2	600	756	783	790	792	792
f_3	900	1006	1033	1040	1042	1042
f_4	400	441	454	458	458	458

Example 8.3.2. Solve the Poissonian equation

$$\nabla^2 f = 8x^2 y^2$$

in the domain of Figure 8.3.3, with $f(x, y) = 0$ on the boundary.

In view of the symmetry of $F(x, y) = 8x^2 y^2$ with respect to the x- and y-axis, there are three unknown values of f (Figure 8.3.3).

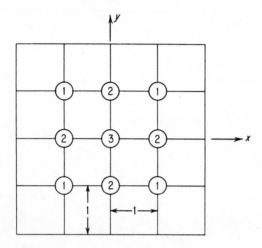

Figure 8.3.3

$$h^2 \, \nabla^2 = (1)^2 \, \nabla^2 f \doteq f_{i+1,j} + f_{i-1,j} + f_{i,j+1} + f_{i,j-1} - 4f_{ij} = (1)^2 8 i^2 j^2.$$

j \ i	1	2	3	F_{ij}
1	-4	2		$8(-1)^2(-1)^2$
2	2	-4	1	$8(-1)^2(0)^2$
3		4	-4	$8(0)^2(0)^2$

$$f_1 = -3, \quad f_2 = -2, \quad f_3 = -2.$$

8.4 Parabolic Equations [Program 8.2]

Parabolic equations, for which $a_{12}^2 - a_{11}a_{22} = 0$ (see Sec. 8.3), depend usually on both space and time variables and, thus, are governed by both boundary and initial conditions.

The *heat-flow equation,*

$$\kappa f_{xx} - f_t = 0,$$ (8.4.1)

with

$$a_{11} = \kappa, \quad a_{12} = a_{22} = 0, \quad a_{12}^2 - a_{11}a_{22} = 0,$$

is a parabolic equation governed by two boundary conditions — say,

$$f(0, t) = 0, \qquad f(L, t) = 0,$$ (a)

and one initial condition — say,

$$f(x, 0) = F(x).$$ (b)

To solve (8.4.1) with conditions (a) and (b), a spacing h for the variable x and a spacing τ for the variable t are selected, by means of which

$$f_{ij} \equiv f(x_i, t_j) = f(0 + ih, 0 + j\tau).$$ (8.4.2)

Approximation of f_{xx} by (3.2.18) and of f_t by (3.2.7),

$$f_{xx,ij} = \frac{1}{h^2}(f_{i+1,j} - 2f_{ij} + f_{i-1,j}),$$

$$f_{t,ij} = \frac{1}{\tau}(f_{i,j+1} - f_{i,j}),$$

transforms (8.4.1) into the finite difference equation

$$\frac{\kappa}{h^2}(f_{i+1,j} - 2f_{ij} + f_{i-1,j}) = \frac{1}{\tau}(f_{i,j+1} - f_{ij}),$$

which, solved for $f_{i,j+1} \equiv f(x_i, t_j + \tau)$, becomes

$$f_{i,j+1} = \frac{\tau\kappa}{h^2}(f_{i+1,j} + f_{i-1,j}) + \left(1 - \frac{2\tau\kappa}{h^2}\right)f_{ij}.$$ (8.4.3)

Equation (8.4.3) gives f at $x = ih$, at a time $t_j + \tau$ in terms of the adjoining values of f at $x = (i - 1)h$ and $x = (i + 1)h$, at a time t_j. Since f is known at $t = 0$, when $f(x, 0) = F(x)$, the *recurrence equation* (8.4.3) allows the evaluation of f at each pivotal point x_i at any time t_j. Equation (8.4.3) becomes particularly simple if, for a given h, τ is chosen so as to make the coefficient of f_{ij} vanish, i.e., if

$$\tau = \frac{h^2}{2\kappa}.$$ (8.4.4)

This value of τ gives the *Bender-Schmidt recurrence equation,*

$$f_{i,j+1} = \tfrac{1}{2}(f_{i+1,j} + f_{i-1,j}),$$ (8.4.5)

which determines the value of f at $x = x_i$, at a time $t = t_j + \tau$, as the average of the values right and left of x_i at a time t_j. Values of τ larger than those of (8.4.4) lead to instability of the solution.

Example 8.4.1. Solve the equation

$$\tfrac{1}{2} f_{xx} - f_t = 0 \tag{c}$$

with the conditions

$$f(0, t) = 0, \quad f(4, t) = 0, \quad f(x, 0) = x(4 - x), \tag{d}$$

using $h = 1$, and τ determined by (8.4.4).

$$\tau = \frac{1^2}{2(\tfrac{1}{2})} = 1; \quad f_{i,j+1} = \tfrac{1}{2} (f_{i+1,j} + f_{i-1,j}).$$

j \ i	0	1	2	3	4
0	0	3.	4.	3.	0
1	0	2.	3.	2.	0
2	0	1.5	2.	1.5	0
3	0	1.0	1.5	1.0	0
4	0	.75	1.0	.75	0
5	0	.50	.75	.50	0
6	0	.375	.50	.375	0
7	0	.250	.375	.250	0
8	0	.1875	.250	.1875	0
9	0	.1250	.1875	.1250	0
10	0	.09375	.1250	.09375	0
...	...	...	...	...	...
...	...	...	...	...	...

8.5 Hyperbolic Equations [Program 8.3]

Hyperbolic equations are also governed by both boundary and initial conditions, if time is one of the independent variables.

The *wave equation* in one dimension,

$$a^2 f_{xx} - f_{tt} = 0, \tag{8.5.1}$$

with

$$a_{11} = a^2, \quad a_{22} = -1, \quad a_{12} = 0; \quad a_{12}^2 - a_{11} a_{22} = a^2 > 0,$$

is a common example of a hyperbolic equation.

Two boundary conditions for (8.5.1) may be

$$f(0, t) = 0, \qquad f(L, t) = 0, \tag{a}$$

and two initial conditions

$$f(x, 0) = F(x), \qquad f_t(x, 0) = 0. \tag{b}$$

To solve (8.5.1), the pivotal value f_{ij} is defined by (8.4.2), with spacings h along the x-axis and τ along the t-axis, and both f_{xx} and f_{tt} are approximated by (3.2.18). Thus, one obtains the difference equation

$$f_{i+1,j} - 2f_{ij} + f_{i-1,j} - \frac{h^2}{a^2\tau^2} (f_{i,j+1} - 2f_{ij} + f_{i,j-1}) = 0,$$

which, solved for $f_{i,j+1}$, becomes the recurrence equation

$$f_{i,j+1} = -f_{i,j-1} + 2\left(1 - \frac{a^2\tau^2}{h^2}\right)f_{ij} + \frac{a^2\tau^2}{h^2}(f_{i+1,j} + f_{i-1,j}). \tag{8.5.2}$$

For a given h, and with a value of τ which makes the coefficient of f_{ij} vanish in (8.5.2), i.e., with $a^2\tau^2/h^2 = 1$, the recurrence equation takes the simplified form

$$f_{i,j+1} = -f_{i,j-1} + f_{i+1,j} + f_{i-1,j} \qquad \left(\frac{a^2\tau^2}{h^2} = 1\right)^*, \tag{8.5.3}$$

which defines f at $x = x_i$, at a time $t_j + \tau$, in terms of f at $x = x_i$, at a time $t_j - \tau$, and of f at the adjoining points $x = x_{i-1}$ and $x = x_{i+1}$, at a time t_j. By (3.2.11), the second initial condition (b),

$$2\tau f_t(x, 0) = f_{i,0+1} - f_{i,0-1} = 0 \quad \therefore \quad f_{i,-1} = f_{i,1}, \tag{c}$$

gives $f_{i,-1}$ in terms of $f_{i,1}$. Substitution of (c) and of the first of conditions (b) in (8.5.3) for $j = 0$ gives the *starting formula*

$$f_{i,1} = \tfrac{1}{2}(f_{i+1,0} + f_{i-1,0}) = \tfrac{1}{2}(F_{i+1} + F_{i-1}). \tag{8.5.4}$$

By means of the $f_{i,1}$ evaluated from (8.5.4), the recurrence equation (8.5.3) allows the determination of f at each point x_i at any time t_j.

Example 8.5.1. Given the initial value $f(x, 0) = F(x) = x(4 - x)$ and conditions (a) and (b), determine numerically the solution of the one-dimensional wave equation (8.5.1) for $a = 2$, with $h = 1$ and $\tau = \tfrac{1}{2}$, i.e., for $a^2\tau^2/h^2 = 1$.

---

* For $a^2\tau^2/h^2 = 1$ the solution of the difference equation is stable and coincides with the solution of the differential equation. For $a^2\tau^2/h^2 > 1$ the solution is unstable; for $a^2\tau^2/h^2 < 1$ the solution is stable but inaccurate.

j \ i	0	1	2	3	4	
0	0	3	4	3	0	$f_{i,0} = F_i$
1	0	2	3	2	0	$f_{i,1}$ from (8.5.4)
2	0	0	0	0	0	
3	0	-2	-3	-2	0	
4	0	-3	-4	-3	0	
5	0	-2	-3	-2	0	$f_{i,j+1}$ from (8.5.3)
6	0	0	0	0	0	
7	0	2	3	2	0	
8	0	3	4	3	0	

The function $f(x, t)$ goes through a complete oscillation in eight steps, indicating a periodic behavior with a period $T = 8\tau = 4$.

PROBLEMS

8.1 Evaluate f_{xx}, f_{yy}, f_{xy}, and $\nabla^2 f$ at the origin (the central point of the following set of pivotal values of f) by finite difference operators with errors of order h^2.

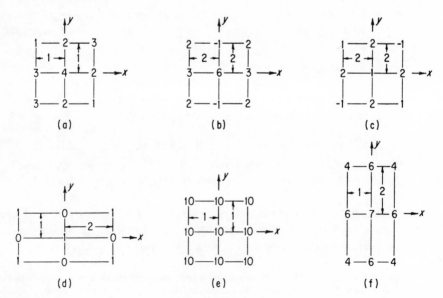

Problem 8.1

8.2 Evaluate by linear interpolation the value of $f(x, y)$ at the given points, by means of the pivotal values of f in Problem 8.1.

(a) $x = .5, y = .5; x = -.25, y = .75$.

(b) $x = 1, y = 1; x = -1, y = 1$.

(c) $x = .65, y = .35; x = -1.25, y = .75$.

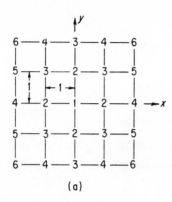

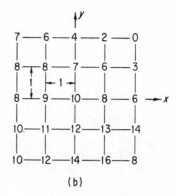

(a)   (b)

Problem 8.2

8.3 Evaluate the value of $f(x, y)$ in Problem 8.2 by quadratic interpolation.

8.4 Evaluate f_{xx}, f_{yy}, f_{xy}, and $\nabla^2 f$ at the origin by finite differences with $h = 2$ and with $h = 1$, and use h^2-extrapolation to improve these values.

8.5 Integrate the following functions over the given domains by the trapezoidal formula, using the indicated spacings. Improve the results by h^2-extrapolations.

(a) $f(x, y) = xy^2; 0 \leq x \leq 1, 0 \leq y \leq 1; h_1 = .5, h_2 = .25$.

(b) $f(x, y) = \sqrt{1 - xy}; 0 \leq x \leq 1, 0 \leq y \leq 1; h_1 = .5, h_2 = .25$.

(c) $f(x, y) = \dfrac{x^2 + y^2}{\sqrt{x^2 - y^2 + 2}}; 0 \leq x \leq 1, 0 \leq y \leq 1; h_1 = .5, h_2 = .25$.

(d) $f(x, y) = \sin x \cos y; 0 \leq x \leq \pi/2, 0 \leq y \leq \pi/2; h_1 = \pi/4, h_2 = \pi/8$.

(e) $f(x, y) = e^{x-y}; 0 \leq x \leq .2, 0 \leq y \leq .2; h_1 = .04, h_2 = .02$.

8.6 Integrate the functions of Problem 8.5 by Simpson's 1/3 rule and improve the results by h^4-extrapolations.

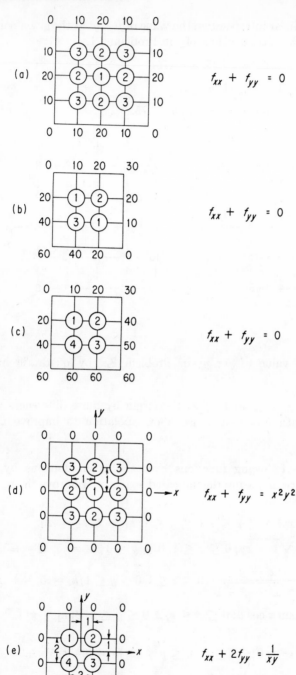

Problem 8.8

8.7 Determine which of the following equations are hyperbolic, parabolic, and elliptic in the given domains for the variables x, y.

(a) $xf_{xx} + yf_{yy} = 0;\ x > 0,\ y > 0.$

(b) $x^2f_{xx} + (1 - y^2)f_{yy} = 0;\ -\infty < x < \infty,\ -1 < y < 1.$

(c) $f_{xx} - 2f_{xy} = 0.$

(d) $f_{xx} + 2f_{xy} + f_{yy} = 0.$

(e) $f_{xx} + 2f_{xy} + 4f_{yy} = 0.$

(f) $f_{xy} - f_x = 0.$

(g) $f_{xx} - 2f_{xy} + f_{yy} = 0.$

8.8 Evaluate $f(x, y)$ at the internal pivotal points of the given domains by solving the difference equations corresponding to the given differential equations. The values of $f(x, y)$ on the boundary are given in the corresponding figures.

8.9 Evaluate $f(x, y)$ at the internal pivotal points of the given domains by cross averaging, after obtaining initial values by diagonal averaging.

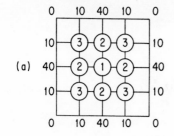

(a) $f_{xx} + f_{yy} = 0$

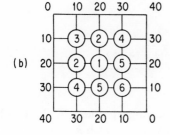

(b) $f_{xx} + f_{yy} = 0$

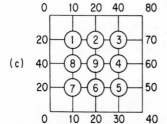

(c) $f_{xx} + f_{yy} = 0$

Problem 8.9

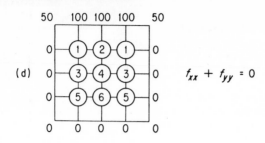

(d) $f_{xx} + f_{yy} = 0$

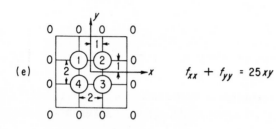

(e) $f_{xx} + f_{yy} = 25xy$

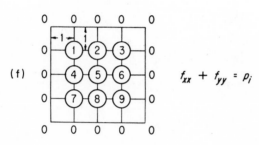

(f) $f_{xx} + f_{yy} = p_i$

i	1	2	3	4	5	6	7	8	9
p_i	10	15	18	12	16	20	14	18	22

Problem 8.9

8.10 Evaluate the pivotal values of the following equations by the Bender-Schmidt recurrence equation for $0 < t < 10\tau$, with $h = 1$.

(a) $f_{xx} - f_t = 0$ $\begin{cases} f(0, t) = f(5, t) = 0; \\ f(x, 0) = x^2(25 - x^2). \end{cases}$

(b) $10f_{xx} - 2f_t = 0$ $\begin{cases} f(0, t) = 0, f(5, t) = 60, \\ f(x, 0) = 20x \text{ for } 0 \le x \le 3 \\ f(x, 0) = 60 \text{ for } 3 \le x \le 5 \end{cases}$

(c) $2f_{xx} - f_t = 0$ $\begin{cases} f(0, t) = 10, f(6, t) = 18, \\ f(x, 0) = x^2/2. \end{cases}$

(d) $4f_{xx} - f_t = 0$ $\qquad$ $\begin{cases} f(0, t) = -10, \; f(5, t) = 10, \\ f(x, 0) = -10 \text{ for } 0 \le x \le 2.5 \\ f(x, 0) = 10 \text{ for } 2.5 \le x \le 5 \end{cases}$

8.11 Evaluate the pivotal values of the following equations by (8.5.3) and (8.5.4) for one-half period of vibration.

(a) $16f_{xx} - f_{tt} = 0$ $\qquad$ $\begin{cases} f(0, t) = f(5, t) = 0; \\ f(x, 0) = x^2(5 - x). \end{cases}$

(b) $25f_{xx} - f_{tt} = 0$ $\qquad$ $\begin{cases} f(0, t) = f(5, t) = 0; \\ f(x, 0) = 2x \text{ for } 0 \le x \le 2.5, \\ f(x, 0) = 10 - 2x \text{ for } 2.5 \le x \le 5. \end{cases}$

(c) $4f_{xx} - f_{tt} = 0$ $\qquad$ $\begin{cases} f(0, t) = f(5, t) = 0; \\ f(x) = 160x^3(5 - x). \end{cases}$

(d) $25f_{xx} - f_{tt} = 0$ $\qquad$ $\begin{cases} f(0, t) = f(5, t) = 0; \\ f(x, 0) = 20x \text{ for } 0 \le x \le 1, \\ f(x, 0) = 25\left(1 - \dfrac{x}{5}\right) \text{ for } 1 \le x \le 5. \end{cases}$

Chapter Two

1. (a) $y_1 = .133$, $n_1 = 4$; $y_2 = -.0625$, $n_2 = 4$

    (c) $y_1 = 2.54$, $n_1 = 4$; $y_2 = .375$, $n_2 = 4$

2. (b) $y_1 = .0499$, $n_1 = 5$; $y_2 = .500$, $n_2 = 1$

    (d) $y_1 = 1.005$, $n_1 = 4$, $y_2 = 8.05$, $n_2 = 5$

3. (a) $y = 1 + \dfrac{x}{2} - \dfrac{x^2}{8} + \dfrac{x^3}{16} - \ldots,\ n = 4$

    (c) $y = 1 - \dfrac{x^4}{4} - \dfrac{3x^8}{32} - \ldots,\ n = 2$

    (e) $y = x - \dfrac{x^3}{6} + \dfrac{x^5}{120} + \ldots,\ n = 2$

    (g) $y = 1 - \dfrac{9x^2}{2} + \dfrac{27x^4}{8} - \dfrac{81x^6}{80} + \ldots,\ n = 4$

4. (b) $y = \sum\limits_{n=0}^{\infty} (-1)^n(x-1)^n$; $n = 3$

(d) $y = \dfrac{e^2}{3} \sum\limits_{n=0}^{\infty} \dfrac{2^n(x-1)^n}{n!}$; $n = 4$

5. (a) $z = x^2 - y^2$; .05 [.05]

(c) $z = x^2 - y^2$; .05 [.04998]

(e) $z = x - y$; .1 [.0964]

6. (b) 12, 25, 44, 48, 24

(d) 25, 71, 154, 240, 120

7. (a) $p_3(x) = (x + \frac{4}{3})^3 - \frac{22}{3}(x + \frac{4}{3}) + \frac{254}{27}$

(c) $p_4(x) = (x + \frac{1}{4})^4 + \frac{5}{8}(x + \frac{1}{4})^2 - \frac{3}{8}(x + \frac{1}{4}) + \frac{269}{256}$

8. (b)

i	f_i	δf_i	$\delta^2 f_i$	$\delta^3 f_i$	$\delta^4 f_i$
0	.43429				
		.43427			
1	.86856		.00004		
		.43432		−.00006	
2	1.30288		−.00002		.00007
		.43430		.00001	
3	1.73718		−.00001		.00001
		.43429		.00002	
4	2.17147		.00001		.00004
		.43430		−.00002	
5	2.60577		−.00001		
		.43429			
6	3.04006				

(d)

i	f_i	δf_i	$\delta^2 f_i$	$\delta^3 f_i$	$\delta^4 f_i$
0	.3420				
		.0164			
1	.3584		−.0002		
		.0162		.0001	
2	.3746		−.0001		−.0001
		.0161		.0000	
3	.3907		−.0001		.0000
		.0160		.0000	
4	.4067		−.0001		
		.0159			
5	.4226				

9. (a) $f_4 = .5646 - .0200 = .5446$ [.5446]

(c) $f_3 = .93011 - .01980 = .91031$ [.91031]

Chapter Three

1. (a) $-.9516, -.9969, -.9997$ [$-1.$]

(c) $-.940$ [$-1.$]

(e) $-.85$ [$-.905$]; $-.85$ [$-.819$]

2. (b) $-.840, -.8405$ [$-.8415$]

(d) $-.20$ [$-.1700$]

3. (a) $-.9064, -.9516, -.9969$ [$-1.$]
$-.8242, -.8201, -.8187$ [$-.8187$]

(c) $-.6748, -.6714, -.6703$ [$-.6703$]
$-.6725, -.671, -.670$ [$-.6703$]

4. (b) $-.8385, -.783, -.728$ [$-.7174$]
$-.8385, -.840, -.840$ [$-.8415$]

5. (a) $f_i''' = \dfrac{1}{2h^3} (-f_{i-2} + 2f_{i-1} - 2f_{i+1} + f_{i+2})$

(c) $f_i{}^{iv} = \dfrac{1}{h^4} (f_i - 4f_{i+1} + 6f_{i-2} - 4f_{i+3} + f_{i+4})$

6. (b) $f_i''' = \dfrac{1}{h^3} (-f_{i-1} + 3f_i - 3f_{i+1} + f_{i+2})$

7. $.4527, .4516, .4512$ [.4512]

8. (b) $.3935$ [.3935]

9. (a) $.5921, .5915$ [.5916]

(c) $f^{(1)} = .7739, .7782, .7746$
$f^{(2)} = .7771, .7773$
$f^{(3)} = .7772$ [.7772]

11. (a) $.9077$ [.9048]

Chapter Four

1. (b) $x_1 = 1$; $x_{2.3} = \pm i$

(d) $x_1 = -1.6474$; $x_{2.3} = .82371 + .73179i$

2. (a) $x_{1,2} = \pm 1$; $x_{3,4} = \pm 2$

(c) $x_{1,2} = 1.2726 \pm 1.3102i$; $x_{3,4} = -.77262 \pm 1.17321i$

(e) $x_{1,2} = 1$; $x_{3,4} = -1 \pm i$

3. (b) $x_1 = -.22147$; $x_{2,3} = -.88926 \pm 1.0076i$

(d) $x_1 = 1.1$; $x_2 = -.6$; $x_{3,4} = -\dfrac{1}{2} \pm \dfrac{\sqrt{7}}{2}i$

(f) $x_{1,2} = 2.1$; $x_{3,4} = -\dfrac{1}{2} \pm \dfrac{\sqrt{11}}{2}i$

4. See Problem 3.

5. $x^4 = N$; $x^{(k+1)} = \dfrac{1}{4}\left(3x^{(k)} + \dfrac{N}{(x^{(k)})^3}\right)$

(a) 3.11; (c) .928; (e) 4.95

6. (b) .3705; (d) 3.0702; (f) .5492

7. See Problem 6.

8. See Problem 6.

9. See Problem 6.

Chapter Five

1. (a) 1.; (c) -63.5538

2. (b) $x_1 = 2.1622$; $x_2 = .45546$; $x_3 = 1.4324$; $x_4 = 1.0811$

(d) $x_1 = -2.1291$; $x_2 = 1.2679$; $x_3 = -1.6112$; $x_4 = 1.0300$

3. (a)
$$\begin{bmatrix} -1. & 1. & 0. \\ 1.5 & -.5 & -.5 \\ -1. & 0. & 1. \end{bmatrix}$$

(c)
$$\begin{bmatrix} .85714 & -.71429 & .57143 & -.42857 & .28571 & -.14286 \\ -.71429 & 1.42857 & -1.14286 & .85714 & -.57143 & .28571 \\ .57143 & -1.14286 & 1.71429 & -1.28571 & .85714 & -.42857 \\ -.42857 & .85714 & -1.28571 & 1.71429 & -1.14286 & .57143 \\ .28571 & -.57143 & .85714 & -1.14286 & 1.42857 & -.71429 \\ -.14286 & .28571 & -.42857 & .57143 & -.71429 & .85714 \end{bmatrix}$$

4. (a) $x_1 = -3.$; $x_2 = 1.5$; $x_3 = 2.$

$x_1 = 3.$; $x_2 = -4.$; $x_3 = 4.$

(c) $x_1 = \frac{33}{7}$; $x_2 = \frac{4}{7}$; $x_3 = \frac{22}{7}$; $x_4 = \frac{8}{7}$; $x_5 = \frac{11}{7}$; $x_6 = \frac{12}{7}$

$x_1 = 3$; $x_2 = -5$; $x_3 = 6$; $x_4 = -6$; $x_5 = 5$; $x_6 = -3$

5. (b) $x_1 = 1$, $x_2 = 2$, $x_3 = 3$, $x_4 = 0$

   (d) $x_1 = 2$, $x_2 = 0$, $x_3 = 1$, $x_4 = 2$, $x_5 = 0$, $x_6 = 1$, $x_7 = 2$

6. (a) $\lambda_1 = 3$, $\begin{bmatrix} 1 \\ 1 \end{bmatrix}$; $\lambda_2 = 1$, $\begin{bmatrix} 1 \\ -1 \end{bmatrix}$

   (c) $\lambda_1 = 0$, $\begin{bmatrix} 1 \\ 1 \\ 1 \end{bmatrix}$; $\lambda_2 = \lambda_3 = 3$, $\begin{bmatrix} 1 \\ 1 \\ -2 \end{bmatrix}$, $\begin{bmatrix} 1 \\ -1 \\ 0 \end{bmatrix}$

   (e) $\lambda_1 = .382$, $\begin{bmatrix} 1. \\ -1.618 \\ 1.618 \\ -1. \end{bmatrix}$; $\lambda_2 = 1.382$, $\begin{bmatrix} 1. \\ -.618 \\ -.618 \\ 1. \end{bmatrix}$;

   $\lambda_3 = 2.618$, $\begin{bmatrix} 1. \\ .618 \\ -.618 \\ -1. \end{bmatrix}$; $\lambda_4 = 3.618$, $\begin{bmatrix} 1. \\ 1.618 \\ 1.618 \\ 1. \end{bmatrix}$

7. (b) $\lambda = 5$, $\begin{bmatrix} 1 \\ -1 \end{bmatrix}$

   (d) $\lambda = 12.935$, $\begin{bmatrix} 1. \\ 1.340 \\ 1.595 \\ 1.340 \\ 1. \end{bmatrix}$

Chapter Six

1. (a) $y^{(1)}(.50) = 1.$; $y^{(2)}(.25) = .5378$, $y^{(2)}(.50) = .9412$, $y^{(2)}(.75) = 1.1092$; $y_{1.2}(.50) = .9216$

   (c) $y^{(1)}(.50) = -2.14$; $y^{(2)}(.25) = -1.590$, $y^{(2)}(.50) = -2.089$, $y^{(2)}(.75) = -1.535$; $y_{1.2}(.50) = -2.072$

   (e) $y^{(1)}(.50) = -.0667$; $y^{(2)}(.25) = -.0461$, $y^{(2)}(.50) = -.0693$, $y^{(2)}(.75) = -.0584$; $y_{1.2}(.50) = -.0702$

   (g) $y_1 = 1.6969$, $y_2 = .3330$, $y_3 = -1.5362$, $y_4 = -1.0392$, $y_5 = 1.0109$, $y_6 = 2.0848$, $y_7 = 1.2303$, $y_8 = -.3560$, $y_9 = -.9825$

   (i) $y_1 = .1736$, $y_2 = .5432$, $y_3 = .9961$, $y_4 = 1.4823$

   (k) $y_1 = -.8949$, $y_2 = -1.1332$, $y_3 = .7174$, $y_4 = .2017$

(m) $y^{(1)} (.2) = 5.446$, $y^{(1)} (.4) = 6.218$, $y^{(1)} (.6) = 6.346$, $y^{(1)} (.8) = 3.872$;
$y^{(2)} (.1) = 2.385$, $y^{(2)} (.2) = 4.027$, $y^{(2)} (.3) = 5.372$, $y^{(2)} (.4) = 6.247$,
$y^{(2)} (.5) = 6.562$, $y^{(2)} (.6) = 6.269$, $y^{(2)} (.7) = 5.372$, $y^{(2)} (.8) = 3.934$,
$y^{(2)} (.9) = 2.082$; $y_{1.2} (.2) = 3.547$, $y_{1.2} (.4) = 6.257$, $y_{1.2} (.6) = 6.243$,
$y_{1.2} (.8) = 3.955$

2. (a) 16., 17.871, 18.495

(c) 32., 42.667, 46.222

(e) 8., 9.37, 9.83

Chapter Seven

1. (a) $y = 1 + x + \dfrac{x^2}{2}$
$y_1 = 1.22$, $y_2 = 1.48$, $y_3 = 1.78$

(c) $y = 10 + 5x^2 - \tfrac{10}{3} x^3$
$y_1 = 10.17$, $y_2 = 10.59$, $y_3 = 11.08$

(e) $y = 10(-1 + 10x - 100x^2)$
$y_1 = -30.$, $y_2 = -130.$, $y_3 = -310.$

(g) $y = 2(1 - 2x + 4x^2)$
$y_1 = 1.52$, $y_2 = 1.68$, $y_3 = 2.48$

(i) $y = 1 + \dfrac{x^2}{2} + \dfrac{x^4}{24}$
$y_1 = 1.02$, $y_2 = 1.08$, $y_3 = 1.19$

(k) $y = \dfrac{x^3}{6} - \dfrac{x^4}{12} - \dfrac{x^5}{120}$
$y_1 = .00120$, $y_2 = .00839$, $y_3 = .0246$

(m) $y = 1 + x^2 + \dfrac{x^4}{12}$
$y_1 = 1.04$, $y_2 = 1.16$, $y_3 = 1.36$

(o) $y = x - \dfrac{x^2}{2} - \dfrac{x^3}{2}$
$y = .176$, $y_2 = .288$, $y_3 = .312$

2. (b) $y_1 = 3.$, $y_2 = 4.444$; (d) $y_1 = 10$, $y_2 = 10.17$;

(f) $y_1 = 1.2$, $y_2 = 1.399$; (h) $y_1 = .6283$, $y_2 = .9908$

3. (a) $y_1 = 1.213$, $y_2 = 1.472$; (c) $y_1 = 10.12$, $y_2 = 10.52$;

(e) $y_1 = -5.$, $y_2 = -3.230$; (g) $y_1 = 1.397$, $y_2 = 1.094$

4. (b) $y_1 = 3.222$, $y_2 = 5.089$; (d) $y_1 = 10.09$, $y_2 = 10.52$;

(f) $y_1 = 1.199$, $y_2 = 1.395$; (h) $y_2 = .5522$

(a)	Problem 5 Predicted	Corrected	Problem 6	Problem 7	Problem 8 Predicted	Corrected
0.00	1.	1.	1.	1.		
.20	1.2000000	1.2200000	1.220000	1.2214000		
.40	1.4600000	1.4860000	1.488400	1.4918179		
.60	1.7780000	1.8098000	1.815848	1.8221063		
.80	2.1654000	2.2041400	2.215334	2.2255206	2.225385	2.225526
1.00	2.6372200	2.6844020	2.702708	2.7182508	2.718088	2.718259
1.20	3.2118460	3.2693086	3.297303	3.3200714	3.319872	3.320088
1.40	3.9116778	3.9816609	4.022710	4.0551351	4.054898	4.055160
1.60	4.7639964	4.8492283	4.907706	4.9529419	4.952659	4.952981
1.80	5.8020275	5.9058306	5.987402	6.0495232	6.049187	6.049578
2.00	7.0662361	7.1926569	7.304630	7.3888876	7.388487	7.388966

(c)						
0.00	10.	10.	10.			
.20	10.0000000	10.1600000	10.180000	10.1748410		
.40	10.4800000	10.5715200	10.614400	10.6042110		
.60	11.0745600	11.0888290	11.157857	11.1404680		
.80	11.6204070	11.5405440	11.637734	11.6105860	11.615563	11.610767
1.00	11.9123970	11.7264700	11.850564	11.8135870	11.809975	11.814108
1.20	11.7264700	11.4450350	11.589852	11.5488220	11.534798	11.550059
1.40	10.8821650	10.5541990	10.707540	10.6751260	10.652846	10.677199
1.60	9.3353970	9.0486000	9.191353	9.1820340	9.161048	9.184490
1.80	7.2562038	7.1075086	7.213815	7.2324932	7.227704	7.233495
2.00	5.0177220	5.0590709	5.101956	5.1343387	5.157042	5.131415

(e)						
0.00	−10.	−10.	−10.	−10.		
.10	0.0000000	−5.0000000	−7.500000	−4.8563640		
.20	−5.0000000	−3.7500000	−5.302734	−3.2689981		
.30	−1.2500000	−2.4218750	−3.784241	−2.4637438		
.40	−2.2656250	−2.0870972	−2.842845	−1.9767603	−3.517033	−1.691131
.50	−1.5737916	−1.7066034	−2.248092	−1.6505075	−2.053362	−1.739542
.60	−1.4589214	−1.4763399	−1.849931	−1.4166872	−1.224710	−1.142335
.70	−1.2634948	−1.2900964	−1.568088	−1.2408936	−1.756583	−1.361832
.80	−1.1304545	−1.1463791	−1.359244	−1.1039111	−.563629	−.840970
.90	−1.0185864	−1.0306069	−1.198749	−.9941647	−1.450244	−1.135608
1.00	−.9268551	−.9357780	−1.071759	−.9042660	−.398181	−.640163
1.10	−.8498719	−.8567108	−.968873	−.8292774	−1.235902	−.987065
1.20	−.7844826	−.7898261	−.883876	−.7657737	−.291904	−.493756
1.30	−.7282848	−.7325355	−.812505	−.7113039	−1.091220	−.882390
1.40	−.6794956	−.6829298	−.751743	−.6640685	−.205226	−.380411
1.50	−.6367584	−.6395711	−.699400	−.6227160	−.987277	−.804651
1.60	−.5990249	−.6013564	−.653845	−.5862116	−.132764	−.288671
1.70	−.5654734	−.5674269	−.613843	−.5537502	−.907907	−.744481
1.80	−.5354509	−.5371035	−.578440	−.5246952	−.071064	−.211825
1.90	−.5084327	−.5098429	−.546888	−.4985372	−.844364	−.696258
2.00	−.4839925	−.4852053	−.518593	−.4748635	−.017579	−.145682

(g)						
0.00	2.	2.	2.	2.		
.20	1.2000000	1.4617600	1.493120	1.4340129		
.40	1.1852800	1.2055094	1.195351	1.1380399		
.60	.9694882	1.0273447	1.021902	.9727077		
.80	.9070366	.9375729	.928862	.8854234	.914281	.883972
1.00	.8783374	.9079551	.898233	.8570887	.865240	.857323
1.20	.9079551	.9442279	.932119	.8896241	.890099	.888458
1.40	1.0167736	1.0797483	1.062057	1.0148247	1.007913	1.014958
1.60	1.2782433	1.4338851	1.404482	1.3609390	1.318786	1.356205
1.80	1.9436637	2.5350080	2.512641	2.7838669	2.309135	2.642294
2.00	4.2274751	8.7427050	10.561899	156.5119900	8.991572	21.887580

*The answers on this page are given as obtained from the computer.

9. (a) $y_1 = 1., \ y_2 = 1.01; \ z_1 = .1, \ z_2 = .2$

(c) $y_1 = 1.022, \ y_2 = 1.100; \ z_1 \doteq 1.2, \ z_2 = 1.419$

10. (b) $y_1 = 1.0002, \ y_2 = 1.0014, \ y_3 = 1.0047$
$y'_1 = .0050, \ y'_2 = .0200, \ y'_3 = .0452$

(d) $y_1 = 1., \ y_2 = .99993, \ y_3 = .99956$
$y'_1 = -.000238, \ y'_2 = .002140, \ y'_3 = .006733$

(f) $y_1 = .005, \ y_2 = .02104, \ y_3 = .04927$
$y'_1 = .10513, \ y'_2 = .22129, \ y'_3 = .34949$

11. (a) $y_4 = 1.0108, \ y_5 = 1.0212$

(d) $y_4 = .99849, \ y_5 = .99661$

(f) $y_4 = .09136, \ y_5 = .14780$

12. (b) $y_1 = 10.06, \ y_2 = 10.81$

(d) $y_1 = 1.005, \ y_2 = 1.020; \ z_1 = .100, \ z_2 = .201$

(f) $y_1 = 1.3002, \ y_2 = 1.0014$

(h) $y_4 = 2.0475$

13. (a) $y_0 = 0., \ y_1 = .5378, \ y_2 = .9412, \ y_3 = 1.1093, \ y_4 = 1.0001$

(c) $y_0 = 0., \ y_1 = -1.5899, \ y_2 = -2.0894, \ y_3 = -1.5346, \ y_4 = .0000$

14. (b) $k = 12.74$

15. (a) $1 + h$ 　　　　　　　　(c) $1 + x(1 - x)h$

(e) $1 + 2yh$ 　　　　　　　(g) $1 + 2(1 - x^2)yh$

16. $1 + \dfrac{h}{2}(f_{y,i} + f_{y,i+1})$

18. $\left(1 + \dfrac{h}{2}f_{y,i}\right)\left(1 + \dfrac{h}{2}f_{y,i+1/2}\right)$

Chapter Eight

1. (b) $-1.5, \ -3.5, \ 0, \ -5$

(d) $-.5, \ -2, \ 0, \ -2.5$

(f) $-2, \ -5, \ 0, \ -2.5$

2. (a) 2.75, 2.4375 　　　　　　(c) 1.1838, 1.6875

3. (b) 3.875, 3.875

4. (a) 1.5, 2, 2.17; 1, 2, 2.33; 0, 0, 0; 2.5, 4, 4.5

5. (b) .8308, .8483, .8542 　　　　(d) .8988, .9744, .9996

6. (a)   .1667, .1667, .1667   (c)   .4877, .4831, .4827

    (e)   .0401336, .0401335, .0401335

7. (b)   elliptic, (d) parabolic, (f) hyperbolic

8. (a) $f_1 = 15$, $f_2 = 15$, $f_3 = 12.5$

    (c) $f_1 = 26\frac{2}{3}$, $f_2 = 33\frac{1}{3}$, $f_3 = 46\frac{2}{3}$, $f_4 = 43\frac{1}{3}$

    (e) $f_1 = -f_2 = f_3 = -f_4 = 4/9$

9. (b) $f_1 = 20$, $f_2 = 20$, $f_3 = 15$, $f_4 = 25$, $f_5 = 20$

    (d) $f_1 = 42.86$, $f_2 = 52.68$, $f_3 = 18.75$

        $f_4 = 25.$, $f_5 = 7.14$, $f_6 = 9.82$

    (f) $f_1 = -8.955$, $f_2 = -13.473$, $f_3 = -11.812$

        $f_4 = -12.348$, $f_5 = -18.125$, $f_6 = -15.777$

        $f_7 = -10.312$, $f_8 = -14.902$, $f_9 = -13.170$

10. (a)

i \ j	0	1	2	3	4	5
0	0.	24.	84.	144.	144.	0.
1	0.	42.	84.	114.	72.	0.
2	0.	42.	78.	78.	57.	0.
3	0.	39.	60.	67.	39.	0.
4	0.	30.	53.25	49.5	33.75	0.
5	0.	26.625	39.75	43.5	24.75	0.
6	0.	19.875	35.063	32.25	21.75	0.
7	0.	17.531	26.063	28.406	16.125	0.
8	0.	13.031	22.969	21.094	14.203	0.
9	0.	11.484	17.063	18.586	10.547	0.
10	0.	8.531	15.035	13.805	9.293	0.
∞	0.	0.	0.	0.	0.	0.

(c)

i \ j	0	1	2	3	4	5	6
0	10.	.5	2.	4.5	8.	12.5	18.
1	10.	6.	2.5	5.	8.5	13.	18.
2	10.	6.25	5.5	5.5	9.	13.25	18.
3	10.	7.75	5.875	7.25	9.375	13.5	18.
4	10.	7.9375	7.5	7.625	10.375	13.688	18.
5	10.	8.75	7.7812	8.9375	10.656	14.188	18.
6	10.	8.8906	8.8437	9.2187	11.563	14.328	18.
7	10.	9.4218	9.0546	10.203	11.773	14.781	18.
8	10.	9.5273	9.8125	10.414	12.492	14.887	18.
9	10.	9.9062	9.9707	11.152	12.650	15.246	18.
10	10.	9.9853	10.529	11.311	13.199	15.325	18.
∞	10.	$11\frac{1}{3}$	$12\frac{2}{3}$	14	$15\frac{1}{3}$	$16\frac{2}{3}$	18.

11. (b)

i j	0	1	2	3	4	5
0	0.	2.	4.	4.	2.	0.
1	0.	2.	3.	3.	2.	0.
2	0.	1.	1.	1.	1.	0.
3	0.	−1.	−1.	−1.	−1.	0.
4	0.	−2.	−3.	−3.	−2.	0.
5	0.	−2.	−4.	−4.	−2.	0.

(d)

i j	0	1	2	3	4	5
0	0.	20.	15.	10.	5.	0.
1	0.	7.5	15.	10.	5.	0.
2	0.	−5.	2.5	10.	5.	0.
3	0.	−5.	−10.	−2.5	5.	0.
4	0.	−5.	−10.	−15.	−7.5	0.
5	0.	−5.	−10.	−15.	−20.	0.

1 On the Programs

The following eight sections contain a collection of complete FORTRAN programs, each accompanied by a flow chart, program notes, beginner's hints, and examples. The programs in Sections 2 through 8 encompass techniques to be found in the corresponding chapters of the book. Thus, the programs numbered 7.1 through 7.8 are based on methods developed in Chapter 7 for integrating initial-value problems. Programs whose identification number contains an A are generalizations of a preceding program; e.g., Program 7.5-A uses the same algorithm as Program 7.5, but uses FUNCTION subprograms instead of arithmetic statement functions and allows more input parameters. Flow charts, notes, and results are not given for most of the A-programs because of their similarity to the program they generalize.

Most of the programs use a simple algorithm for the method considered so that the pertinent numerical technique may be exhibited in a short program. Suggestions for more general algorithms are given in the notes and hints.

The flow charts vary in the amount of detail shown. The charts for some of the simpler programs show every calculation and indicate every loop explicitly, while the charts of some of the longer, more complex programs show only the possible alternatives in the calculation. In such cases a single flow-chart box may indicate much calculation, possibly many loops.

An effort has been made to include every aspect of FORTRAN in these programs, since the mastering of the language is often hampered by a lack of programs illustrating the use of the uncommon statements, specifications, and controls. The following reference table is a list of definitions and typical examples of FORTRAN statements and specifications, with a reference to as many as three programs where they are used (although some specifications and statements are used in almost every program).

Designation	Typical Form	Programs
A-field specification	FORMAT (A3)	8.1, 8.2, 8.3
Arithmetic statement function	G(X,Y,Z) = X*Y/Z	7.5, 3.2, 4.9
Array	F(I,J)	2.2, 4.5, 5.5
Array names without subscript		
in COMMON	COMMON A, Y	6.2, 6.1
in input	READ 998, A	4.6, 4.4, 4.2
in output	PUNCH 997, A, X, XI	4.4, 4.2
in SUBROUTINE	SUBROUTINE QUART (C,XR,XI)	4.5, 4.1, 4.3
Call link of job, statement	CALL CHAIN (2,A4)	9.4
CALL EXIT statement	CALL EXIT	9.2
CALL subroutine statement	CALL BAND3(N)	6.2, 4.3, 9.6
Chain job control card	* CHAIN (1,A4)	9.4
Comment	C PROGRAM 2.1	2.1, 7.6, 9.8
COMMON Statement	COMMON A, Y	6.2, 6.1
Computed GO TO statement	GO TO (1030,1032), IPATH	4.3, 4.8, 9.4
Continuation of statement	1 7TH)	2.2, 8.1, 7.4
CONTINUE statement	10 CONTINUE	3.3, 5.2, 5.3
Control character for printer	FORMAT (1H1)	9.2
Data control card	* DATA	9.4
Date control card	* DATE 3/29/64	9.4
DIMENSION statement	DIMENSION F(20,20)	2.2, 5.5, 5.3
DO statements	DO 10 I = 2, N	2.1, 3.4, 9.3
	DO 10 K = 1, N, 4	2.3
E-field specification	FORMAT (3E10.0)	7.8, 5.3
END statement	END	2.1, 2.2, 2.3
EQUIVALENCE statement	EQUIVALENCE (AQ,BQ)	4.5
Exponentiation of floating point number		
to fixed point power	H4 = H**4	6.3, 6.2, 4.3
to floating point power	Z = −(2.*Q)**EX	4.3, 6.2
F-field specification	FORMAT (F10.2)	2.3, 2.2, 3.4
FORMAT specification	FORMAT (I5/(5E15.7))	2.1, 3.4, 9.6
FUNCTION statement	FUNCTION FR(X)	6.2, 7.5-A, 9.9
GO TO statement	GO TO 2	4.9, 3.4, 9.9
H-field specification	FORMAT (4HX(I))	3.3, 5.5, 9.6
Identification control card	* PROGRAM 9.4	9.4
I-field specification	FORMAT (I27)	3.4, 5.5, 9.6
IF statement	1F(K-M2) 10, 10, 11	3.4, 4.8, 9.3
IF SENSE SWITCH statement	IF (SENSE SWITCH 1) 30, 40	9.8, 6.1, 8.4

Designation	Typical Form	Programs
Label object deck, control card	* LABEL	9.5, 9.4
List in input statement	READ 996, (Y(I), I = 1,N)	5.2, 9.6, 9.8
List in output statement	PUNCH 997, (I,X(I), 1 = I,N)	5.5, 9.6, 9.8
List machine language coding, control card	* LIST8	9.4, 9.5
Pack output tape	* PACK	9.4, 9.5
PAUSE statement	PAUSE 00020	7.1, 9.8
Pause control card	* PAUSE	9.4
PRINT statement	PRINT 998, A, B, EXACT	3.2-A, 9.9, 9.9-A
PUNCH statement	PUNCH 996, X, P	2.1, 5.1, 8.4
READ statement	READ 999, A, B	3.2, 9.6, 9.8
READ INPUT TAPE statement	READ INPUT TAPE 5, 998, U, V, LAST	9.2, 9.4
Repetition number	FORMAT (2F10.0)	3.2, 5.5, 8.1
RETURN statement	RETURN	4.1, 9.1, 4.5
Scale factor	FORMAT (1PEI4.7)	9.2, 9.4
Slash specification	FORMAT (/)	6.2, 5.1, 5.4
Statement number	24 PUNCH 993	6.3, 8.1, 9.3
STOP statement	STOP 00002	7.4, 9.3, 9.9
SUBROUTINE statement	SUBROUTINE CUBIC (A,XR,XI)	4.3, 9.3, 9.7
Subscripted variable	A(I,J+2)	6.3, 3.3, 9.6
Symbol table control card	* SYMBOL TABLE	9.4, 9.5
WRITE OUTPUT TAPE statement	WRITE OUTPUT TAPE 6, 997, U, V, X, Y	9.2, 9.4
X-field specification	FORMAT (21X)	2.1, 3.3, 9.6
Execution control card	* XEQ	9.4

Program 2.1 uses the "nested-binomial" approach (Sec. 2.4) to evaluate the polynomial

$$p_n(x) = a_n x^n + a_{n-1} x^{n-1} + a_{n-2} x^{n-2} + \cdots + a_1 x + a_0.$$

The nested binomial at any stage

$$\cdots (((a_n)x + a_{n-1})x + a_{n-2})x + \cdots$$

is indicated by the floating-point variable P, which is initially a_n. At each subsequent stage i a new binomial is generated by multiplying the previous binomial by x and adding $a_{n-(i-1)}$. The $(n+1)$st term a_0 is added separately because zero cannot be used as a subscript in FORTRAN. The example shown in the results evaluates the first six terms of the power series expansions of e^{-x}.

Beginner's Hints

(a) The symbol = means "replace by"; thus the statement

P = P*X + A(N1)

does not indicate equality, but means that A(N1) is added to the product of P and X, and the result stored under the name P. The previous value of P is thus lost.

(b) With N1 previously defined as N−I+1, A(N1) must be used rather than the improperly subscripted variable A(N−I+1), because the most general form of a subscript in FORTRAN is a constant times the subscript, plus a constant, e.g., 6*I − 219.

```
C       PROGRAM 2.1
C       EVALUATION OF A POLYNOMIAL
C
        DIMENSION  A(50)
        PUNCH 995
        READ   999,  N,  AO,  (A(I),  I=1,N)
        PUNCH 998,  N,  AO,  (I,  A(I),  I=1,N)
   1    READ 997, X
        P = A(N)
        DO  10   I = 2,  N
        N1 = N + 1 - I
  10    P = P*X + A(N1)
        P = P*X + AO
        PUNCH 996, X, P
        GO TO 1
C
 995    FORMAT (// 21X, 24HRESULTS FROM PROGRAM 2.1 // 19X, 28HEVALUATION
       1OF THE POLYNOMIAL / 5X,56HP(X) = A(N)*X**N + A(N-1)*X**(N-1) + ...
       2 + A(1)*X + A(0))
 996    FORMAT (/ 24X,  4HX  = E16.7 / 22X, 6HP(X) = E16.7)
 997    FORMAT (F10.0)
 998    FORMAT (// 22X, 20HPOLYNOMIAL OF DEGREE I2 / 22X, 6HA(0) = E16.7 /
       1 (22X, 2HA(   I1,   3H) = E16.7))
 999    FORMAT (I5/(5E15.7))
        END
```

EVALUATION OF THE POLYNOMIAL
P(X) = A(N)*X**N + A(N-1)*X**(N-1) + ... + A(1)*X + A(0)

```
POLYNOMIAL OF DEGREE 5
A(0) =    1.0000000E+00
A(1) =   -1.0000000E+00
A(2) =    5.0000000E-01
A(3) =   -1.6666667E-01
A(4) =    4.1666667E-02
A(5) =   -8.3333333E-03

 X  =    2.0000000E-01
P(X) =    8.1873070E-01

 X  =    4.0000000E-01
P(X) =    6.7031470E-01

 X  =    6.0000000E-01
P(X) =    5.4875200E-01

 X  =    8.0000000E-01
P(X) =    4.4900270E-01

 X  =    1.0000000E+00
P(X) =    3.6666660E-01
```

Flow Chart 2.1

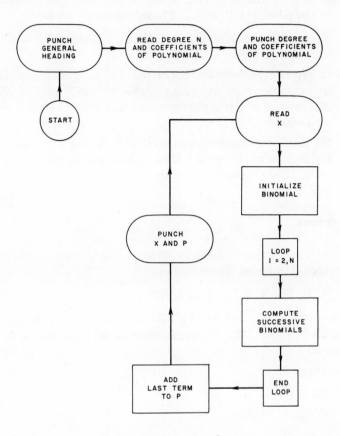

Program 2.2 reads the values of a function f at n points and computes its differences through the $(n-1)$st. $F(K, I)$ is the $(k-1)$st difference of f at the $(i-1)$st point; $F(1, I) \equiv f_{i-1}$. The results shown are for

(a) a third-degree polynomial; notice that the third difference is constant and all higher differences are zero;

(b) an exponential function; notice that the ratio of any two consecutive differences at any point is $e^h - 1$ (.6487 for $h = .5$), while the ratio of a given difference for any two successive points is e^{-h} (.6065 for $h = .5$);

(c) the same third-degree polynomial as in (a), with two digits of f at the fifth point transposed, thus introducing an error of .09 at that point. The propagation of this error may be seen by comparison with (a).

Beginner's Hints

(a) Notice that parentheses in input or output list-statements may take the place of DO loops. The statement

```
1    READ 999, N, (F(1,I), I = 1, N)
```

causes the reading (according to FORMAT statement 999) of the quantities: N, F(1,1), F(1,2), ..., F(1,N). The same result could have been achieved by three statements

```
     READ  n₁, N
     DO 2 I = 1, N
2    READ  n₂, F(1,I)
```

where n_1 and n_2 specify appropriate formats. The left parenthesis in the list statement 1 may be interpreted as the beginning of a DO loop with the limits of the indexing variable I given just before the matching right parenthesis.

(b) The statements that have a C in the first column are comments. They are not processed by the compiler and are simply listed as they appear. They may be used for any purpose the programmer desires, e.g., to identify the program and/or to explain it, or simply to leave an almost blank line for the sake of appearance.

```
C       PROGRAM 2.2
C       TABLE OF DIFFERENCES
C
        DIMENSION F(20, 20)
        PUNCH 997
    1   READ 999, N, (F(1,I), I = 1,N)
        PUNCH 996
        DO  10   K = 2, N
        M = N + 1 - K
        DO  10   I = 1, M
   10   F(K,I) = F(K-1,I+1) - F(K-1,I)
        DO  20   I = 1, N
        L = I - 1
        M = N + 1 - I
   20   PUNCH 998, L, (F(K,I), K = 1,M)
        GO TO 1
  996   FORMAT ( / 59H  I   Y(I)   1ST    2ND    3RD    4TH    5TH    6TH
       1     7TH )
  997   FORMAT (// 19X, 24HRESULTS FROM PROGRAM 2.2
       1          // 23X, 17HDIFFERENCE TABLES )
  998   FORMAT (I4, 8F7.3)
  999   FORMAT (I5/(8F10.0))
        END
```

RESULTS FROM PROGRAM 2.2

DIFFERENCE TABLES

I	Y(I)	1ST	2ND	3RD	4TH	5TH	6TH	7TH
0	1.000	2.375	2.250	.750	0.000	0.000	0.000	0.000
1	3.375	4.625	3.000	.750	0.000	0.000	0.000	
2	8.000	7.625	3.750	.750	0.000	0.000		
3	15.625	11.375	4.500	.750	0.000			
4	27.000	15.875	5.250	.750				
5	42.875	21.125	6.000					
6	64.000	27.125						
7	91.125							

I	Y(I)	1ST	2ND	3RD	4TH	5TH	6TH	7TH
0	2.718	1.764	1.143	.743	.482	.307	.219	.093
1	4.482	2.907	1.886	1.225	.789	.526	.312	
2	7.389	4.793	3.111	2.014	1.315	.838		
3	12.182	7.904	5.125	3.329	2.153			
4	20.086	13.029	8.454	5.482				
5	33.115	21.483	13.936					
6	54.598	35.419						
7	90.017							

I	Y(I)	1ST	2ND	3RD	4TH	5TH	6TH	7TH
0	1.000	2.375	2.250	.750	0.000	-.090	.540	-1.890
1	3.375	4.625	3.000	.750	-.090	.450	-1.350	
2	8.000	7.625	3.750	.660	.360	-.900		
3	15.625	11.375	4.410	1.020	-.540			
4	27.000	15.785	5.430	.480				
5	42.785	21.215	5.910					
6	64.000	27.125						
7	91.125							

Flow Chart 2.2

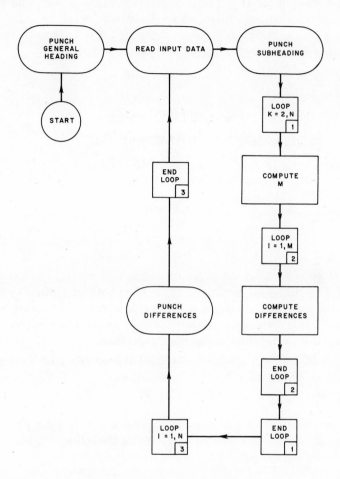

Program 2.3 computes the values of $f(x) = \sin(\pi/6 + x)$ by Taylor series. F(I) is the value of the $(i - 1)$st derivative of $f(x)$ at $x = 0$. The value of $f(x)$ at $x = 0$ is identical with its zero-order derivative F(1).

The variable SERIES is the sum of the first $i - 1$ terms of the series expansion of $f(x)$ about $\pi/6$. The ith term of the series,

$$\frac{\pi f^{(i-1)} x^{i-1}}{6(i-1)!} \, ,$$

is added to the series by the FORTRAN statement

20   SERIES = SERIES + F(I)*XRAD**(I-1)/FACT

XRAD is the value of X in radians, and FACT contains $(i - 1)!$. The first DO loop (to 10) computes the values of F(I) which will be needed in the second DO loop (to 20), which sums the series.

Beginner's Hints

(a) The statement numbered 20 contains both exceptions to the rule that all the quantities on the right-hand side of the = sign must be in the same mode: It is permissible to use fixed-point quantities as subscripts or as exponents in an otherwise floating-point expression.

(b) A DO loop will always be executed at least once, for the first value of the index. Thus even if N = 1, the statement

DO 20 I = 2, N

will cause execution of the loop for the value I = 2. Thus Program 2.3 always computes at least the first two terms of the series.

```
C       PROGRAM 2.3
C       TAYLOR SERIES CALCULATION OF SIN(PI/6 + X)
C
        DIMENSION F(50)
        PUNCH 999
        PI = 3.1415927
  1     READ 998, XDEG, N
        XRAD = XDEG*PI/180.
        EXACT = SINF(PI/6. + XRAD)
        DO  10   K = 1, N, 4
        F(K) = .5
        F(K+1) = SQRTF(3.)/2.
        F(K+2) = -.5
 10     F(K+3) = -F(2)
        SERIES = F(1)
        FACT = 1.
        DO  20   I = 2, N
        AI = I-1
        FACT = AI*FACT
 20     SERIES = SERIES + F(I)*XRAD**(I-1)/FACT
        ERROR = (EXACT-SERIES)/EXACT*100.
        PUNCH 997, XDEG, XRAD, N, SERIES, EXACT, ERROR
        GO TO 1
C
997     FORMAT (F10.2, F9.3, I6, F13.8, F12.8, F11.6)
998     FORMAT (F10.0, I5)
999     FORMAT (// 20X, 24HRESULTS FROM PROGRAM 2.3 // 11X,
       1 42HTAYLOR SERIES CALCULATION OF SIN(PI/6 + X) // 7X, 1HX 8X, 1HX
       2 7X, 1HN 6X, 6HSERIES 6X, 5HEXACT 6X, 7HPERCENT / 4X, 23HDEGREES
       3RADIANS  TERMS 4X, 6HRESULT 6X, 6HSIN(X) 6X, 5HERROR/)
        END
```

RESULTS FROM PROGRAM 2.3

TAYLOR SERIES CALCULATION OF SIN(PI/6 + X)

X DEGREES	X RADIANS	N TERMS	SERIES RESULT	EXACT SIN(X)	PERCENT ERROR
10.00	.174	2	.65114994	.64278760	-1.300949
10.00	.174	3	.64353451	.64278760	-.116198
10.00	.174	4	.64276713	.64278760	.003184
10.00	.174	5	.64278646	.64278760	.000177
10.00	.174	6	.64278762	.64278760	-.000003
30.00	.523	2	.95344984	.86602537	-10.094908
30.00	.523	3	.88491092	.86602537	-2.180715
30.00	.523	4	.86419162	.86602537	.211743
30.00	.523	5	.86575748	.86602537	.030933
30.00	.523	6	.86604149	.86602537	-.001861
60.00	1.047	4	.96698960	1.00000000	3.301040
60.00	1.047	5	.99204337	1.00000000	.795670
60.00	1.047	6	1.00113180	1.00000000	-.113180
60.00	1.047	7	1.00021600	1.00000000	-.021600
60.00	1.047	8	.99997870	1.00000000	.002130
60.00	1.047	9	.99999663	1.00000000	.000340
60.00	1.047	10	1.00000020	1.00000000	-.000020

Flow Chart 2.3

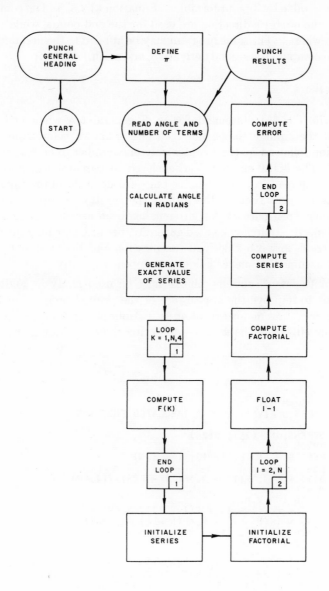

Program 3.1 computes the first derivative of a tabulated function at all the points of the table by 3-point formulas. Equation (3.2.8) and its companion slanted in the opposite direction are used for the end points, while (3.2.11) is used elsewhere. (The same program may be applied to the first derivative in order to compute the second derivative, and so on.)

Beginner's Hints

(a) The FORMAT statement 999 is of general use when neither the number of the input variables nor their size is known beforehand. The I5 specification followed by the / causes only one number to be read from the first card. The 8E10.0 specification, enclosed in parentheses, causes eight numbers to be read from each succeeding card until the entire input list is read. This happens because the format specification is repeated starting from the last open parentheses, after it has been executed the first time. The E10.0 specification may be used generally, because punching the decimal point overrides any other decimal specification and the exponent E+00 is implicitly assumed whenever E does not appear explicitly.

(b) With few exceptions, blanks may be used freely in FORTRAN expressions to improve the appearance of the printed program or for any other purpose. The major exception is in Hollerith statements, i.e., those of the form wH, where the w spaces following the H (including any blanks) are counted.

```
C       PROGRAM 3.1
C       FIRST DERIVATIVE OF A TABULATED FUNCTION
C
        DIMENSION F(25), D(25)
        PUNCH 997
1       READ 999, N, H, (F(I), I = 1,N)
        PUNCH 996, H
        D(1) = (-3.*F(1) + 4.*F(2) - F(3))/(2.*H)
        M = N - 1
        DO 10 I = 2,M
10      D(I) = (-F(I - 1) + F(I + 1))/(2.*H)
        D(N) = (F(N - 2) - 4.*F(N - 1) + 3.*F(N))/(2.*H)
        PUNCH 998, (I, F(I), D(I), I = 1,N)
        GO TO 1
C
996     FORMAT ( / 18X, 4HH = E14.7 )
997     FORMAT ( // 15X, 24HRESULTS FROM PROGRAM 3.1 )
998     FORMAT ( / 7X, 5HPOINT 5X, 8HFUNCTION 8X, 10HDERIVATIVE /
     1          (I10, 2E17.7))
999     FORMAT (I5 / (8E10.0))
        END
```

RESULTS FROM PROGRAM 3.1

H = 1.0000000E-01

POINT	FUNCTION	DERIVATIVE
1	0.0000000E-99	0.0000000E-99
2	1.0000000E-02	2.0000000E-01
3	4.0000000E-02	4.0000000E-01
4	9.0000000E-02	6.0000000E-01
5	1.6000000E-01	8.0000000E-01
6	2.5000000E-01	1.0000000E+00
7	3.6000000E-01	1.2000000E+00

Flow Chart 3.1

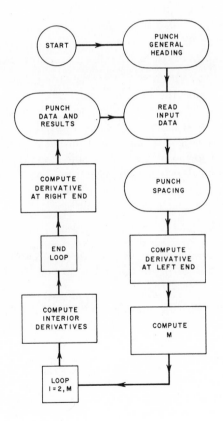

Program 3.2 computes the integral of a function from $X = A$ to $X = B$ by Simpson's 1/3 rule (3.2.27) with different spacings. The number of divisions (DIV), the result of the numerical integration (SUM), and the exact result (EXACT) are punched in tabular form for each pair of limits A, B.

Beginner's Hints

(a) In this program the function to be integrated, $x^2 e^{-x^3}$, is defined by the arithmetic statement function

F(X) = X**2*EXPF($-$X**3)

Any other function could be integrated by this program by suitably changing the F(X) definition (and the EXACT result, if known).

(b) This program can be made into a FUNCTION subprogram (see Notes, Program 6.2) so that it may be used as part of another program. The function to be integrated, F(X), can also be made a FUNCTION subprogram so that it may be changed without recompiling the rest of the program. See Programs 3.2-A and 9.9 for more refined programs using this algorithm.

(c) Notice that the output statement lists three floating-point variables (DIV, SUM, EXACT), while the output format (997) contains specifications for one fixed- and two floating-point variables. This apparent contradiction is used here to show that in some versions of FORTRAN a floating-point number need not be changed to fixed-point format in order to appear in the output in fixed-point form (or vice versa), since the proper formatting does the "fixing" automatically. The number of divisions (DIV) in this program must be an integer and hence would naturally be a fixed-point number. But since it appears in a floating-point calculation,

H = (B$-$A)/DIV

it was read in as a floating-point number, used in two calculations in this form, and then outputted in its natural fixed-point format by use of the format specification I10 in 997.

Program 3.2-A uses a FUNCTION subprogram RICHEX for h^n Richardson extrapolations to improve the results. Notice that for Simpson's 1/3 rule $n = 4$.

```
C       PROGRAM 3.2 (SEE ALSO PROGRAMS 3.2-A AND 9.9)
C       INTEGRATION BY SIMPSON-S 1/3 RULE
C
        F(X) = X**2*EXPF(-X**3)
        READ 999, A, B
        EXACT = (EXPF(-A**3) - EXPF(-B**3))/3.
        PUNCH 998, A, B
   1    READ 999, DIV
        H = (B-A)/DIV
        X = A
        NUM = DIV/2.
        SUM = 0.
        DO  2   I = 1, NUM
        SUM = SUM + H/3.*(F(X) + 4.*F(X+H) + F(X+2.*H))
   2    X = X + 2.*H
        PUNCH 997, DIV, SUM, EXACT
        GO·TO 1
C
997     FORMAT (I10, 2E20.7)
998     FORMAT (// 15X, 24HRESULTS FROM PROGRAM 3.2 //17X, 21HLIMITS OF IN
       1TEGRATION / 23X, 3HA = F6.2 / 23X, 3HB = F6.2 // 5X, 9HDIVISIONS
       2 6X, 8HINTEGRAL 13X, 5HEXACT  )
999     FORMAT (2F10.0)
        END



C       PROGRAM 3.2-A
C       INTEGRATION BY SIMPSON-S 1/3 RULE WITH RICHARDSON-S EXTRAPOLATIONS
C
        READ  999, A, B
        EXACT = FEXACT (A,B)
        PRINT 998, A, B, EXACT
   1    READ 997, DIV, NPATH
        EXTR = 0.
        H = (B-A)/DIV
        X = A
        NUM = DIV/2.
        SUM = 0.
        F1 = F(A)
        DO  2   I = 1, NUM
        F3 = F(X + 2.*H)
        SUM = SUM + F1 + 4.*F(X + H) + F3
        F1 = F3
   2    X = X + 2.*H
        SUM = H/3.*SUM
        GO TO (4,3), NPATH
   3    EXTR = RICHEX (4, H, H1, SUM, SUM1)
   4    PRINT 996, DIV, H, SUM, EXTR
        SUM1 = SUM
        H1 = H
        GO TO 1
C
996     FORMAT (I6, F10.5, 2E17.7)
997     FORMAT (2I5)
998     FORMAT (// 14X, 26HRESULTS FROM PROGRAM 3.2-A //17X, 21HLIMITS OF
       1INTEGRATION / 23X, 3HA = F6.2 / 23X, 3HB = F6.2 // 12X, 16HEXACT S
       2OLUTION =E14.7//4X,3HDIV 6X,!HH 8X,8HINTEGRAL 7X,13HEXTRAPOLATION)
999     FORMAT (2E10.3)
        END
```

RESULTS FROM PROGRAM 3.2

LIMITS OF INTEGRATION
A = 0.00
B = 1.00

DIVISIONS	INTEGRAL	EXACT
2	2.0839604E-01	2.1070686E-01
4	2.1090315E-01	2.1070686E-01
8	2.1071763E-01	2.1070686E-01
16	2.1070747E-01	2.1070686E-01
32	2.1070684E-01	2.1070686E-01

```
C       RICHARDSON-S EXTRAPOLATION OF ORDER N
        FUNCTION RICHEX (N, H, H1, SUM, SUM1)
        FAC = (H1/H)**N
        RICHEX = (FAC*SUM - SUM1)/(FAC - 1.)
        RETURN
        END
```

```
        FUNCTION F(X)
        F = X**2*EXPF(-X**3)
        RETURN
        END
```

```
        FUNCTION FEXACT(A,B)
        FEXACT = (EXPF(-A**3) - EXPF(-B**3))/3.
        RETURN
        END
```

RESULTS FROM PROGRAM 3.2-A

LIMITS OF INTEGRATION
A = -1.00
B = 1.00

EXACT SOLUTION = 7.8346746E-01

DIV	H	INTEGRAL	EXTRAPOLATION
4	.50000	8.5030103E-01	0.0000000E-99
6	.33333	8.0485385E-01	7.9366685E-01
8	.25000	7.9170591E-01	7.8562031E-01
16	.12500	7.8412482E-01	7.8361946E-01
32	.06250	7.8351142E-01	7.8347053E-01

Flow Chart 3.2

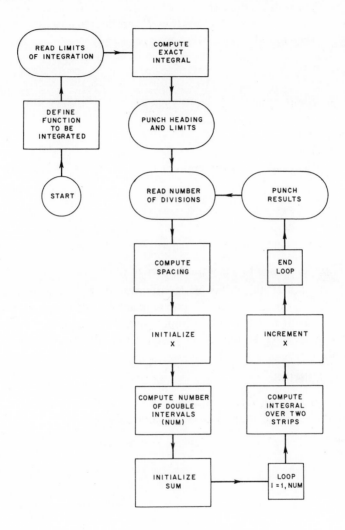

Program 3.3 uses Lagrangian interpolation (Sec. 3.5) to evaluate a function $f(x)$ at x_0. $f(x)$ is defined by the n unevenly spaced points x_i, f_i $(i = 1, n)$. For each value of x_0, the n quantities P_i are first computed; the value $f_0 = f(x_0)$ is then found by (3.5.3):

$$F_0 = \sum_{i=1}^{N} P_i F_i. \tag{a}$$

In the results, $f(x) = x^3$.

Beginner's Hints

(a) Notice that (a) is represented in FORTRAN by the three statements

```
      F0 = 0.
      DO  20  I = 1,N
 20   F0 = F0 + P(I)*F(I)
```

where $F0 = 0.$ is used to initialize the sum of the series.

(b) The CONTINUE statement is often found at the end of a DO loop. It is not an executed statement and is usually used either to provide a needed statement number or to comply with the rule against ending a DO loop with a transfer statement (e.g., IF or GO TO). In Program 3.3 the statement

```
 10   CONTINUE
```

allows the program to skip statement 9 (and still remain within the DO loop) for the case when I and J have the same value.

```
C         PROGRAM 3.3
C         PROGRAM FOR LAGRANGIAN INTERPOLATION
C         UNEVENLY SPACED PIVOTAL POINTS
          DIMENSION X(50), P(50),  F(50)
          PUNCH 994
          READ 999, N,  (X(I), F(I), I=1,N)
    1     READ 998, XO
          DO 10 J=1, N
          P(J) = 1
          DO 10 I=1,N
          IF (I-J) 9, 10, 9
    9     P(J) = P(J)*(XO-X(I))/(X(J)-X(I))
   10     CONTINUE
          FO = 0.
          DO 20 I=1,N
   20     FO = FO + P(I)*F(I)
          PUNCH 997
          PUNCH 996, (I, X(I), F(I), P(I), I=1,N)
          PUNCH 995, XO, FO
          GO TO 1
  994     FORMAT (// 19X, 24HRESULTS FROM PROGRAM 3.3 )
  995     FORMAT (/9X, 6HAT X = F5.2, 21H THE VALUE OF F(X) IS F12.7 )
  996     FORMAT (I10, 3F14.7)
  997     FORMAT (// 9X, 1HI 8X, 4HX(I) 10X, 4HF(I) 9X, 6HP(X,I) )
  998     FORMAT (8F10.0)
  999     FORMAT (I5/(8F10.0))
          END
```

```
I          X(I)           F(I)            P(X,I)
1       1.0000000       1.0000000       -.2222222
2       2.0000000       8.0000000        .8000000
3       4.0000000      64.0000000        .4444444
4       7.0000000     343.0000000       -.0222222
```

AT X = 3.00 THE VALUE OF F(X) IS 26.9999980

```
I          X(I)           F(I)            P(X,I)
1       1.0000000       1.0000000        .4444444
2       2.0000000       8.0000000      -1.0000000
3       4.0000000      64.0000000       1.1111110
4       7.0000000     343.0000000        .4444444
```

AT X = 6.00 THE VALUE OF F(X) IS 215.9999700

```
I          X(I)           F(I)            P(X,I)
1       1.0000000       1.0000000      -1.3333333
2       2.0000000       8.0000000       2.8000000
3       4.0000000      64.0000000      -2.3333331
4       7.0000000     343.0000000       1.8666665
```

AT X = 8.00 THE VALUE OF F(X) IS 511.9999500

Flow Chart 3.3

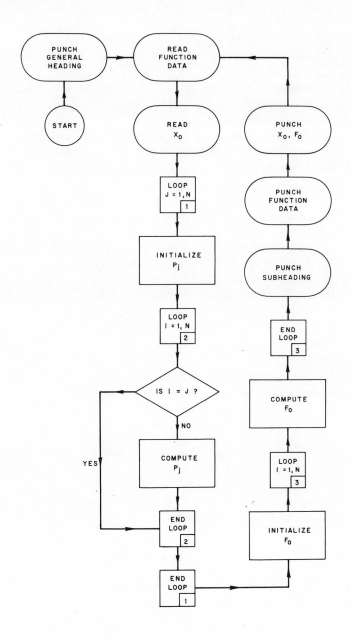

Program 3.4 evaluates a function y at x_0, by Aitken-Neville interpolations of order m, from a set of n pivotal values, evenly spaced by h and starting at $x = x_1$.

Whenever possible, the range of $m + 1$ points used in the interpolation is chosen so as to have x_0 fall (a) in the middle interval of the interpolating range for m odd, and (b) in the interval to the left of the middle point of the interpolating range for m even. When x_0 is near the ends of the range of the n pivotal values, the first or last $m + 1$ points of this range are used in the interpolation.

The integer L indicates in which interval of the interpolating range x_0 falls: L $= 1$ means that x_0 falls between the first and second interpolating points, L $= 2$ between the second and third, and so on. Statement 10 determines L when x_0 is near the left end of the range of pivotal points (K $<$ M2); statement 20 determines L when x_0 is in the middle of the range; statement 21 determines L when x_0 is near the right end of the range (K $>$ N $-$ M2).

The DO 22 loop chooses the $m + 1$ points used in the interpolation for the given value of x_0. The nested DO 23 loop performs successive linear interpolations on the points chosen by the DO 22 loop. The index I shifts the interpolation formula along the points used in the interpolation, the index J indicates the order of the successive interpolations. For a given order of interpolation m the PUNCH 994 statement punches out the results of all the successive interpolations. The last punched result is the interpolated value of order m at x_0.

The pivotal values in the results are those of $y = x^3$ so that for $m \geq 3$ the interpolated values are the correct values of the function y.

Beginner's Hint

For m odd, the integer M2 locates the middle interval of the interpolation range. For m even, M2 locates the interval to the *left* of the middle interpolation point, since the calculation of (M $+ 1)/2$ in fixed-point mode causes the truncation of noninteger numbers. For example, for $m = 2$ the fixed-point variable M2 has the value M2 $= (2 + 1)/2 =$ fixed-point $1.5 = 1$.

```
C       PROGRAM 3.4
C       AITKEN-NEVILLE INTERPOLATIONS UP TO ORDER M
C
        DIMENSION Y(100), Z(100)
        PUNCH 999
        READ 998, N, X1, H, (Y(I), I = 1,N)
        X = X1
        DO 1 I = 1,N
        X = X + H
    1   PUNCH 997, I, X, Y(I)
    2   READ 998, M, X0
        M2 = (M + 1)/2
        K = X0/H + 1.
        IF (K - M2) 10, 10, 11
   10   L = K
        GO TO 12
   11   IF (N - K - M2) 21, 21, 20
   20   L = M2
        GO TO 12
   21   L = M + 1 - N + K
   12   M1 = M + 1
        DO 22 I = 1, M1
        I1 = I + K - L
   22   Z(I) = Y(I1)
        AK = K
        AL = L
        P = (X0 - X1 - (AK - AL)*H)/H
        DO 24 J = 1,M
        PUNCH 995, J, X0
        AJ = J
        MJ = M + 1 - J
        DO 23 I = 1, MJ
        AI = I
   23   Z(I) = ((AI - P + AJ - 1.)*Z(I) + (P - AI + 1.)*Z(I + 1))/AJ
        DO 24 I = 1, MJ
        IEND = I + J
   24   PUNCH 994, I, IEND, Z(I)
        GO TO 2
C
  994   FORMAT (I25, I13, F15.4)
  995   FORMAT ( // 16X, 23HINTERPOLATIONS OF ORDER I2, 9H FOR X0 = F6.3
       1              / 20X, 9H1ST POINT 4X, 10HLAST POINT 4X, 5HY(X0) )
  997   FORMAT ( I27, F10.3, F11.4 )
  998   FORMAT (I10,2E10.0 / (8E10.0))
  999   FORMAT ( // 24X, 24HRESULTS FROM PROGRAM 3.4
       1          // 24X, 24HPOINT      X          Y(X) )
        END
```

RESULTS FROM PROGRAM 3.4

POINT	X	Y(X)
1	1.000	0.0000
2	2.000	1.0000
3	3.000	8.0000
4	4.000	27.0000
5	5.000	64.0000

INTERPOLATIONS OF ORDER 1 FOR X0 = 3.400

1ST POINT	LAST POINT	Y(X0)
1	2	17.8000
2	3	34.6000
3	4	41.8000

INTERPOLATIONS OF ORDER 2 FOR X0 = 3.400

1ST POINT	LAST POINT	Y(X0)
1	3	37.9600
2	4	39.6400

INTERPOLATIONS OF ORDER 3 FOR X0 = 3.400

1ST POINT	LAST POINT	Y(X0)
1	4	39.3040

INTERPOLATIONS OF ORDER 1 FOR X0 = .400

1ST POINT	LAST POINT	Y(X0)
1	2	.4000
2	3	-3.2000
3	4	-22.4000
4	5	-69.2000

INTERPOLATIONS OF ORDER 2 FOR X0 = .400

1ST POINT	LAST POINT	Y(X0)
1	3	-.3200
2	4	2.5600
3	5	15.0400

INTERPOLATIONS OF ORDER 3 FOR X0 = .400

1ST POINT	LAST POINT	Y(X0)
1	4	.0640
2	5	.0640

INTERPOLATIONS OF ORDER 4 FOR X0 = .400

1ST POINT	LAST POINT	Y(X0)
1	5	.0640

Flow Chart 3.4

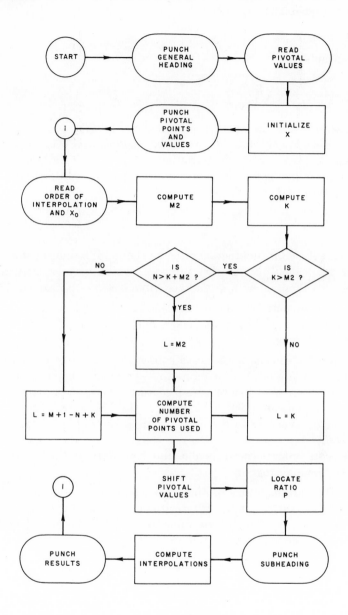

Program 4.1 is a subroutine subprogram named QUAD which computes the roots of the quadratic equation

$$a_1 x^2 + a_2 x + a_3 = 0$$

by the formula

$$x_{1,2} = -\frac{a_2}{2a_1} \pm \sqrt{\left(\frac{a_2}{2a_1}\right)^2 - \frac{a_3}{a_1}}.$$

The discriminant of the equation is represented by DISC and the real parts of the two roots by XR1 and XR2. Since the imaginary parts of the two roots differ only in sign, only their magnitude, XI, is given. The program may follow either of two paths, depending on whether DISC < 0 so that XI $\neq 0$; or DISC ≥ 0 so that XI $= 0$.

Beginner's Hints

(a) A *subroutine* subprogram often has no input or output statements. It must be "called" by another program, which may be a "mainline" program (see Program 4.2), or another subprogram (see Program 4.3).

(b) The naming of subprograms varies from system to system. In some versions of FORTRAN the names must not end in F if they are four or more letters long.

(c) When a dimensioned (i.e., a subscripted) variable is used *without* subscript as an argument of a subroutine statement, all the values of the variable are made available to the subroutine. Thus, when A(I) is written as A in the statement SUBROUTINE QUAD (A, XR1, XR2, XI) all three values of A(I) are made available to the subprogram, as if A(1), A(2), and A(3) had been listed.

(d) A subprogram must have a statement RETURN which returns control to the calling program.

(e) The formula used in this program leads to significant loss of accuracy whenever a_2^2 is much greater than $4a_1 a_3$. In this case it is better to find the greater root in absolute value from the formula and then find the smaller root by dividing this greater root into a_3/a_1.

```
C        PROGRAM 4.1
C        SOLUTION OF THE QUADRATIC EQUATION
C        A(1)*X*X + A(2)*X + A(3) = 0.
C
         SUBROUTINE QUAD (A, XR1, XR2, XI)
         DIMENSION A(3)
         X1 = -A(2)/(2.*A(1))
         DISC = X1*X1 - A(3)/A(1)
         IF(DISC) 10,20,20
10       X2 = SQRTF(-DISC)
         XR1 = X1
         XR2 = X1
         XI = X2
         GO TO 30
20       X2 = SQRTF(DISC)
         XR1 = X1 + X2
         XR2 = X1 - X2
         XI  = 0.
30       RETURN
         END
```

Flow Chart 4.1

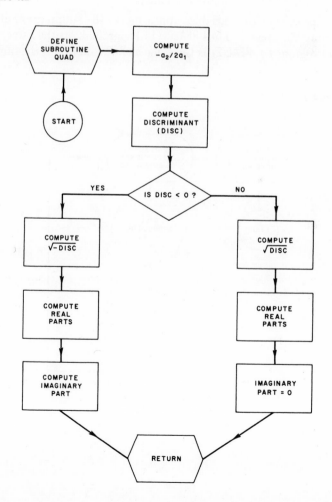

Program 4.2 reads the coefficients, a_i $(i = 1, 2, 3)$, of the quadratic equation

$$a_1 x^2 + a_2 x + a_3 = 0,$$

calls the subroutine subprogram (Program 4.1) which computes the roots, and then punches coefficients and roots in a self-explanatory format.

Beginner's Hints

(a) The three a_i are read by the statement

```
1    READ 998,  A
```

since whenever a dimensioned variable is used without a subscript in an input-output statement, the whole array is included in the statement. In this program A is dimensioned as A(3). Thus the three values A(1), A(2), and A(3) are all read by the above statement.

(b) Notice that the variables appearing in the subprogram definition are "dummy variables." Thus REAL(1) in Program 4.2 is the same variable as XR1 in Program 4.1, REAL(2) is the same as XR2, and RTI1 is the same as XI.

Flow Chart 4.2

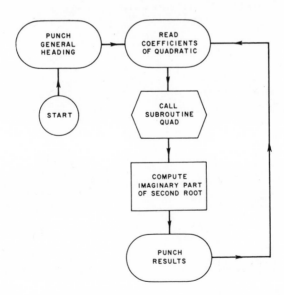

```
C       PROGRAM 4.2
C       CALLS QUADRATIC EQUATION SUBROUTINE
C
        PUNCH 999
        DIMENSION A(3), REAL(2)
   1    READ 998, A
        CALL QUAD (A, REAL(1), REAL(2), RTI1)
        RTI2 = -RTI1
        PUNCH 997, A, REAL(1), RTI1, REAL(2), RTI2
        GO TO 1
 997    FORMAT (/ 15X, 7HA(1) = E10.3 / 15X, 7HA(2) = E10.3 / 15X,
       1 7HA(3) = E10.3 // 18X, 22HREAL PART    IMAGINARY / 6X, 8H1ST ROOT
       2 2(3X, E10.3) / 6X, 8H2ND ROOT 2(3X, E10.3))
 998    FORMAT (3F10.0)
 999    FORMAT (// 12X, 24HRESULTS FROM PROGRAM 4.2 // 8X,    31HROOTS OF
       1 THE QUADRATIC EQUATION / 9X, 30HA(1)*X**2 + A(2)*X + A(3) = 0.  )
        END
```

RESULTS FROM PROGRAM 4.2

ROOTS OF THE QUADRATIC EQUATION
A(1)*X**2 + A(2)*X + A(3) = 0.

```
              A(1) =  1.000E-00
              A(2) =  1.000E-00
              A(3) =  1.000E-00

                    REAL PART     IMAGINARY
          1ST ROOT  -5.000E-01     8.660E-01
          2ND ROOT  -5.000E-01    -8.660E-01

              A(1) =  1.000E-00
              A(2) = -3.000E-00
              A(3) =  2.000E-00

                    REAL PART     IMAGINARY
          1ST ROOT   2.000E-00     0.000E-99
          2ND ROOT   1.000E-00    -0.000E-99

              A(1) =  5.000E-00
              A(2) =  3.000E-00
              A(3) =  1.000E-00

                    REAL PART     IMAGINARY
          1ST ROOT  -3.000E-01     3.316E-01
          2ND ROOT  -3.000E-01    -3.316E-01
```

Program 4.3 is a subroutine subprogram which computes the roots of the cubic equation

$$a_1x^3 + a_2x^2 + a_3x + a_4 = 0. \tag{a}$$

The coefficients a_i are assumed real, so that (a) must have at least one real root. The program first computes a real root and uses this root to reduce the cubic to a quadratic, then calls Program 4.1 to compute the remaining two (possibly complex) roots.

The cubic (a) can always be reduced to a cubic without the second-degree term:

$$z^3 + 3Pz + 2Q = 0, \tag{b}$$

by the linear transformation

$$x = z - \frac{a_2}{3a_1} \tag{c}$$

(Sec. 2.4), where

$$2Q = \frac{a_4}{a_1} - \frac{a_2a_3}{3a_1^2} + \frac{2a_2^3}{27a_1^3}, \tag{d}$$

$$3P = \frac{a_3}{a_1} - \frac{a_2^2}{3a_1^2}. \tag{e}$$

A root of (b) is always given by

$$z = [\sqrt{P^3 + Q^2} - Q]^{1/3} - [\sqrt{P^3 + Q^2} + Q]^{1/3}. \tag{f}$$

The body of the program is concerned with finding the branches of the square and cube roots in (f) which make z real. When $a_4 = 0$, $x = 0$ is a real root of (a). When $Q = 0$, $z = 0$ is a real root of (b). Since a change in the sign of Q changes the sign of the roots of (b), only $Q > 0$ need be considered. Thus, for $a_4 \neq 0$ and $Q > 0$ a real root of (b) is given by one of the five cases listed below:

(1) $P^3 + Q^2 < 0$;

$$z = -2\sqrt{-P} \cos\left[\frac{1}{3}\tan^{-1}\left(\frac{\sqrt{-P^3 - Q^2}}{Q}\right)\right]. \tag{g}$$

(2) $P^3 + Q^2 = 0$; $z = -2Q^{1/3}$. \tag{h}

(3) $P^3 + Q^2 > 0$, $P < 0$;

$$z = -[Q + \sqrt{P^3 + Q^2}]^{1/3} - [Q - \sqrt{P^3 + Q^2}]^{1/3}. \tag{i}$$

(4) $P^3 + Q^2 > 0$, $P = 0$; $z = -(2Q)^{1/3}$. \tag{j}

(5) $P^3 + Q^2 > 0$, $P > 0$;

$$z = [\sqrt{P^3 + Q^2} - Q]^{1/3} - [\sqrt{P^3 + Q^2} + Q]^{1/3}. \tag{k}$$

```
C     PROGRAM 4.3
C     SOLUTION OF CUBIC EQUATION
C     A(1)*X**3 + A(2)*X**2 + A(3)*X + A(4) = 0.
C
      SUBROUTINE CUBIC  (A, XR, XI)
      DIMENSION A(4), XR(3), AQ(3)
      IPATH = 2
      EX = 1./3.
      IF (A(4))  1006, 1004, 1006
 1004 XR(1) = 0.
      GO TO 1034
 1006 A2 = A(1)*A(1)
      Q = (27.*A2*A(4) - 9.*A(1)*A(2)*A(3) + 2.*A(2)**3)/(54.*A2*A(1))
      IF (Q) 1010, 1008, 1014
 1008 Z = 0.
      GO TO 1032
 1010 Q = -Q
      IPATH = 1
 1014 P = (3.*A(1)*A(3) - A(2)*A(2))/(9.*A2)
      ARG = P*P*P + Q*Q
      IF (ARG) 1016, 1018, 1020
 1016 Z = -2.*SQRTF(-P)*COSF(ATANF(SQRTF(-ARG)/Q)/3.)
      GO TO 1028
 1018 Z = -2.*Q**EX
      GO TO 1028
 1020 SARG = SQRTF(ARG)
      IF (P) 1022, 1024, 1026
 1022 Z = -(Q + SARG)**EX - (Q - SARG)**EX
      GO TO 1028
 1024 Z = -(2.*Q)**EX
      GO TO 1028
 1026 Z = (SARG - Q)**EX - (SARG + Q)**EX
 1028 GO TO (1030, 1032), IPATH
 1030 Z = -Z
 1032 XR(1) = (3.*A(1)*Z - A(2))/(3.*A(1))
 1034 AQ(1) = A(1)
      AQ(2) = A(2) + XR(1)*A(1)
      AQ(3) = A(3) + XR(1)*AQ(2)
      CALL QUAD  (AQ, XR(2), XR(3), XI)
      RETURN
      END
```

(a) The computed GO TO statement is used in statement 1028. The computer is instructed to go to statement 1030 or 1032 depending on whether the variable IPATH is 1 or 2.

(b) The exponentiation (**) subroutine behaves differently depending on whether the exponent is a floating-point or a fixed-point number. When the exponent is a fixed-point number, e.g., as in the statement following 1006,

A(2)**3

the result is computed by multiplying A(2) by itself two times; A(2) may then be negative or zero without causing complications. If, on the other hand, the exponent is a floating-point number, e.g., as in statement 1024,

(2.*Q)**EX

the result is computed as

EXPF(EX*LOGF(2.*Q))

which fails if Q is zero or negative. Thus, when a number is to be taken to a floating-point exponent one must make certain that the number is positive.

An integer exponent is usually written as a fixed-point variable because calculations using fixed-point (e.g., 2) exponents are generally faster than those using floating-point (e.g., 2.) exponents.

Flow Chart 4.3

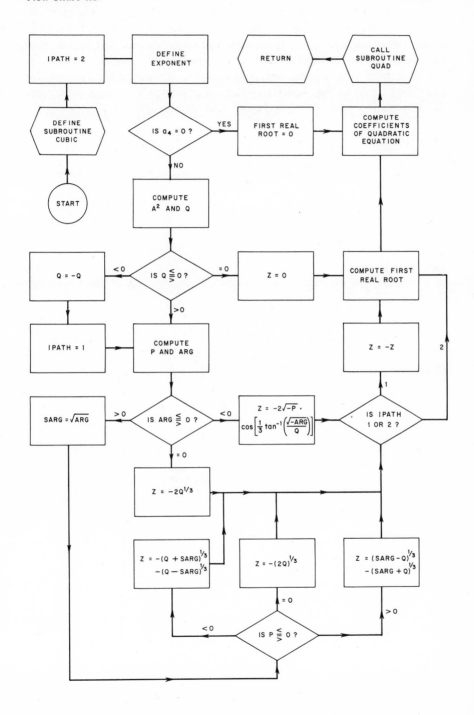

Program 4.4 serves as an input-output vehicle for Program 4.3, SUBROUTINE CUBIC. It punches a general heading, reads the coefficients of the cubic to be solved, calls Program 4.3 which computes the roots, and then punches both coefficients and roots. Since all three roots are punched in a format with both real and imaginary parts, the program provides the necessarily real root with a zero imaginary part and sets the imaginary part of the third root equal to the negative of the imaginary part of the second root, the only imaginary part which the subprogram must provide.

Beginner's Hint

Notice that the DIMENSION statement need not be the first statement in a program. In some versions of FORTRAN it must precede the first use of a dimensioned variable, except as an argument of a statement defining a subprogram.

Flow Chart 4.4

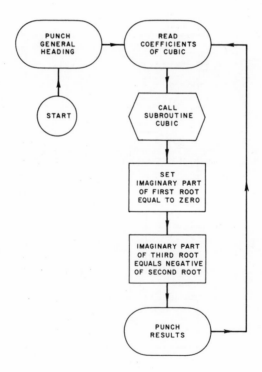

```
C       PROGRAM 4.4
C       CALLS CUBIC EQUATION SUBROUTINE
C
        PUNCH 999
        DIMENSION A(4), X(3), XI(3)
      1 READ 998, A
        CALL CUBIC (A, X, XI(2))
        XI(1) = 0.
        XI(3) = -XI(2)
        PUNCH 997, A, X, XI
        GO TO 1
    999 FORMAT (24X,24HRESULTS FROM PROGRAM 4.4/21X,31HSOLUTIONS OF THE CU
       1BIC EQUATION/15X,42HA(1)*X**3 + A(2)*X**2 + A(3)*X + A(4) = 0.)
    998 FORMAT (4F10.0)
    997 FORMAT (//7X, 4HA(1)13X, 4HA(2)13X, 4HA(3)13X, 4HA(4)/
       1 4(2X, E14.7, 1X) //22X, 8H1ST ROOT 9X, 8H2ND ROOT 9X, 8H3RD ROOT/
       2 7X, 9HREAL PART 3(3X, E14.7)/16H  IMAGINARY PART 3(3X, E14.7))
        END
```

                          RESULTS FROM PROGRAM 4.4
                       SOLUTIONS OF THE CUBIC EQUATION
                   A(1)*X**3 + A(2)*X**2 + A(3)*X + A(4) = 0.

	A(1)	A(2)	A(3)	A(4)
	1.0000000E+00	0.0000000E-99	0.0000000E-99	1.0000000E+00
		1ST ROOT	2ND ROOT	3RD ROOT
REAL PART		-1.0000000E+00	5.0000000E-01	5.0000000E-01
IMAGINARY PART		0.0000000E-99	8.6602540E-01	-8.6602540E-01

	A(1)	A(2)	A(3)	A(4)
	3.1000000E+01	4.1000000E+01	5.1000000E+01	6.1000000E+01
		1ST ROOT	2ND ROOT	3RD ROOT
REAL PART		-1.2581081E+00	-3.2236274E-02	-3.2236274E-02
IMAGINARY PART		0.0000000E-99	1.2502034E+00	-1.2502034E+00

	A(1)	A(2)	A(3)	A(4)
	1.0000000E+00	-3.0000000E+00	3.0000000E+00	-1.0000000E+00
		1ST ROOT	2ND ROOT	3RD ROOT
REAL PART		1.0000000E+00	1.0000000E+00	1.0000000E+00
IMAGINARY PART		0.0000000E-99	0.0000000E-99	-0.0000000E-99

Program 4.5 is a subroutine subprogram which computes the roots of the quartic (fourth-degree) equation

$$c_1 x^4 + c_2 x^3 + c_3 x^2 + c_4 x + c_5 = 0 \tag{a}$$

by Brown's method (Sec. 4.1).

```
C       PROGRAM 4.5
C       SOLUTION OF QUARTIC EQUATION USING BROWN-S METHOD
        SUBROUTINE QUART (C, XR, XI)
        DIMENSION C(5), XR(4), XI(4), AC(4), AQ(3), BQ(3), RT(3)
        EQUIVALENCE (AQ,BQ)
        A3 = C(2)/C(1)
        A2 = C(3)/C(1)
        A1 = C(4)/C(1)
        AO = C(5)/C(1)
        A  = A3/2.
        AC(1) = 1.
        AC(2) = -A2
        AC(3) = A1*A3 - 4.*AO
        AC(4) = AO*(4.*A2 - A3*A3) - A1*A1
        CALL CUBIC (AC, RT, RTI)
        IF(RTI)  20, 10, 20
10      IF (RT(1) - RT(2))  11, 12, 12
11      RT(1) = RT(2)
12      IF (RT(1) - RT(3))  13, 20, 20
13      RT(1) = RT(3)
20      B = RT(1)/2.
        IF (B*B - AO)  22,22,24
22      D = 0.
        CA = SQRTF(A*A + 2.*B - A2)
        GO TO 25
24      D = SQRTF(B*B - AO)
        CA = -(A1/2. - A*B)/D
25      AQ(1) = 1.
        AQ(2) = A - CA
        AQ(3) = B - D
        CALL QUAD (AQ, XR(1), XR(2), XI(1))
        BQ(2) = A + CA
        BQ(3) = B + D
        CALL QUAD (BQ, XR(3), XR(4), XI(3))
        XI(2) = -XI(1)
        XI(4) = -XI(3)
        RETURN
        END
```

(a) Notice that the four statements following the dimension statement convert the quartic from (a) to

$$x^4 + a_3 x^3 + a_2 x^2 + a_1 x + a_0 = 0,$$

so that the arithmetic statements in the program may closely resemble the equations of Section 4.1, where Brown's method is presented. However, (a) was chosen as the form of the quartic for input purposes because

(1) zero subscripts are not allowed in FORTRAN,

(2) it is convenient to use entire arrays as SUBROUTINE arguments,

(3) it is helpful not to have the coefficient of x^4 necessarily be unity, and

(4) the capital letter A is used in another sense in the equations of the text.

(b) A subroutine subprogram must be called by another program, which may be either another subprogram or a "mainline" program (e.g., Program 4.6).

(c) Notice that this subprogram QUART calls subprograms CUBIC (Program 4.3 for solving a cubic equation) and QUAD (Program 4.1 for solving a quadratic equation), while CUBIC, in turn, also calls QUAD.

(d) The EQUIVALENCE statement causes the values of two or more variables to be stored in the same location, i.e., to be considered as the same number. The statement saves storage space; it causes no confusion in this program because AQ and BQ are never needed at the same time.

Flow Chart 4.5

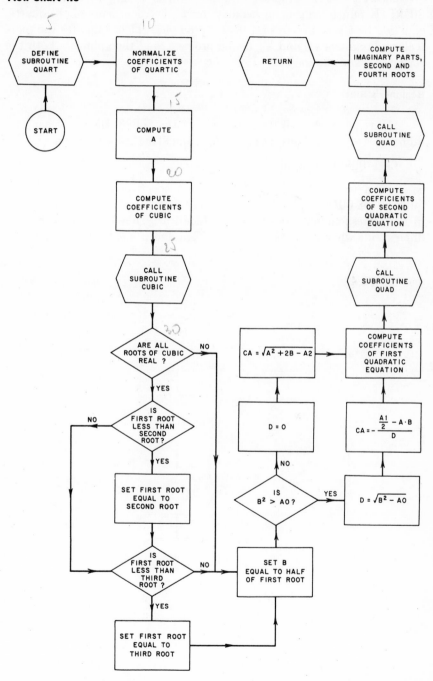

Program 4.6 serves as an input-output program for Program 4.5, SUBROUTINE QUART. It punches a general heading, reads the coefficients of the quartic equation that is to be solved, calls Program 4.5 which computes the roots (calling Programs 4.3 and 4.1 in the process), and then punches both the coefficients and the roots.

Beginner's Hint

Notice again that all the arguments of the SUBROUTINE statement are dummy arguments. Thus the arrays A, R, and RI in the CALL statement

CALL QUART (A, R, RI)

correspond to the arrays C, XR, and XI, respectively, in the statement SUBROUTINE QUART (C, XR, XI) of Program 4.5. Notice that the dimensioning in the corresponding arrays must be identical. Thus A and C each have dimension 5 while R, RI, XR, and XI all have dimension 4.

Flow Chart 4.6

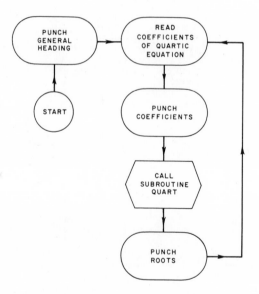

```
C       PROGRAM 4.6
C       CALLS QUARTIC EQUATION SUBROUTINE
C
        DIMENSION A(5), R(4), RI(4)
        PUNCH 996
   1    READ 999, A
        PUNCH 998, (I, A(I), I = 1, 5)
        CALL QUART (A, R, RI)
        PUNCH 997, (I, R(I), RI(I), I = 1, 4)
        GO TO 1
 996    FORMAT(// 17X, 24HRESULTS FROM PROGRAM 4.6 / 12X, 33HSOLUTIONS OF
       1THE QUARTIC EQUATION / 57H   A(1)*X**4 + A(2)*X**3 + A(3)*X**2 + A(
       24)*X + A(5) = 0. )
 997    FORMAT(/10X, 4HROOT 5X,9HREAL PART 8X,9HIMAGINARY/(11X,I2,2E17.7))
 998    FORMAT(//22X, 12HCOEFFICIENTS / 19X 1HI 8X, 4HA(I)/(18X,I2,E17.7))
 999    FORMAT(5F10.0)
        END
```

```
                 RESULTS FROM PROGRAM 4.6
              SOLUTIONS OF THE QUARTIC EQUATION
     A(1)*X**4 + A(2)*X**3 + A(3)*X**2 + A(4)*X + A(5) = 0.
```

$$A_1 x^4 + A_2 x^3 + A_3 x^2 + A_4 x + A_5 = 0$$

```
                      COEFFICIENTS
                  I        A(I)
                  1    1.0000000E+00
                  2    0.0000000E-99
                  3    0.0000000E-99
                  4    0.0000000E-99
                  5    1.0000000E+00


        ROOT      REAL PART          IMAGINARY
          1    7.0710675E-01      7.0710685E-01
          2    7.0710675E-01     -7.0710685E-01
          3   -7.0710675E-01      7.0710685E-01
          4   -7.0710675E-01     -7.0710685E-01


                      COEFFICIENTS
                  I        A(I)
                  1    1.0000000E+00
                  2    0.0000000E-99
                  3    0.0000000E-99
                  4    0.0000000E-99
                  5   -1.0000000E+00


        ROOT      REAL PART          IMAGINARY
          1    1.0000000E+00      0.0000000E-99
          2   -1.0000000E+00     -0.0000000E-99
          3    0.0000000E-99      1.0000000E+00
          4    0.0000000E-99     -1.0000000E+00
```

Program 4.7 uses Newton's method of tangents (Sec. 4.2) to find the roots of the particular transcendental equation

$$f(x) = \tan x - x = 0, \tag{a}$$

which is used in the program in the equivalent form

$$\sin x - x \cos x = 0.$$

After each root has been located, the program increments that root by π and uses this incremented value as the starting point for the next higher root. This procedure is suggested by the fact that, for large n, the nth root of (a) is approximately given by $\dfrac{2n - 1}{2}\,\pi$. This approximate (asymptotic) value of the root is punched out with each root. The steps by which the root is approached, including the values of $f(x)$ and $f'(x)$ at each step, are also shown.

Beginner's Hint

Notice how the conversion from floating-point to fixed-point mode is used to round off a number. The integer AN in the expression

    ASYMP = AN*PI/2.

must be a floating-point number to agree with the mode of the rest of the expression. To compute AN, the fixed-point number

    N = 2.*X0/PI + .9999999

is first computed, and then this integer is "floated":

    AN = N

Program 4.7-A extends synthetic substitution (Sec. 2.4) and the Newton-Raphson method (Sec. 4.2) to the evaluation of *all* the roots (real and complex) of algebraic equations with real or complex coefficients. The starting value of each root is arbitrarily chosen as $i(\sqrt{-1})$.

This program calls subroutine POLAR for the polar form of complex numbers.

```
C       PROGRAM 4.7
C       ROOTS OF A TRANSCENDENTAL EQUATION
C       NEWTON-S METHOD
C
        PI = 3.1415927
        PUNCH 999
1       READ 998, X0
4       PUNCH 997
5       F0 = SINF(X0) - X0*COSF(X0)
        F1 = X0*SINF(X0)
        PUNCH 995, X0, F0, F1
        X1 = X0 - F0/F1
        IF (X1 - X0) 10, 20, 10
10      X0 = X1
        GO TO 5
20      N = 2.*X0/PI + .9999999
        AN = N
        M = (N + 1)/2
        ASYMP = AN*PI/2.
        PUNCH 996, M, X0, AN, ASYMP
        X0 = X0 + PI
        GO TO 4
995     FORMAT (F7.2, 2E19.7)
996     FORMAT (/ 14X, 4HROOT I2, 2H = E14.7 / 13X, I2 7H*PI/2 = E14.7)
997     FORMAT (/ 47H      X            FUNCTION            DERIVATIVE      )
998     FORMAT (F10.0)
999     FORMAT (// 13X, 24HRESULTS FROM PROGRAM 4.7 // 15X,
       1 19HROOTS OF TAN(X) = X )
        END
```

RESULTS FROM PROGRAM 4.7

ROOTS OF TAN(X) = X

X	FUNCTION	DERIVATIVE
5.00	-2.3772351E+00	-4.7946213E+00
4.50	-4.7384460E-02	-4.4069153E+00
4.49	-1.1161000E-04	-4.3861548E+00
4.49	-2.1000000E-07	-4.3861052E+00

ROOT 2 = 4.4934095E+00
3*PI/2 = 4.7123890E+00

X	FUNCTION	DERIVATIVE
7.63	-6.8245890E-01	7.4526756E+00
7.72	1.0135110E-02	7.6639481E+00
7.72	2.0300000E-06	7.6613316E+00
7.72	4.9000000E-07	7.6613313E+00

ROOT 3 = 7.7252519E+00
5*PI/2 = 7.8539815E+00

X	FUNCTION	DERIVATIVE
10.86	4.0330590E-01	-1.0776928E+01
10.90	-1.5783000E-03	-1.0858843E+01
10.90	-3.7400000E-06	-1.0858555E+01

ROOT 4 = 1.0904122E+01
7*PI/2 = 1.0995574E+01

X	FUNCTION	DERIVATIVE
14.04	-2.8691090E-01	1.3987018E+01
14.06	4.5025000E-04	1.4030845E+01
14.06	1.2600000E-06	1.4030781E+01

ROOT 5 = 1.4066194E+01
9*PI/2 = 1.4137167E+01

X	FUNCTION	DERIVATIVE
17.20	2.2279080E-01	-1.7164464E+01
17.22	-1.6725000E-04	-1.7191813E+01
17.22	-1.2610000E-05	-1.7191795E+01

ROOT 6 = 1.7220756E+01
11*PI/2 = 1.7278759E+01

X	FUNCTION	DERIVATIVE
20.36	-1.8212210E-01	2.0328103E+01
20.37	8.2380000E-05	2.0346810E+01
20.37	8.9000000E-07	2.0346802E+01

ROOT 7 = 2.0371303E+01
13*PI/2 = 2.0420352E+01

Flow Chart 4.7

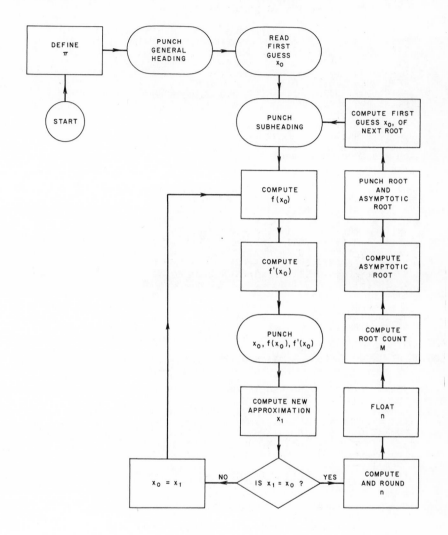

```
C       PROGRAM 4.7-A
C       NEWTON-S METHOD FOR ROOTS OF POLYNOMIALS WITH COMPLEX COEFFICIENTS
C       USING COMPLEX SYNTHETIC SUBSTITUTION
C
        DIMENSION AR(50), AI(50), BR(50), BI(50), CR(50), CI(50)
        PRINT 994
  1     READ 999, NDEG, EPS
        N1 = NDEG + 1
        N = NDEG
        READ 998, (AR(I), AI(I), I = 1,N1)
        PRINT 997, NDEG, (I, AR(I), AI(I), I = 1, N1)
        PRINT 996, EPS
        BR(1) = AR(1)
        BI(1) = AI(1)
        CR(1) = AR(1)
        CI(1) = AI(1)
        DO 300 NROOT = 1, NDEG
        X = 0.
        Y = 1.
  10    DO 100 I = 2,N1
        BR(I) = AR(I) + BR(I-1)*X - BI(I-1)*Y
 100    BI(I) = AI(I) + BR(I-1)*Y + BI(I-1)*X
        DO 200 I = 2,N
        CR(I) = BR(I) + CR(I-1)*X - CI(I-1)*Y
 200    CI(I) = BI(I) + CR(I-1)*Y + CI(I-1)*X
        DEN = CR(N)**2 + CI(N)**2
        X = X - (BR(N1)*CR(N) + BI(N1)*CI(N))/DEN
        Y = Y + (BR(N1)*CI(N) - BI(N1)*CR(N))/DEN
        IF (BR(N1)**2 + BI(N1)**2 - EPS) 250,250,10
 250    N1 = N1 - 1
        N = N - 1
        DO 260 I = 2, N1
        AR(I) = BR(I)
 260    AI(I) = BI(I)
        CALL POLAR (X,Y,RHO,PHI)
 300    PRINT 995, NROOT, X, Y, RHO, PHI
        GO TO 1
C
 994    FORMAT (// 23X, 26HRESULTS FROM PROGRAM 4.7-A )
 995    FORMAT (7X, I3, 3F13.7, F13.6)
 996    FORMAT ( / 33X, 5HROOTS / 27X, 9HEPSILON = E8.1  // 14X, 9HREAL P
       1ART 4X, 9HIMAGINARY 5X, 7HMODULUS 7X, 5HANGLE )
 997    FORMAT (// 25X, 20HPOLYNOMIAL OF DEGREE I2 // 30X, 12HCOEFFICIENTS
       1 // 27X, 9HREAL PART 4X, 9HIMAGINARY / (20X, I3, 2F13.7))
 998    FORMAT (2E10.0)
 999    FORMAT (I5, E10.3)
        END


        SUBROUTINE POLAR (X, Y, RHO, PHI)
        RHO = SQRTF(X*X + Y*Y)
        PHI = 180.*ATANF(Y/ABSF(X))/3.1415927
        IF(X) 10,40,40
  10    IF(Y) 20,30,30
  20    PHI = -180. - PHI
        GO TO 40
  30    PHI = 180. - PHI
  40    RETURN
        END
```

POLYNOMIAL OF DEGREE 6

COEFFICIENTS

	REAL PART	IMAGINARY
1	1.0000000	0.0000000
2	-3.0000000	1.0000000
3	2.0000000	-3.0000000
4	1.0000000	2.0000000
5	-3.0000000	1.0000000
6	2.0000000	-3.0000000
7	0.0000000	2.0000000

ROOTS
EPSILON = 1.0E-13

	REAL PART	IMAGINARY	MODULUS	ANGLE
1	.5000000	.8660254	1.0000000	59.999996
2	.5000000	-.8660253	.9999999	-59.999989
3	1.0000001	0.0000000	1.0000000	-.000003
4	0.0000000	-1.0000001	1.0000000	-90.000020
5	-1.0000000	0.0000000	1.0000000	180.000000
6	1.9999999	0.0000000	1.9999998	0.000000

POLYNOMIAL OF DEGREE 9

COEFFICIENTS

	REAL PART	IMAGINARY
1	1.0000000	0.0000000
2	0.0000000	0.0000000
3	0.0000000	0.0000000
4	0.0000000	0.0000000
5	0.0000000	-81.0000000
6	0.0000000	32.0000000
7	0.0000000	0.0000000
8	0.0000000	0.0000000
9	0.0000000	0.0000000
10	2592.0000000	0.0000000

ROOTS
EPSILON = 1.0E-07

	REAL PART	IMAGINARY	MODULUS	ANGLE
1	0.0000000	-2.0000000	2.0000000	-90.000010
2	-1.1480503	2.7716386	2.9999999	112.500010
3	1.9021131	-.6180340	2.0000000	-17.999999
4	-2.7716387	-1.1480503	3.0000000	-157.500010
5	1.1755704	1.6180342	2.0000000	54.000004
6	-1.9021129	-.6180342	1.9999998	-162.000000
7	-1.1755711	1.6180281	1.9999955	126.000120
8	2.7716355	1.1480497	2.9999968	22.500011
9	1.1479946	-2.7716196	2.9999611	-67.500838

Program 4.8 evaluates a root of $f(x) = 0$ by the bisection method (Sec. 4.3). The process is started at a point x to the left of the root with an increment h.

The first IF statement checks whether $f(x)$ and $f(x + h)$ have opposite or equal signs. NPATH is set equal to 1 initially. Thus, for equal signs, statement 4 shifts x to $x + h$ until a separation interval is located, i.e., A and B have different signs. From there on NPATH = 2, and statement 5 causes the interval h to be halved at each step.

The second IF statement terminates the program as soon as h is less than a permissible error EPS.

Beginner's Hint

An arithmetic statement function is used to define F(X) in this program. A FUNCTION subprogram (see Notes, Program 6.2) could have been used to define F(X), but it is not practical to use such subprograms when the mainline program is very short, as in this case.

Flow Chart 4.8

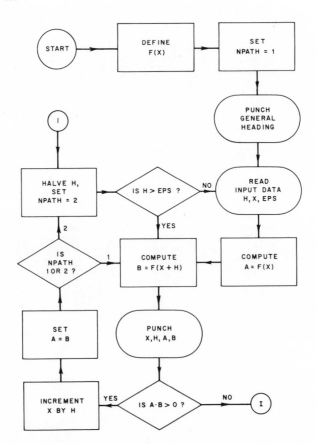

```
C       PROGRAM 4.8
C       BISECTION METHOD FOR THE REAL ROOTS OF THE EQUATION F(X) = 0.
C
        F(X) = SINF(X) - X*COSF(X)
        NPATH = 1
        PUNCH 999
1       READ 998, H, X, EPS
2       A = F(X)
3       B = F(X + H)
        PUNCH 997, X, H, A, B
        IF (A*B) 5,5,4
4       X = X + H
        A = B
        GO TO (3,5), NPATH
5       H = H/2.
        NPATH = 2
        IF (H - EPS) 1,1,3
C
997     FORMAT (16X, 2F8.4, 2F11.4)
998     FORMAT (3E10.0)
999     FORMAT (// 24X, 24HRESULTS FROM PROGRAM 4.8
       1        // 21X, 1HX, 7X, 1HH 8X, 4HF(X) 6X, 6HF(X+H))
        END
```

RESULTS FROM PROGRAM 4.8

X	H	F(X)	F(X+H)
2.0000	1.0000	1.7415	3.1110
3.0000	1.0000	3.1110	1.8577
4.0000	1.0000	1.8577	-2.3772
4.0000	.5000	1.8577	-.0289
4.0000	.2500	1.8577	1.0008
4.2500	.1250	1.0008	.5046
4.3750	.0625	.5046	.2420
4.4375	.0312	.2420	.1075
4.4687	.0156	.1075	.0395
4.4843	.0078	.0395	.0053
4.4921	.0039	.0053	-.0117
4.4921	.0019	.0053	-.0032
4.4921	.0009	.0053	.0010
4.4931	.0004	.0010	-.0010
4.4931	.0002	.0010	0.0000
4.4934	.0001	0.0000	-.0005

Program 5.1 computes the determinant (DETERM) of a square matrix of order n by the method of pivotal condensation (Sec. 5.1). The basic algorithm of the program is that used in (5.1.5):

$$a_{ij} \rightarrow a_{ij} - a_{il} \frac{a_{lj}}{a_{ll}} = a_{ij} - a_{lj} \frac{a_{il}}{a_{ll}}.$$

Since the ratio a_{il}/a_{ll} is independent of the summation index j, this ratio is computed once for each value of i

RATIO = A(I,L)/A(L,L)

and then used for each value of j

A(I,J) = A(I,J) − A(L,J)*RATIO

Beginner's Hints

(a) The size of the matrix for which the program can compute the determinant is limited by the DIMENSION statement. In this program the order n of the matrix is arbitrarily limited to 30 by the DIMENSION statement A(30,30). The student should not infer from this that the method fails for matrices with $n > 30$, or that it will always evaluate the determinant to the same number of significant figures, if $n \leq 30$.

(b) In this program the matrix is read in and printed out by rows, i.e., the elements are stored in the following order:

$$a_{11}, a_{12}, a_{13}, \ldots, a_{1n}, a_{21}, a_{22}, \ldots, a_{2n}, \ldots, a_{nn}.$$

This happens because the input/output list statement

..... , ((A(I,J), J = 1,N), I = 1,N)

is equivalent to the nested DO loop

```
        DO n₁ I = 1, N
        DO n₁ J = 1, N
n₁   ..... ,        A(I,J)
```

If the indexing is omitted, e.g., READ 999, A, then arrays are read in and printed out by columns, i.e., in the following order:

$$a_{11}, a_{21}, a_{31}, \ldots, a_{n1}, a_{12}, a_{22}, a_{32}, \ldots, a_{n2}, \ldots, a_{nn}.$$

```
C       PROGRAM 5.1
C       DETERMINANT BY PIVOTAL CONDENSATION
C
        PUNCH 996
        DIMENSION A(30,30)
  1     READ   999, N,((A(I,J), J = 1,N), I = 1,N)
        PUNCH 998, N,((A(I,J), J = 1,N), I = 1,N)
        K = 2
        L = 1
  5     DO 10 I = K,N
        RATIO = A(I,L)/A(L,L)
        DO 10 J = K,N
 10     A(I,J) = A(I,J) - A(L,J)*RATIO
        IF(K - N) 15,20,20
 15     L = K
        K = K + 1
        GO TO 5
 20     DETERM = 1
        DO 25 L = 1,N
 25     DETERM = DETERM*A(L,L)
        PUNCH 997, DETERM
        GO TO 1
C
996     FORMAT (// 24X, 24HRESULTS FROM PROGRAM 5.1 )
997     FORMAT (/ 12X, 33HTHE DETERMINANT OF THIS MATRIX IS E15.7)
998     FORMAT (// 27X, 15HMATRIX OF ORDER I2 // (4E17.7))
999     FORMAT (I5/(8F10.0))
        END
```

RESULTS FROM PROGRAM 5.1

MATRIX OF ORDER 2

1.0000000E+00   3.0000000E+00   2.0000000E+00   4.0000000E+00

THE DETERMINANT OF THIS MATRIX IS -2.0000000E+00

MATRIX OF ORDER 3

1.0000000E+00   1.0000000E+00   1.0000000E+00   1.0000000E+00
2.0000000E+00   3.0000000E+00   1.0000000E+00   4.0000000E+00
9.0000000E+00

THE DETERMINANT OF THIS MATRIX IS 2.0000000E+00

MATRIX OF ORDER 4

2.0000000E+00   4.0000000E+00   6.0000000E+00   8.0000000E+00
3.0000000E+00   1.0000000E+00   2.0000000E+00   1.0000000E+00
1.0000000E+00   2.0000000E+00   -2.0000000E+00   2.0000000E+00
2.0000000E+00   3.0000000E+00   4.0000000E+00   1.0000000E+00

THE DETERMINANT OF THIS MATRIX IS -2.2800000E+02

MATRIX OF ORDER 4

1.2000000E+00   2.1000000E+00   -1.1000000E+00   4.0000000E+00
-1.1000000E+00   2.0000000E+00   3.1000000E+00   3.9000000E+00
-2.1000000E+00   -2.2000000E+00   3.7000000E+00   1.6000000E+01
-1.0000000E+00   -2.3000000E+00   4.7000000E+00   1.2000000E+01

THE DETERMINANT OF THIS MATRIX IS -3.1064278E+02

MATRIX OF ORDER 6

2.0000000E+00   1.0000000E+00   0.0000000E-99   0.0000000E-99
0.0000000E-99   0.0000000E-99   1.0000000E+00   2.0000000E+00
1.0000000E+00   0.0000000E-99   0.0000000E-99   0.0000000E-99
0.0000000E-99   1.0000000E+00   2.0000000E+00   1.0000000E+00
0.0000000E-99   0.0000000E-99   0.0000000E-99   0.0000000E-99
1.0000000E+00   2.0000000E+00   1.0000000E+00   0.0000000E-99
0.0000000E-99   0.0000000E-99   0.0000000E-99   1.0000000E+00
2.0000000E+00   1.0000000E+00   0.0000000E-99   0.0000000E-99
0.0000000E-99   0.0000000E-99   1.0000000E+00   2.0000000E+00

THE DETERMINANT OF THIS MATRIX IS 7.0000022E+00

Flow Chart 5.1

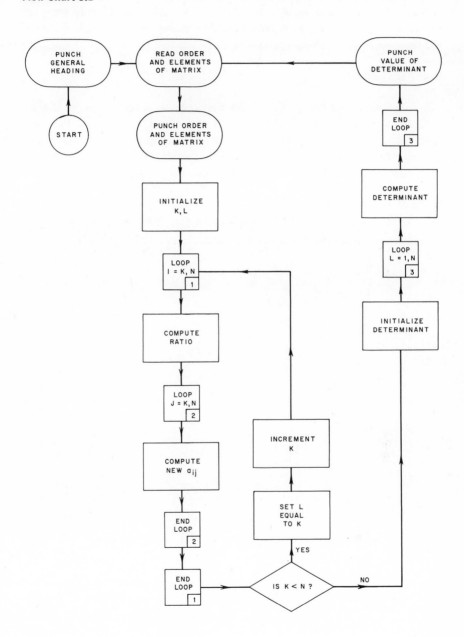

Program 5.2 uses the Gauss elimination method (Sec. 5.2) to solve a system of simultaneous linear equations. The simple algorithm of this program makes it ideal for pedagogical purposes. The generally superior algorithm of the Gauss-Jordan method is presented in Program 9.7.

Beginner's Hints

(a) Notice that this program fails when any term on the diagonal A(I,I) becomes zero. It is known a priori in many physical problems that this cannot happen, and in most cases where it does happen the equations can be renumbered to obviate this occurrence. However, in most computations involving the solution of simultaneous equations, a more sophisticated method (like that of Program 9.7) should be used, which will determine whether any A(I,I) is zero.

(b) The variable RATIO of Program 5.1 could also be used here; it would save a division at each calculation of the new A(I,J) and Y(J).

```
C       PROGRAM 5.2
C       SOLUTION OF SIMULTANEOUS EQUATIONS
C       METHOD OF GAUSS
C
        DIMENSION  A(50,50), Y(50), X(50)
        PUNCH 999
   1    READ 998, N, ((A(I,J), J = 1,N), I = 1,N)
        PUNCH 997, N, ((I,J,A(I,J), J = 1,N), I = 1,N)
   2    READ 996, (Y(I), I = 1,N)
        PUNCH 995, (I,Y(I), I = 1,N)
        M = N - 1
        DO  10   I = 1,M
        L = I + 1
        DO  10    J = L,N
        IF  (A(J,I))  6, 10, 6
   6    DO  8   K = L,N
   8    A(J,K) = A(J,K) - A(I,K)*A(J,I)/A(I,I)
        Y(J) = Y(J) - Y(I)*A(J,I)/A(I,I)
  10    CONTINUE
        X(N) = Y(N)/A(N,N)
        PUNCH 994, N, X(N)
        DO  30   I = 1,M
        K = N - I
        L = K + 1
        DO  20    J = L,N
  20    Y(K) = Y(K) - X(J)*A(K,J)
        X(K) = Y(K)/A(K,K)
  30    PUNCH 993, K, X(K)
        GO TO 1
 993    FORMAT (11X, I5, E16.7)
 994    FORMAT (/ 16X, 15HSOLUTION VECTOR / 15X, 1HI 6X, 4HX(I) /
       1 (11X, I5, E16.7))
 995    FORMAT (/ 16X, 15HCONSTANT VECTOR / 15X, 1HI 6X, 4HY(I) /
       1 (11X, I5, E16.7))
 996    FORMAT (8F10.0)
 997    FORMAT (// 45H  SOLUTION OF SIMULTANEOUS EQUATIONS OF ORDER I2 //
       1 14X, 22HMATRIX OF COEFFICIENTS / 13X, 1HI 4X, 1HJ 7X, 6HA(I,J) /
       2 (9X, 2I5, E17.7))
 998    FORMAT (I5/(8F10.0))
 999    FORMAT (// 12X, 24HRESULTS FROM PROGRAM 5.2)
        END
```

SOLUTION OF SIMULTANEOUS EQUATIONS OF ORDER 5

MATRIX OF COEFFICIENTS

I	J	A(I,J)
1	1	1.0000000E+00
1	2	1.0000000E+00
1	3	1.0000000E+00
1	4	1.0000000E+00
1	5	1.0000000E+00
2	1	1.0000000E+00
2	2	2.0000000E+00
2	3	3.0000000E+00
2	4	4.0000000E+00
2	5	5.0000000E+00
3	1	1.0000000E+00
3	2	4.0000000E+00
3	3	9.0000000E+00
3	4	1.6000000E+01
3	5	2.5000000E+01
4	1	1.0000000E+00
4	2	8.0000000E+00
4	3	2.7000000E+01
4	4	6.4000000E+01
4	5	1.2500000E+02
5	1	1.0000000E+00
5	2	1.6000000E+01
5	3	8.1000000E+01
5	4	2.5600000E+02
5	5	6.2500000E+02

CONSTANT VECTOR

I	Y(I)
1	1.5000000E+01
2	5.5000000E+01
3	2.2500000E+02
4	9.7900000E+02
5	4.4250000E+03

SOLUTION VECTOR

I	X(I)
5	5.0000000E+00
4	4.0000000E+00
3	3.0000000E+00
2	2.0000000E+00
1	1.0000000E+00

Flow Chart 5.2

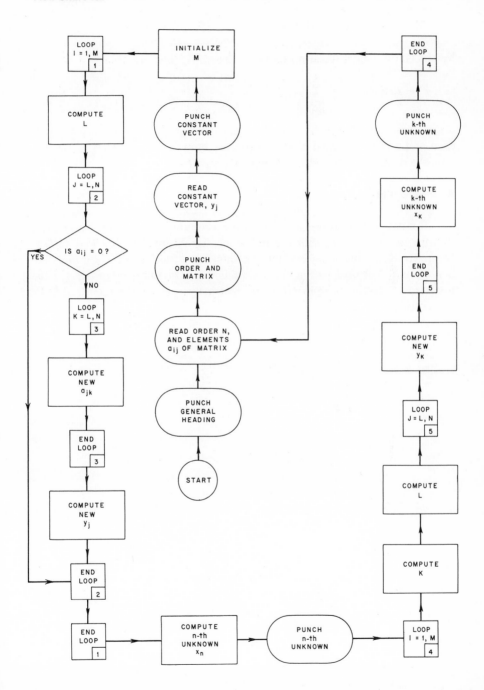

Program 5.3 solves a system of linear simultaneous equations

$$\sum_{j=1}^{N} a_{ij}x_j = y_i \qquad (i = 1, n)$$

by the Gauss-Seidel iteration method (Sec. 5.4). The variable

$$P = a_{ii}x_i = y_i - \sum_{\substack{j=1 \\ j \neq i}}^{n} a_{ij}x_j$$

is evaluated for each x_i by using the last computed value of x_j ($j \neq i$) at each step. It is assumed that the process converges, and that a_{ii} is the largest absolute-value coefficient in the ith equation.

Beginner's Hint

Iterative procedures are usually terminated when two successive iterates agree to a specified number of significant figures. The rather complicated calculations determining this "iteration cut-off" are omitted here so as to not obscure the basic simplicity of the iterative process. This program stops the process after an arbitrarily specified number (ITLAST) of iterations.

```
C       PROGRAM 5.3
C       GAUSS-SEIDEL ITERATION OF SIMULTANEOUS EQUATIONS
C
        DIMENSION A(30,30), X(30), Y(30)
        PUNCH 997
  1     READ  999, N, ITLAST, ((A(I,J), J = 1,N), Y(I), I = 1,N)
        PUNCH 996, N, ((A(I,J), J = 1, N), I = 1, N)
        PUNCH 995, (Y(I), I = 1, N)
        DO 10 I = 1,N
 10     X(I) = 0.
        IT = 1
 20     PUNCH 994, IT
        DO 60 I = 1,N
        P = Y(I)
        DO 50 J = 1,N
        IF(I-J) 40,50,40
 40     P = P - A(I,J)*X(J)
 50     CONTINUE
        X(I) = P/A(I,I)
 60     PUNCH 998, I, X(I)
        IT = IT + 1
        IF(IT - ITLAST) 20,20,1
C
994     FORMAT (/24X, 9HITERATION I2)
995     FORMAT (/ 22X, 15HCONSTANT VECTOR / (3E18.7) // 22X,
       1 15HSOLUTION VECTOR)
996     FORMAT (// 21X, 15HMATRIX OF ORDER I2 // (3E18.7))
997     FORMAT (// 17X, 24HRESULTS FROM PROGRAM 5.3)
998     FORMAT (20X, I2, E16.7)
999     FORMAT(2I5/(8F10.0))
        END
```

MATRIX OF ORDER 3

1.0000000E+01	2.0000000E+00	1.0000000E+00
2.0000000E+00	2.0000000E+01	-2.0000000E+00
-2.0000000E+00	3.0000000E+00	1.0000000E+01

CONSTANT VECTOR

| 9.0000000E+00 | -4.4000000E+01 | 2.2000000E+01 |

SOLUTION VECTOR

ITERATION 1
1   9.0000000E-01
2   -2.2900000E+00
3   3.0670000E+00

ITERATION 2
1   1.0513000E+00
2   -1.9984300E+00
3   3.0097890E+00

ITERATION 3
1   9.9870710E-01
2   -1.9988918E+00
3   2.9994089E+00

ITERATION 4
1   9.9983750E-01
2   -2.0000429E+00
3   2.9999803E+00

ITERATION 5
1   1.0000105E+00
2   -2.0000030E+00
3   3.0000030E+00

ITERATION 6
1   1.0000003E+00
2   -1.9999997E+00
3   2.9999999E+00

ITERATION 7
1   1.0000000E+00
2   -2.0000000E+00
3   3.0000000E+00

ITERATION 8
1   1.0000000E+00
2   -2.0000000E+00
3   3.0000000E+00

Flow Chart 5.3

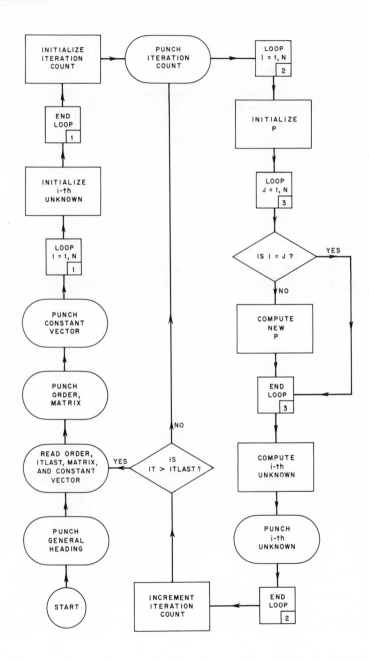

211

Program 5.4 computes the eigenvalues of a *symmetric* matrix A of the third order:

$$A = \begin{bmatrix} a_{11} & a_{12} & a_{13} \\ a_{12} & a_{22} & a_{23} \\ a_{13} & a_{23} & a_{33} \end{bmatrix}.$$

The coefficients of the cubic characteristic equation are formed by expanding the determinant of the matrix $(\lambda I - A)$; a subroutine subprogram (Program 4.3) is then called to solve the equation. This method of finding the eigenvalues as the roots of the determinantal equation is impractical for matrices of large order. More efficient procedures are based on iterative methods of successive approximation and interpolation, in which the determinant is successively evaluated for trial values of the eigenvalue parameter.

Beginner's Hint

Only the six distinct elements of the matrix

$$\begin{array}{ccc} a_{11} & a_{12} & a_{13} \\ & a_{22} & a_{23} \\ & & a_{33} \end{array}$$

are shown in the output to emphasize that in this program the matrix must be symmetric — a sufficient condition for the existence of only real eigenvalues.

Flow Chart 5.4

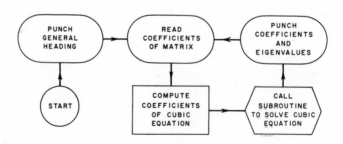

212

```
C       PROGRAM 5.4
C       EIGENVALUES OF A SYMMETRIC MATRIX OF THIRD ORDER
C
        DIMENSION C(4), EIGEN(3)
        PUNCH 997
   1    READ 999, A11, A12, A13, A22, A23, A33
        C(1) = 1.
        C(2) = -(A11 + A22 + A33)
        C(3) = A11*A22 + A11*A33 + A22*A33 - A12*A12 - A13*A13 - A23*A23
        C(4) = -A11*A22*A33 - 2.*A12*A13*A23 + A11*A23*A23 + A22*A13*A13
       1       + A33*A12*A12
        CALL CUBIC (C, EIGEN, XI)
        PUNCH 998, A11, A12, A13, A22, A23, A33, EIGEN
        GO TO 1
C
  997   FORMAT ( // 24X, 24HRESULTS FROM PROGRAM 5.4 )
  998   FORMAT ( // 33X, 6HMATRIX // 9X, 3E17.7 / 26X, 2E17.7 / 43X,
       1          E17.7 // 31X, 11HEIGENVALUES / (26X, E17.7))
  999   FORMAT (8E10.0)
        END
```

RESULTS FROM PROGRAM 5.4

MATRIX

1.0000000E+00	0.0000000E-99	0.0000000E-99
	1.0000000E+00	0.0000000E-99
		1.0000000E+00

EIGENVALUES
1.0000000E+00
1.0000000E+00
1.0000000E+00

MATRIX

1.0000000E+01	2.0000000E+00	1.0000000E+00
	1.0000000E+01	2.0000000E+00
		1.0000000E+01

EIGENVALUES
1.3372281E+01
9.0000001E+00
7.6277189E+00

Program 5.5 computes the largest eigenvalue of a matrix of order n by iteration (Sec. 5.5). The matrix is A(I,J); X(J) is the eigenvector (with its first component normalized, i.e., set equal to 1), and Y(I) is the product at any stage of A(I,J) and X(J). The eigenvalue is Y(1). The iteration continues until the iteration counter ITERA reaches ITLAST (see Notes, Program 5.3). The eigenvector is printed after the final iteration.

Beginner's Hints

(a) Notice that X(1) is always unity, and hence, it is unnecessary to begin the DO loop (ending at 30) with I = 1, for which value the loop would merely compute again X(1) = 1.

(b) To emphasize the fact that Y(1) is the eigenvalue, the name EIGEN could be put into equivalence with Y(1):

EQUIVALENCE (Y(1), EIGEN)

The variable EIGEN may then be used in the output statement

PUNCH 998, ITERA, EIGEN

(c) This method fails when the two largest eigenvalues λ_1, λ_2 have the same modulus or when the starting eigenvector is orthogonal to the eigenvector associated with λ_1.

(d) This method converges rapidly when the ratio $|\lambda_1|/|\lambda_2|$ is much larger than one.

```
C       PROGRAM 5.5
C       LARGEST EIGENVALUE OF MATRIX BY ITERATION
C
        DIMENSION A(25, 25), X(25), Y(25)
  1     READ 999, N, ITLAST, ((A(I, J), J = 1, N), I = 1, N)
        PUNCH 996, ((I, J, A(I,J), J = 1,N), I = 1,N)
        ITERA = 1
        X(1) = 1.
        DO 10 I = 2, N
 10     X(I) = 0.
        PUNCH 995
 15     DO 20 I = 1, N
        Y(I) = 0.
        DO 20 J = 1, N
 20     Y(I) = Y(I) + A(I,J)*X(J)
        DO 30 I = 2, N
 30     X(I) = Y(I)/Y(1)
        PUNCH 998, ITERA, Y(1)
        ITERA = ITERA + 1
        IF(ITERA - ITLAST) 15,15,40
 40     PUNCH  997, (I, X(I), I = 1, N)
        GO TO 1
C
995     FORMAT ( / 24X, 23HITERATION    EIGENVALUE )
996     FORMAT ( // 24X, 24HRESULTS FROM PROGRAM 5.5 /// 25X,
        1          22HMATRIX OF COEFFICIENTS // 25X, 18HI   J        A(I,J)
        2          / (22X, 2I4, E17.7))
997     FORMAT (/ 31X, 11HEIGENVECTOR / (I29, E19.7))
998     FORMAT (I29, E19.7 )
999     FORMAT (2I5/(8E10.0))
        END
```

RESULTS FROM PROGRAM 5.5

MATRIX OF COEFFICIENTS

I	J	A(I,J)
1	1	1.0000000E+01
1	2	2.0000000E+00
1	3	1.0000000E+00
2	1	2.0000000E+00
2	2	1.0000000E+01
2	3	2.0000000E+00
3	1	1.0000000E+00
3	2	2.0000000E+00
3	3	1.0000000E+01

ITERATION	EIGENVALUE
1	1.0000000E+01
2	1.0500000E+01
3	1.1028571E+01
4	1.1541450E+01
5	1.1998652E+01
6	1.2376304E+01
7	1.2669187E+01
8	1.2885564E+01
9	1.3039877E+01
10	1.3147274E+01

	EIGENVECTOR
1	1.0000000E+00
2	1.1417934E+00
3	9.3722736E-01

Flow Chart 5.5

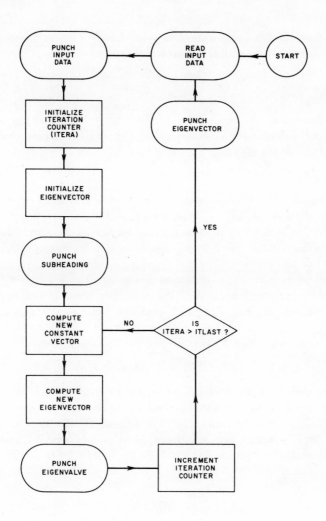

Program 6.1 solves the boundary-value problem of Example 6.1.1,

$$y'' - y = 0, \quad y(0) = 0, \quad y(1) = 1,$$

by the second-order finite difference equation (6.1.2), and compares the approximate solutions with the exact solution,

$$y(x) = \frac{\sinh x}{\sinh 1}.$$

N is the number of unknown pivotal values while STRIPS is the number of strips. Each difference equation contains at most three nonzero coefficients, indicated in the Ith equation by

A(I,1), A(I,2), A(I,3)

The right side of the Ith equation is called A(I,4). The exact solution at the point X(I) is called EXACT(I). These six quantities are evaluated in the DO loop ending at statement 10. The right-hand side is then corrected for the known values Y0 and Y1 at $x = 0$ and $x = 1$, respectively, and the first coefficient of the first equation and the third coefficient of the last equation are set equal to zero. The system of linear equations in the Y(I) is then solved by the subprogram SUBROUTINE BAND3(N), which is designed to solve equations whose coefficients form a centered band matrix three elements wide.

The problem solved by this program is the special case

F(X) = 0, G(X) = − 1, FR(X) = 0, XA = 0, YA = 0, XB = 1, YB = 1

of the general class of problems solved by Program 6.2, where extensive use is made of FUNCTION subprograms. This program, which introduces the COMMON statement and the SUBROUTINE BAND3(N), but uses the by-now familiar arithmetic statement functions, is meant to serve as a "stepping stone" to Program 6.2.

```
        SUBROUTINE BAND3 (N)
        DIMENSION A(100, 4), X(100)
        COMMON A, X
        M = N - 1
        DO 10 I = 2, M
        A(I,2) = A(I,2)*A(I-1,2) - A(I,1)*A(I-1,3)
        A(I,3) = A(I,3)*A(I-1,2)
   10   A(I,4) = A(I,4)*A(I-1,2) - A(I,1)*A(I-1,4)
        X(N) = (A(N,4)*A(N-1,2) - A(N,1)*A(N-1,4))/
   1          (A(N,2)*A(N-1,2) - A(N,1)*A(N-1,3))
        DO 20 I = 1, M
        J = N - I
   20   X(J) = (A(J,4) - A(J,3)*X(J+1))/A(J,2)
        RETURN
        END
```

```
C       PROGRAM 6.1
C       PROGRAM FOR SOLVING A PARTICULAR BOUNDARY VALUE PROBLEM
C       DETERMINES COEFFICIENTS AT PIVOTAL POINTS
C       THEN SOLVES SIMULTANEOUS EQUATIONS
C       AND COMPARES THE RESULTS WITH THE EXACT SOLUTION
C
        DIMENSION A(100,4), Y(100), EXACT(100), X(100)
        COMMON A, Y
        F(Z)  =   0.
        G(Z)  =  -1.
        FR(Z) =   0.
        SINH(Z) = (EXPF(Z) - EXPF(-Z))/2.
        PUNCH 995
        Y0  =  0.
        Y1  =  1.
        CONS = SINH(1.)
   1    READ 999, N
        PUNCH 994, N
        STRIPS = N + 1
        H = 1./STRIPS
        X(1) = H
        DO 10   I  = 1, N
        A(I,1)  =   1. - H/2.*F(X(I))
        A(I,2)  =  -(2. - H*H*G(X(I)))
        A(I,3)  =   1. + H/2.*F(X(I))
        A(I,4)  =   H*H*FR(X(I))
        EXACT(I) = SINH(X(I))/CONS
   10   X(I + 1) = X(I) + H
        A(1,4) = A(1,4) - A(1,1)*Y0
        A(1,1) = 0.
        A(N,4) = A(N,4) - A(N,3)*Y1
        A(N,3) = 0.
        IF(SENSE SWITCH 2) 22,24
   22   PUNCH 998, (I, (A(I,J), J = 1,4), I = 1,N)
   24   CALL BAND3 (N)
        PUNCH 996, (I, X(I), Y(I), EXACT(I), I = 1,N)
        PUNCH 993
        GO TO 1
C
  993   FORMAT (/ 22X, 30H****************************** )
  994   FORMAT (// 20X,   31HTHE NUMBER OF PIVOTAL POINTS IS I3 )
  995   FORMAT (// 25X, 24HRESULTS FROM PROGRAM 6.1 )
  996   FORMAT ( / 16X, 1HI 5X, 4HX(I) 8X, 4HY(I) 10X, 8HEXACT(I) /
       1          (I17, F9.4, 2E16.7))
  998   FORMAT ( / 26X, 22HMATRIX OF COEFFICIENTS // 5X, 1HI 6X, 6HA(I,1)
       1          10X, 6HA(I,2) 10X, 6HA(I,3) 10X, 6HA(I,4) / (I6,4E16.7))
  999   FORMAT(I5)
        END
```

(a) The COMMON statement links the storage of two or more programs or subprograms. It is used to establish a correspondence between variables in successive mainline programs, or variables in a mainline program and in its subprograms. In the latter case it is not necessary to name the variables as arguments of the subprogram. Thus, the variables A and X are not named as arguments of the subprogram BAND3; only N is named. But A and X are mentioned in the COMMON statement of the subprogram, and this suffices to identify them with the corresponding variables A and Y of the mainline Program 6.1. Notice that the variables in COMMON in the subprogram are dummy variables, i.e., X in the BAND3 subprogram becomes Y in Program 6.1.

(b) Generally speaking, variables that are mentioned in COMMON statements are stored starting from the last positions in memory. Thus, in our case,

COMMON A, Y

(where A has dimension 100×4 and Y has dimension 100), the value of A(1,1) is in the last address of memory, with the rest of A in the next 399 addresses. Y(1) and the rest of Y follow in the next 100 addresses. Y(100) is thus found in the 500th from last address in memory. It is thus possible to have variables from different programs in the same positions in storage, even though their dimensions are different.

(c) Some versions of FORTRAN store last in memory those variables which appear both in COMMON and EQUIVALENCE statements (Program 4.6), so that it is not enough to know the order of appearance of the variables in COMMON and their dimensions. The EQUIVALENCE statements must be included in the calculation of the location of a given variable.

(d) The IF (SENSE SWITCH 2) 22, 24 statement is used to by-pass the punching of the A(I,J) matrix.

Flow Chart 6.1

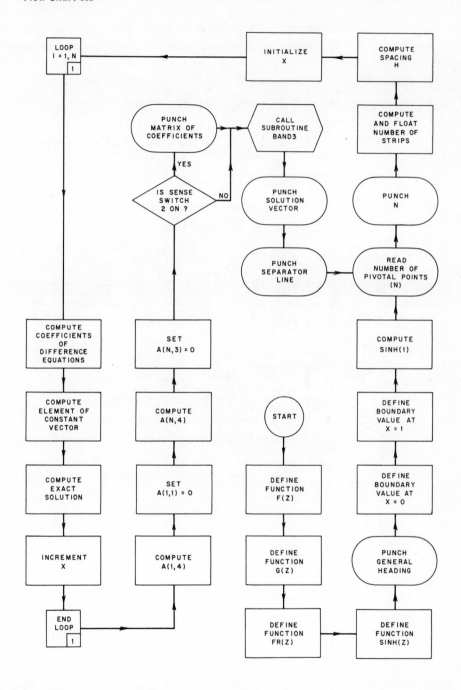

RESULTS FROM PROGRAM 6.1

THE NUMBER OF PIVOTAL POINTS IS 3

MATRIX OF COEFFICIENTS

I	A(I,1)	A(I,2)	A(I,3)	A(I,4)
1	0.0000000E-99	-2.0625000E+00	1.0000000E+00	0.0000000E-99
2	1.0000000E+00	-2.0625000E+00	1.0000000E+00	0.0000000E-99
3	1.0000000E+00	-2.0625000E+00	0.0000000E-99	-1.0000000E+00

I	X(I)	Y(I)	EXACT(I)
1	.2500	2.1511473E-01	2.1495242E-01
2	.5000	4.4367415E-01	4.4340943E-01
3	.7500	6.9996324E-01	6.9972422E-01

****

THE NUMBER OF PIVOTAL POINTS IS 7

MATRIX OF COEFFICIENTS

I	A(I,1)	A(I,2)	A(I,3)	A(I,4)
1	0.0000000E-99	-2.0156250E+00	1.0000000E+00	0.0000000E-99
2	1.0000000E+00	-2.0156250E+00	1.0000000E+00	0.0000000E-99
3	1.0000000E+00	-2.0156250E+00	1.0000000E+00	0.0000000E-99
4	1.0000000E+00	-2.0156250E+00	1.0000000E+00	0.0000000E-99
5	1.0000000E+00	-2.0156250E+00	1.0000000E+00	0.0000000E-99
6	1.0000000E+00	-2.0156250E+00	1.0000000E+00	0.0000000E-99
7	1.0000000E+00	-2.0156250E+00	0.0000000E-99	-1.0000000E+00

I	X(I)	Y(I)	EXACT(I)
1	.1250	1.0666332E-01	1.0664195E-01
2	.2500	2.1499327E-01	2.1495242E-01
3	.3750	3.2668248E-01	3.2662585E-01
4	.5000	4.4347612E-01	4.4340943E-01
5	.6250	5.6719907E-01	5.6713033E-01
6	.7500	6.9978448E-01	6.9972422E-01
7	.8750	8.4330397E-01	8.4326547E-01

****

Program 6.2 solves the linear second-order differential equation

$$\frac{d^2y}{dx^2} + f(x)\frac{dy}{dx} + g(x) = F(x)$$

with the value of $y(x)$ specified at $x = a$ and $x = b$:

$$y(a) = y_a, \qquad y(b) = y_b.$$

In the program

$$f(x) \longrightarrow \mathsf{F(X)}$$
$$g(x) \longrightarrow \mathsf{G(X)}$$
$$F(x) \longrightarrow \mathsf{FR(X)}$$

and the exact solution of the equation is called FEXACT(X). The four functions F(X), G(X), FR(X), and FEXACT(X) are defined by FUNCTION subprograms. Since the coefficients of the linear equations for the unknowns form a band matrix of width three, the special SUBROUTINE subprogram introduced in Program 6.1, BAND3(N), is called to solve these simultaneous equations.

Beginner's Hints

(a) The FUNCTION subprogram differs from the SUBROUTINE subprogram in one important respect: The result of a FUNCTION subprogram is always a single number, and hence a FUNCTION subprogram can be placed on the right-hand side of an arithmetic expression. The first appearance of a FUNCTION subprogram in Program 6.2 is in the statement

$$\mathsf{A(I,1) = 1. - H/2.*F(X(I))}$$

Notice that F has not been previously defined. The computer knows that F is not a subscripted variable because it does *not* appear in a DIMENSION statement and, hence, must be a FUNCTION subprogram.

(b) In the example shown, F is the simple function

$$\mathsf{F = -14./X}$$

but F could be defined as any other function without changing the main program (Program 6.2). FUNCTION subprograms are most useful because they can be used to "read in" functions which are not yet defined at the time the main program is written or compiled.

(c) Notice that each FUNCTION subprogram is a separate FORTRAN program which must be compiled; each must have a FUNCTION statement to define the function name and its arguments. (There may be more than one argument; only the result must be single-valued.) The name of the function must appear at least once (as the variable) on the left-hand side of an arithmetic statement, e.g.,

FR = 2.*X**3

or in an input statement list. There must be at least one argument. There must be a RETURN statement, which returns control to the mainline program, and, as with all FORTRAN programs, there must be an END card which signals the computer that there are no more statements in this program.

(d) Notice that a FUNCTION subprogram can call a SUBROUTINE subprogram, and vice versa; for example, the FUNCTION FEXACT calls the SUBROUTINE subprogram BESSEL.

(e) The boundary problem of this program has the solution

$$y(x) = 2 - 2x^{7.5} \frac{J_3(.4x^{2.5})}{J_3(.4)}.$$

The Bessel functions are computed by Program 9.3, SUBROUTINE BESSEL (ARG,N,BJN,BYN,BI,BK). Notice that as the number of pivotal points is increased, the approximate solution comes closer to the exact solution, which remains practically equal to 2 up to $x \doteq .75$, and then falls sharply to zero.

(f) The rules for naming FUNCTION subprograms vary with different versions of FORTRAN. In FORTRAN IV, there are no unusual restrictions; the rules for naming functions are the same as those for naming variables. In FORTRAN II, some versions require that the name should not end in F if it is more than three letters long.

(g) Notice that the arguments in FUNCTION subprograms are dummy arguments, as they are in SUBROUTINE subprograms. Thus, the subscripted variable X(I) is used as an argument of each of the FUNCTION subprograms in Program 6.2, even though a subscripted variable may not be used as an argument of the FUNCTION statement itself.

(h) As in Program 6.1, a COMMON statement is used to link Program 6.2 and SUBROUTINE BAND3(N).

(i) When the exact solution is unknown, as is usually the case, a dummy function should be used with this program, e.g.,

FEXACT = 0.

```
C         PROGRAM 6.2
C         PROGRAM FOR SOLVING THE SECOND ORDER DIFFERENTIAL EQUATION
C         DDY + F(X)*DY + G(X)*Y = FR(X)
C         WITH Y SPECIFIED AT X = A AND X = B
C
          DIMENSION A(100,4), Y(100), EXACT(100), X(100)
          COMMON A, Y
          PUNCH 995
          READ 992, XA, YA, XB, YB
    1     READ 999, N
          PUNCH 994, N
          STRIPS = N + 1
          H = (XB - XA)/STRIPS
          X(1)= XA + H
          DO 10  I = 1, N
          A(I,1)  = 1. - H/2.*F(X(I))
          A(I,2)  =  -(2. - H*H*G(X(I)))
          A(I,3)  = 1. + H/2.*F(X(I))
          A(I,4)  =  H*H*FR(X(I))
          EXACT(I) = FEXACT(X(I))
   10     X(I + 1) = X(I) + H
          A(1,4) = A(1,4) - A(1,1)*YA
          A(1,1) = 0.
          A(N,4) = A(N,4) - A(N,3)*YB
          A(N,3) = 0.
          IF(SENSE SWITCH 2) 24,22
   22     PUNCH 998, (I, (A(I,J), J = 1,4), I = 1,N)
   24     CALL BAND3 (N)
          PUNCH 996, (I, X(I), Y(I), EXACT(I), I = 1,N)
          PUNCH 993
          GO TO 1
C
  992     FORMAT (8E10.0)
  993     FORMAT (/ 22X, 30H**************************** )
  994     FORMAT (// 20X,  31HTHE NUMBER OF PIVOTAL POINTS IS I3 )
  995     FORMAT (// 25X, 24HRESULTS FROM PROGRAM 6.2 )
  996     FORMAT ( / 16X, 1HI 5X, 4HX(I) 8X, 4HY(I) 10X, 8HEXACT(I) /
         1          (I17, F9.4, 2E16.7))
  998     FORMAT ( / 26X, 22HMATRIX OF COEFFICIENTS // 5X, 1HI 6X, 6HA(I,1)
         1          10X, 6HA(I,2) 10X, 6HA(I,3) 10X, 6HA(I,4) / (I6,4E16.7))
  999     FORMAT(I5)
          END
```

```
      FUNCTION F(X)
      F = -14./X
      RETURN
      END




      FUNCTION G(X)
      G = X**3
      RETURN
      END




      FUNCTION FR(X)
      FR = 2.*X**3
      RETURN
      END




      FUNCTION FEXACT(X)
      ARG = .4*X**2.5
      CALL BESSEL (ARG, 3, BJN, XX1, XX2, XX3)
      CALL BESSEL (.4, 3, CONS, XX1, XX2, XX3)
      FEXACT = -2.*BJN*X**7.5/CONS + 2.
      RETURN
      END




      SUBROUTINE BAND3 (N)
      DIMENSION A(100, 4), X(100)
      COMMON A, X
      M = N - 1
      DO 10 I = 2, M
      A(I,2) = A(I,2)*A(I-1,2) - A(I,1)*A(I-1,3)
      A(I,3) = A(I,3)*A(I-1,2)
   10 A(I,4) = A(I,4)*A(I-1,2) - A(I,1)*A(I-1,4)
      X(N) = (A(N,4)*A(N-1,2) - A(N,1)*A(N-1,4))/
     1       (A(N,2)*A(N-1,2) - A(N,1)*A(N-1,3))
      DO 20 I = 1, M
      J = N - I
   20 X(J) = (A(J,4) - A(J,3)*X(J+1))/A(J,2)
      RETURN
      END
```

Flow Chart 6.2

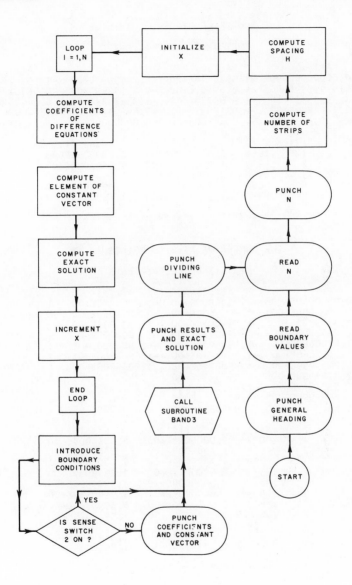

START

PUNCH
GENERAL
HEADING

READ
BOUNDARY
VALUES

READ
N

PUNCH
N

COMPUTE
NUMBER OF
STRIPS

COMPUTE
SPACING
H

INITIALIZE
X

LOOP
I = 1,N

COMPUTE
COEFFICIENTS
OF
DIFFERENCE
EQUATIONS

COMPUTE
ELEMENT OF
CONSTANT
VECTOR

COMPUTE
EXACT
SOLUTION

INCREMENT
X

END
LOOP

INTRODUCE
BOUNDARY
CONDITIONS

IS SENSE
SWITCH
2 ON ?

YES

NO

PUNCH
COEFFICIENTS
AND CONSTANT
VECTOR

CALL
SUBROUTINE
BAND3

PUNCH RESULTS
AND EXACT
SOLUTION

PUNCH
DIVIDING
LINE

RESULTS FROM PROGRAM 6.2

THE NUMBER OF PIVOTAL POINTS IS 5

MATRIX OF COEFFICIENTS

I	A(I,1)	A(I,2)	A(I,3)	A(I,4)
1	0.0000000E-99	-1.9998714E+00	-5.9999999E+00	-1.5999742E+01
2	4.4999999E+00	-1.9989712E+00	-2.4999999E+00	2.0576126E-03
3	3.3333333E+00	-1.9965278E+00	-1.3333333E+00	6.9444426E-03
4	2.7499999E+00	-1.9917696E+00	-7.4999990E-01	1.6460901E-02
5	2.3999999E+00	-1.9839250E+00	0.0000000E-99	3.2150196E-02

I	X(I)	Y(I)	EXACT(I)
1	.1666	2.0177177E+00	2.0000000E+00
2	.3333	1.9940945E+00	1.9999999E+00
3	.4999	2.0366137E+00	1.9999384E+00
4	.6666	1.9304110E+00	1.9953929E+00
5	.8333	2.3190574E+00	1.8694094E+00

****

THE NUMBER OF PIVOTAL POINTS IS 11

MATRIX OF COEFFICIENTS

I	A(I,1)	A(I,2)	A(I,3)	A(I,4)
1	0.0000000E-99	-1.9999960E+00	-5.9999998E+00	-1.5999991E+01
2	4.5000000E+00	-1.9999679E+00	-2.5000000E+00	6.4300401E-05
3	3.3333333E+00	-1.9998915E+00	-1.3333333E+00	2.1701385E-04
4	2.7500000E+00	-1.9997428E+00	-7.5000000E-01	5.1440321E-04
5	2.4000000E+00	-1.9994977E+00	-4.0000000E-01	1.0046937E-03
6	2.1666666E+00	-1.9991320E+00	-1.6666660E-01	1.7361107E-03
7	1.9999999E+00	-1.9986216E+00	1.0000000E-07	2.7568796E-03
8	1.8749999E+00	-1.9979424E+00	1.2500010E-01	4.1152257E-03
9	1.7777777E+00	-1.9970704E+00	2.2222230E-01	5.8593740E-03
10	1.6999999E+00	-1.9959813E+00	3.0000010E-01	8.0375498E-03
11	1.6363636E+00	-1.9946511E+00	0.0000000E-99	1.0697978E-02

I	X(I)	Y(I)	EXACT(I)
1	.0833	2.0000000E+00	2.0000000E+00
2	.1666	2.0000000E+00	2.0000000E+00
3	.2499	1.9999999E+00	2.0000000E+00
4	.3333	2.0000001E+00	1.9999999E+00
5	.4166	2.0000000E+00	1.9999960E+00
6	.4999	2.0000000E+00	1.9999384E+00
7	.5833	2.0000001E+00	1.9993780E+00
8	.6666	1.9994796E+00	1.9953929E+00
9	.7499	1.9916817E+00	1.9730683E+00
10	.8333	1.9294092E+00	1.8694094E+00
11	.9166	1.5774774E+00	1.4558285E+00

****

THE NUMBER OF PIVOTAL POINTS IS 23

MATRIX OF COEFFICIENTS

I	A(I,1)	A(I,2)	A(I,3)	A(I,4)
1	0.0000000E-99	-1.9999999E+00	-5.9999998E+00	-1.5999999E+01
2	4.4999999E+00	-1.9999990E+00	-2.4999999E+00	2.0093875E-06
3	3.3333332E+00	-1.9999967E+00	-1.3333332E+00	6.7816818E-06
4	2.7500001E+00	-1.9999920E+00	-7.5000010E-01	1.6075096E-05
5	2.4000001E+00	-1.9999844E+00	-4.0000010E-01	3.1396671E-05
6	2.1666667E+00	-1.9999729E+00	-1.6666670E-01	5.4253447E-05
7	2.0000001E+00	-1.9999570E+00	-1.0000000E-07	8.6152463E-05
8	1.8750000E+00	-1.9999357E+00	1.2500000E-01	1.2860076E-04
9	1.7777778E+00	-1.9999085E+00	2.2222220E-01	1.8310537E-04
10	1.7000000E+00	-1.9998745E+00	3.0000000E-01	2.5117335E-04
11	1.6363636E+00	-1.9998329E+00	3.6363640E-01	3.3431173E-04
12	1.5833333E+00	-1.9997830E+00	4.1666670E-01	4.3402754E-04
13	1.5384615E+00	-1.9997241E+00	4.6153850E-01	5.5182784E-04
14	1.5000000E+00	-1.9996554E+00	5.0000000E-01	6.8921967E-04
15	1.4666667E+00	-1.9995762E+00	5.3333330E-01	8.4771004E-04
16	1.4375000E+00	-1.9994856E+00	5.6250000E-01	1.0288060E-03
17	1.4117647E+00	-1.9993830E+00	5.8823530E-01	1.2340146E-03
18	1.3888889E+00	-1.9992676E+00	6.1111110E-01	1.4648429E-03
19	1.3684210E+00	-1.9991387E+00	6.3157900E-01	1.7227980E-03
20	1.3500000E+00	-1.9989954E+00	6.5000000E-01	2.0093866E-03
21	1.3333333E+00	-1.9988370E+00	6.6666670E-01	2.3261163E-03
22	1.3181818E+00	-1.9986628E+00	6.8181820E-01	2.6744937E-03
23	1.3043478E+00	-1.9984720E+00	0.0000000E-99	3.0560261E-03

I	X(I)	Y(I)	EXACT(I)
1	.0416	2.0000001E+00	2.0000000E+00
2	.0833	2.0000000E+00	2.0000000E+00
3	.1249	1.9999999E+00	2.0000000E+00
4	.1666	2.0000000E+00	2.0000000E+00
5	.2083	1.9999999E+00	2.0000000E+00
6	.2499	2.0000000E+00	2.0000000E+00
7	.2916	1.9999999E+00	2.0000000E+00
8	.3333	1.9999998E+00	1.9999999E+00
9	.3749	1.9999995E+00	1.9999992E+00
10	.4166	1.9999985E+00	1.9999960E+00
11	.4583	1.9999938E+00	1.9999833E+00
12	.4999	1.9999731E+00	1.9999384E+00
13	.5416	1.9998951E+00	1.9997953E+00
14	.5833	1.9996348E+00	1.9993780E+00
15	.6249	1.9988540E+00	1.9982495E+00
16	.6666	1.9967078E+00	1.9953929E+00
17	.7083	1.9912262E+00	1.9885669E+00
18	.7499	1.9780801E+00	1.9730683E+00
19	.7916	1.9482288E+00	1.9394435E+00
20	.8333	1.8836220E+00	1.8694095E+00
21	.8749	1.7496186E+00	1.7288134E+00
22	.9166	1.4820489E+00	1.4558293E+00
23	.9583	9.6576352E-01	9.4169270E-01

****

Program 6.3 solves the fourth-order boundary-value problem

$$y^{iv} - 16y = x,$$
$$y(0) = 0, \qquad y''(0) = 0, \qquad y(1) = 0, \qquad y'(1) = 0,$$

by second-order finite differences, and compares the approximate solutions with the exact solution. N is the number of pivotal points and STRIPS is the number of strips.

Because the equation contains a fourth derivative, the finite difference equations contain five pivotal values. The use of central differences requires that two additional points be considered on either side of the range of pivotal points. Thus, in the initial formulation of the equations, we consider the coefficients A(I,J) where I designates the number of the equation from 1 to N and J designates the number of the unknown from 1 to N + 4.

The DO loops ending at statement 8 set all the coefficients initially to zero; the next five statements define the five nonzero terms in the Ith equation. The right-hand side or constant vector, C(I,1), is set initially equal to xh^4. However, the first and last members of this vector are modified by the boundary conditions as follows:

(a) at $x = 0$, $h^2y''(0) = y_{-1} - 2y_0 + y_1 = 0$.

But $y(0) = y_0 = 0$, hence: $y_{-1} = -y_1$. Thus the coefficient of y_1 in the equation for I = 1 becomes

$$A(1,3) = A(1,3) - A(1,1)$$

(b) at $x = 1$, $2hy'(1) = y_{n+4} - y_{n+2} = 0$,
hence $y_{n+2} = y_{n+4}$, and the coefficient of y_{n+2} in the equation for I = N becomes

$$A(N,N+2) = A(N,N+2) + A(N,N+4)$$

We may thus reduce our system to the N unknowns B(I,J), where for each I and J,

$$B(I,J) = A(I,J+2)$$

i.e., the unknowns are shifted to the left by two, since the first and last two pivotal values are not independent unknowns, but are related to the other unknowns through the boundary conditions. The statement CALL MATINV calls a general SUBROUTINE subprogram (Program 9.7) for the solution of linear equations.

```
C       PROGRAM 6.3
C       SOLVES A FOURTH ORDER BOUNDARY VALUE PROBLEM
C
        SINH(X) = (EXPF(X) - EXPF(-X))/2.
        COSH(X) = (EXPF(X) + EXPF(-X))/2.
        DIMENSION A(22,22), C(18,1), B(18,18), EXACT(18)
        PUNCH 998
    1   READ 999, N
        STRIPS = N + 1
        H = 1./STRIPS
        X = H
        PUNCH 997, N
        DEN = SINF(2.)*COSH(2.) - COSF(2.)*SINH(2.)
        CONA = (COSH(2.)/16. - SINH(2.)/32.)/DEN
        CONB = (SINF(2.)/32. - COSF(2.)/16.)/DEN
        M = N + 4
        H4 = H**4
        DO  10   I = 1, N
        DO   8   J = 1, M
    8   A(I,J) = 0
        A(I,I) = 1.
        A(I,I + 1) = -4.
        A(I,I + 2) = (6. - 16.*H4)
        A(I,I + 3) = -4.
        A(I,I + 4) = 1.
        C(I,1) = X*H4
        EXACT(I) = CONA*SINF(2.*X) + CONB*SINH(2.*X) - X/16.
   10   X = X + H
        A(1,3) = A(1,3) - A(1,1)
        A(N,N + 2) = A(N,N + 2) + A(N,N + 4)
        DO  20   I = 1, N
        DO  20   J = 1, N
   20   B(I,J) = A(I,J + 2)
        IF (SENSE SWITCH 1)  24, 22
   22   PUNCH 996, ((I, J, B(I,J), J = 1, N), I = 1, N)
        PUNCH 995, (I, C(I,1), I = 1, N)
        GO TO 26
   24   PUNCH 993
   26   CALL MATINV (B, N, C, 1, DETERM, ID)
        PUNCH 994, (I, C(I,1), EXACT(I), I = 1, N)
        PUNCH 992
        GO TO 1
C
  992   FORMAT (/ 8X, 37H*********************************** )
  993   FORMAT (/ 12X, 29HSENSE SWITCH 1 ON, MATRIX AND / 13X, 27HCONSTANT
       2 VECTOR NOT PRINTED)
  994   FORMAT (/ 19X, 15HSOLUTION VECTOR / 10X, 1HI 7X, 4HY(I) 12X,
       2 5HEXACT / (8X, I3, 2E16.7))
  995   FORMAT (/ 19X, 15HCONSTANT VECTOR / 18X, 1HI 8X, 4HC(I) /
       2       (16X, I3, E16.7))
  996   FORMAT (/ 15X, 22HMATRIX OF COEFFICIENTS / 14X, 1HI 4X, 1HJ 8X,
       2 6HA(I,J) / (10X, 2I5, E18.7))
  997   FORMAT (// 16X, I3 15H POINT SOLUTION)
  998   FORMAT (// 14X, 24HRESULTS FROM PROGRAM 6.3 // 5X, 43HFOURTH ORDER
       2 ORDINARY DIFFERENTIAL EQUATION / 15X, 22HBOUNDARY VALUE PROBLEM)
  999   FORMAT (I5)
        END
```

(a) The IF(SENSE SWITCH 1) statement is used to control the output. If the sense switch is off, the computer goes to statement 22, and the coefficient matrix and constant vector are punched. If the sense switch is on, control goes to statement 24, and the punching of the matrix and constant vector is by-passed.

(b) The constant vector $C(I,1)$ is dimensioned as a two-dimensional variable with the second subscript 1, because in the subprogram MATINV the constant $C(I,J)$ is designed to accommodate a number M of constant vectors for the same $N \times N$ matrix. Since we have used only a single constant vector in any of the programs of this book, M was set equal to 1 in the program MATINV.

(c) Program 6.3-A uses FUNCTION subprograms to define the variable coefficients and the right-hand function of a nonhomogeneous fourth-order equation.

The boundary conditions specify the function and either its first or second derivative at either end of the interval.

Flow Chart 6.3

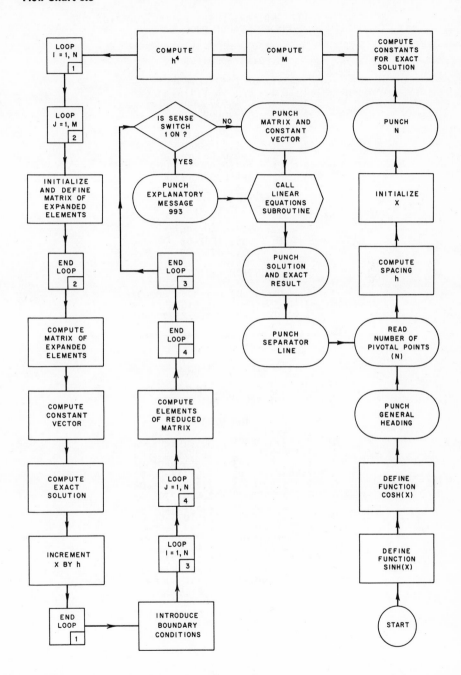

RESULTS FROM PROGRAM 6.3

FOURTH ORDER ORDINARY DIFFERENTIAL EQUATION BOUNDARY VALUE PROBLEM

3 POINT SOLUTION

MATRIX OF COEFFICIENTS

I	J	A(I,J)
1	1	4.9375000E+00
1	2	-4.0000000E+00
1	3	1.0000000E+00
2	1	-4.0000000E+00
2	2	5.9375000E+00
2	3	-4.0000000E+00
3	1	1.0000000E+00
3	2	-4.0000000E+00
3	3	6.9375000E+00

CONSTANT VECTOR

I	C(I)
1	9.7656250E-04
2	1.9531250E-03
3	2.9296875E-03

SOLUTION VECTOR

I	Y(I)	EXACT
1	2.5470273E-03	1.9711180E-03
2	3.4043535E-03	2.5107540E-03
3	2.0180286E-03	1.2721770E-03

****

15 POINT SOLUTION

SENSE SWITCH 1 ON, MATRIX AND
CONSTANT VECTOR NOT PRINTED

SOLUTION VECTOR

I	Y(I)	EXACT
1	5.6677271E-04	5.5719120E-04
2	1.1068675E-03	1.0879660E-03
3	1.5946985E-03	1.5669940E-03
4	2.0068571E-03	1.9711180E-03
5	2.3231851E-03	2.2804200E-03
6	2.5278295E-03	2.4792770E-03
7	2.6102722E-03	2.5573820E-03
8	2.5663340E-03	2.5107540E-03
9	2.3991502E-03	2.3427060E-03
10	2.1201098E-03	2.0647860E-03
11	1.7497721E-03	1.6976990E-03
12	1.3187504E-03	1.2721770E-03
13	8.6857553E-04	8.2986800E-04
14	4.5254408E-04	4.2415800E-04
15	1.3656277E-04	1.2105100E-04

****

```
C      PROGRAM 6.3-A
C      SOLVES THE GENERAL FOURTH ORDER DIFFERENTIAL EQUATION
C      D4Y + F3(X)*D3Y + F2(X)*D2Y + F1(X)*DY + F0(X)*Y = FR(X)
C      WITH THE FUNCTION AND EITHER THE 1ST OR THE 2ND DERIVATIVE
C      GIVEN AT EACH END OF THE INTERVAL (A,B)
C
       DIMENSION A(22,22), C(18,1), B(18,18), EXACT(18)
       PUNCH 998
       READ  991, NLEFT, NRIGHT, AOL, AOR, A1L, A1R, A2L, A2R
       PUNCH 990, NLEFT, NRIGHT, AOL, AOR, A1L, A1R, A2L, A2R
C
C      NLEFT (NRIGHT) = 1 IF THE 1ST DERIVATIVE IS SPECIFIED AT THAT END
C                     = 2 IF THE 2ND DERIVATIVE IS SPECIFIED AT THAT END
C      AOL, A1L, A2L (AOR, A1R, A2R) ARE THE VALUES OF THE FUNCTION AND
C                     THE 1ST AND 2ND DERIVATIVES AT THE LEFT (RIGHT) END
C
1      READ 999, N
       STRIPS = N + 1
       H = 1./STRIPS
       X = H
       PUNCH 997, N
       M = N + 4
       H2 = H*H
       H3 = H*H2
       H4 = H*H3
       DO  10   I = 1, N
       DO   8   J = 1, M
8      A(I,J) = 0.
       FO = FUNO(X)
       F1 = FUN1(X)
       F2 = FUN2(X)
       F3 = FUN3(X)
       FR = FUNR(X)
       A(I,I) = 1. - H/2.*F3
       A(I,I + 1) = -4. + H*F3 + H2*F2 - H3/2.*F1
       A(I,I + 2) = 6. - 2.*H2*F2 + H4*FO
       A(I,I + 3) = -4. - H*F3 + H2*F2 + H3/2.*F1
       A(I,I + 4) = 1. + H/2.*F3
       C(I,1) = H4*FR
       EXACT(I) = FEXACT(X)
10     X = X + H
       C(2,1) = C(2,1) - A(2,2)*AOL
       C(N - 1,1) = C(N - 1,1) - A(N - 1,N + 3)*AOR
       GO TO (12,14), NLEFT
12     A(1,3) = A(1,3) + A(1,1)
       C(1,1) = C(1,1) + 2.*H*A(1,1)*A1L - A(1,2)*AOL
       GO TO 15
14     A(1,3) = A(1,3) - A(1,1)
       C(1,1) = C(1,1) - A(1,1)*(H2*A2L + 2.*AOL) - A(1,2)*AOL
15     GO TO (16,18), NRIGHT
16     A(N,N + 2) = A(N,N + 2) + A(N,N + 4)
       C(N,1) = C(N,1) + 2.*H*A(N,N + 4)*A1R - A(N,N + 3)*AOR
       GO TO 19
18     A(N,N + 2) = A(N,N + 2) - A(N,N + 4)
       C(N,1) = C(N,1) - A(N,N + 4)*(H2*A2R + 2.*AOR) - A(N,N + 3)*AOR
19     CONTINUE
       DO  20   I = 1, N
       DO  20   J = 1, N
20     B(I,J) = A(I,J + 2)
       IF (SENSE SWITCH 1)  24, 22
```

```
 22    PUNCH 996, ((I, J, B(I,J), J = 1, N), I = 1, N)
       PUNCH 995, (I, C(I,1), I = 1, N)
 24    CALL MATINV (B, N, C, 1, DETERM, ID)
       PUNCH 994, (I, C(I,1), EXACT(I), I = 1, N)
       PUNCH 992
       GO TO 1
C
990    FORMAT ( / 13X, 7HNLEFT = I2, 9X, 8HNRIGHT = I2 / 12X, 5HAOL =
      1 F7.4, 6X, 5HAOR = F7.4 / 12X, 5HA1L = F7.4, 6X, 5HA1R = F7.4 /
      2 12X, 5HA2L = F7.4, 6X, 5HA2R = F7.4 )
991    FORMAT (2I5 / 6E10.3)
992    FORMAT (/ 8X, 37H************************************* )
994    FORMAT (/ 19X, 15HSOLUTION VECTOR / 10X, 1HI 7X, 4HY(I) 12X,
      2 5HEXACT / (8X, I3, 2E16.7))
995    FORMAT (/ 19X, 15HCONSTANT VECTOR / 18X, 1HI 8X, 4HC(I) /
      2         (16X, I3, E16.7))
996    FORMAT (/ 15X, 22HMATRIX OF COEFFICIENTS / 14X, 1HI 4X, 1HJ 8X,
      2 6HA(I,J) / (10X, 2I5, E18.7))
997    FORMAT (// 16X, I3 15H POINT SOLUTION)
998    FORMAT (// 14X, 26HRESULTS FROM PROGRAM 6.3-A//5X, 43HFOURTH ORDER
      2 ORDINARY DIFFERENTIAL EQUATION / 15X, 22HBOUNDARY VALUE PROBLEM)
999    FORMAT (I5)
       END




       FUNCTION FUNO(X)
       FUNO = 1./X**4
       RETURN
       END

       FUNCTION FUN1(X)
       FUN1 = -3./X**3
       RETURN
       END

       FUNCTION FUN2(X)
       FUN2 = 1./X**2
       RETURN
       END

       FUNCTION FUN3(X)
       FUN3 = -1./X
       RETURN
       END

       FUNCTION FUNR(X)
       FUNR = 1. + 2./X**4
       RETURN
       END

       FUNCTION FEXACT(X)
       FEXACT = 2. + X**4
       RETURN
       END
```

FOURTH ORDER ORDINARY DIFFERENTIAL EQUATION
BOUNDARY VALUE PROBLEM

NLEFT = 2   NRIGHT = 1
AOL = 2.0000   AOR = 3.0000
A1L = 0.0000   A1R = 4.0000
A2L = 0.0000   A2R = 0.0000

3 POINT SOLUTION

SOLUTION VECTOR

I	Y(I)	EXACT
1	2.6076114E+00	2.0039062E+00
2	2.6957548E+00	2.0625000E+00
3	2.6248170E+00	2.3164062E+00

****

7 POINT SOLUTION

SOLUTION VECTOR

I	Y(I)	EXACT
1	1.9938664E+00	2.0002441E+00
2	1.9956799E+00	2.0039062E+00
3	2.0131851E+00	2.0197753E+00
4	2.0595725E+00	2.0625000E+00
5	2.1538165E+00	2.1525878E+00
6	2.3206740E+00	2.3164062E+00
7	2.5906554E+00	2.5861816E+00

****

15 POINT SOLUTION

SOLUTION VECTOR

I	Y(I)	EXACT
1	1.9996735E+00	2.0000152E+00
2	1.9997927E+00	2.0002441E+00
3	2.0008650E+00	2.0012359E+00
4	2.0037533E+00	2.0039062E+00
5	2.0096936E+00	2.0095367E+00
6	2.0202942E+00	2.0197753E+00
7	2.0375332E+00	2.0366363E+00
8	2.0637587E+00	2.0625000E+00
9	2.1016864E+00	2.1001129E+00
10	2.1543994E+00	2.1525878E+00
11	2.2253475E+00	2.2234039E+00
12	2.3183471E+00	2.3164062E+00
13	2.4375811E+00	2.4358062E+00
14	2.5875973E+00	2.5861816E+00
15	2.7733104E+00	2.7724761E+00

****

Program 7.1 computes the solution of the initial-value problem

$$\frac{dy}{dx} = \frac{1}{2}(1 + x)y^2, \qquad y(0) = 1,$$

by the Euler predictor-corrector method (Sec. 7.2). At each time-step, FP and FC are the predicted and corrected values of dy/dx; YP and YC are the predicted and corrected values of y. H is the increment and XLAST is the value of x at which the program is terminated. The exact solution and the per cent error are computed at each stage.

Beginner's Hints

(a) The first statement,

F(X,Y) = .5*(1.+X)*Y*Y

is called an arithmetic statement function ; F(X,Y) is defined by a single arithmetic statement and applies only to the particular program or subprogram in which its definition appears. Some versions of FORTRAN require that the name of an arithmetic statement function be at least four letters long and end in F. With such versions the above function F would be invalid.

(b) Notice that the arguments of an arithmetic statement function are really dummy variables. Thus, while F is defined as F(X,Y), either variable may be replaced with another variable or expression; e.g., Y is replaced by YP in the statement

FC = F(X,YP)

(c) Notice that the program is terminated by the IF statement

IF (X − XLAST) 10,20,20

Thus as long as X is less than XLAST the computation continues, but if X is equal to or greater than XLAST the program stops.

Program 7.1-A generalizes Program 7.1 by means of FUNCTION subprograms and an arbitrary starting point.

```
C       PROGRAM 7.1
C       EULER PREDICTOR-CORRECTOR INTEGRATION OF DY/DX = F(X,Y)
C
        F(X,Y) = .5*(1. + X)*Y*Y
        READ 999, H, XLAST
        X = 0.
        YC = 1.
        FP = F(X,YC)
        PUNCH 998, X, FP, YC
 10     X = X + H
        YP = YC + H*FP
        FC = F(X,YP)
        YC = YC + .5*H*(FP+FC)
        YEXACT = 4./(4.-2.*X-X*X)
        ERROR = (YEXACT-YC)/YEXACT*100.
        PUNCH 997, X, YP, FC, YC, YEXACT, ERROR
        FP = FC
        IF (X - XLAST) 10,20,20
 20     PAUSE 00020
        GO TO 10
C
997     FORMAT (F7.2, 5F12.7)
998     FORMAT (// 23X, 24HRESULTS FROM PROGRAM 7.1 // 29X,
       1 12HEULER METHOD // 5X, 1HX 4X, 9HPREDICTED 5X, 6HF(X,Y) 4X,
       2 9HCORRECTED 5X, 5HEXACT 7X, 7HPERCENT / 14X, 1HY 23X, 1HY 11X,
       3 1HY 10X, 5HERROR / F7.2, 12X, F12.7, 12X, F12.7)
999     FORMAT (2F10.0)
        END
```

RESULTS FROM PROGRAM 7.1

EULER METHOD

X	PREDICTED Y	F(X,Y)	CORRECTED Y	EXACT Y	PERCENT ERROR
0.00		.5000000		1.0000000	
.10	1.0500000	.6063750	1.0553187	1.0554089	.0085464
.20	1.1159562	.7472149	1.1229981	1.1235955	.0531686
.30	1.1977195	.9324457	1.2069811	1.2084592	.1223127
.40	1.3002256	1.1834106	1.3127739	1.3157894	.2291780
.50	1.4311149	1.5360672	1.4487477	1.4545454	.3985918
.60	1.6023544	2.0540316	1.6282526	1.6393442	.6765876
.70	1.8336557	2.8579491	1.8738516	1.8957345	1.1543230
.80	2.1596465	4.1976655	2.2266323	2.2727272	2.0281756
.90	2.6463988	6.6532551	2.7691783	2.8776978	3.7710526
1.00	3.4345038	11.7958160	3.6916318	4.0000000	7.7092050
1.10	4.8712134	24.9151550	5.5271803	6.7796610	18.4740900
1.20	8.0186958	70.7294290	10.3094090	25.0000000	58.7623640

Flow Chart 7.1

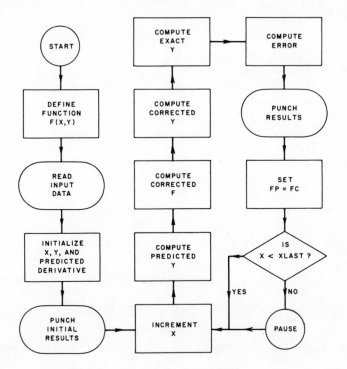

```
C       PROGRAM 7.1-A
C       EULER PREDICTOR-CORRECTOR INTEGRATION OF DY/DX = F(X,Y)
C
        READ 999, H, XLAST, X, YC
        FP = F(X,YC)
        PUNCH 998, X, FP, YC
10      X = X + H
        YP = YC + H*FP
        FC = F(X,YP)
        YC = YC + .5*H*(FP+FC)
        YEXACT = EXACT(X)
        ERROR = (YEXACT-YC)/YEXACT*100.
        PUNCH 997, X, YP, FC, YC, YEXACT, ERROR
        FP = FC
        IF (X - XLAST) 10,20,20
20      PAUSE 00020
        GO TO 10
C
997     FORMAT (F7.2, 5F12.7)
998     FORMAT (// 23X, 26HRESULTS FROM PROGRAM 7.1-A // 29X,
       1 12HEULER METHOD // 5X, 1HX 4X, 9HPREDICTED 5X, 6HF(X,Y) 4X,
       2 9HCORRECTED 5X, 5HEXACT 7X, 7HPERCENT / 14X, 1HY 23X, 1HY 11X,
       3 1HY 10X, 5HERROR / F7.2, 12X, F12.7, 12X, F12.7)
999     FORMAT (4E10.0)
        END




        FUNCTION F(X,Y)
        F = .5*(1. + X)*Y*Y
        RETURN
        END




        FUNCTION EXACT(X)
        EXACT = 4./(4.-2.*X-X*X)
        RETURN
        END
```

Program 7.2 solves the initial-value problem of Program 7.1 by a second-order Runge-Kutta method. The basic equations are (c) and (7.3.1) of Section 7.3:

$$\Delta' y_i = hf(x_i, y_i),$$

$$\overline{\Delta} y_i = hf\left(x_i + \frac{h}{2}, \; y_i + \frac{1}{2}\Delta' y_i\right),$$

$$y_{i+1} = y_i + \overline{\Delta} y_i.$$

In the program $\Delta' y_i$ is DEL1 and $\overline{\Delta} y_i$ is DEL2. The exact solution is evaluated at each step and the per cent error is shown with the results.

Beginner's Hint

Notice that an argument of an arithmetic statement function may be an expression. Thus even though F is defined as F(X,Y), the dummy variables X and Y are in fact expressions in the statement

DEL2 = H*F(X + H/2., Y + DEL1/2.)

Flow Chart 7.2

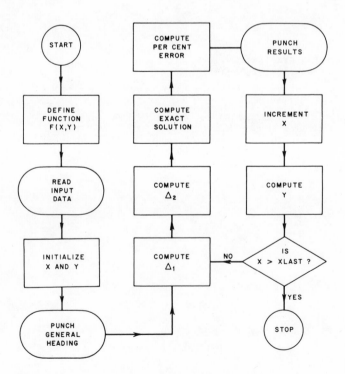

```
C       PROGRAM 7.2
C       SECOND ORDER RUNGE-KUTTA INTEGRATION OF DY/DX = F(X,Y)
C
        F(X,Y) = .5*(1. + X)*Y*Y
        READ 999, H, XLAST
        X = 0.
        Y = 1.
        PUNCH 998
   1    DEL1 = H*F(X,Y)
        DEL2 = H*F(X + H/2., Y + DEL1/2.)
        YEXACT = 4./(4. - 2.*X - X*X)
        ERROR = (YEXACT - Y)/YEXACT*100.
        PUNCH 997, X, Y, DEL1, DEL2, YEXACT, ERROR
        X = X + H
        Y = Y + DEL2
        IF (X - XLAST) 1,1,2
   2    STOP
C
997     FORMAT (F7.2, 5F12.6)
998     FORMAT (// 23X, 24HRESULTS FROM PROGRAM 7.2 // 19X, 33HA SECOND OR
       1DER RUNGE-KUTTA METHOD // 60X, 7HPERCENT / 5X, 1HX 8X, 1HY 9X,
       2 7HDELTA 1 5X, 7HDELTA 2 5X, 7HEXACT Y 6X, 5HERROR)
999     FORMAT (2F10.0)
        END
```

RESULTS FROM PROGRAM 7.2

A SECOND ORDER RUNGE-KUTTA METHOD

X	Y	DELTA 1	DELTA 2	EXACT Y	PERCENT ERROR
0.00	1.000000	.050000	.055157	1.000000	0.000000
.10	1.055157	.061234	.067787	1.055408	.023791
.20	1.122944	.075660	.084212	1.123595	.057903
.30	1.207157	.094719	.106232	1.208459	.107732
.40	1.313389	.120749	.136824	1.315789	.182377
.50	1.450213	.157733	.181201	1.454545	.297804
.60	1.631415	.212921	.249167	1.639344	.483656
.70	1.880582	.300610	.360894	1.895734	.799246
.80	2.241477	.452179	.563221	2.272727	1.375004
.90	2.804699	.747301	.984936	2.877697	2.536708
1.00	3.789635	1.436133	2.082735	4.000000	5.259125
1.10	5.872370	3.620897	6.345264	6.779661	13.382531
1.20	12.217634	16.419763	46.944378	25.000000	51.129464

Program 7.3 solves the initial-value problem of Programs 7.1 and 7.2 by a fourth-order Runge-Kutta method. The basic equations are (7.3.3):

$$\Delta' y_i = h f(x_i, y_i),$$

$$\Delta'' y_i = h f\left(x_i + \frac{h}{2}, y_i + \frac{\Delta' y_i}{2}\right),$$

$$\Delta''' y_i = h f\left(x_i + \frac{h}{2}, y_i + \frac{\Delta'' y_i}{2}\right),$$

$$\Delta^{iv} y_i = h f(x_i + h, y_i + \Delta''' y_i),$$

$$y_{i+1} = y_i + \frac{1}{6}\left(\Delta' y_i + 2\,\Delta'' y_i + 2\,\Delta''' y_i + \Delta^{iv} y_i\right).$$

The correspondence between these symbols and the floating-point variables in the program is

$$\Delta' y_i \longrightarrow \text{DEL1}$$
$$\Delta'' y_i \longrightarrow \text{DEL2}$$
$$\Delta''' y_i \longrightarrow \text{DEL3}$$
$$\Delta^{iv} y_i \longrightarrow \text{DEL4}$$
$$y_i \longrightarrow \text{Y}$$
$$x_i \longrightarrow \text{X}$$

The output includes the computed value of y_i for each x_i as well as the exact solution (**YEXACT**) and the per cent error (**ERROR**).

```
C       PROGRAM 7.3
C       FOURTH ORDER RUNGE-KUTTA INTEGRATION OF DY/DX = F(X,Y)
C
        F(X,Y) = .5*(1. + X)*Y*Y
        READ 999, H, XLAST
        X = 0.
        Y = 1.
        PUNCH 998
    1   YEXACT = 4./(4. - 2.*X - X*X)
        ERROR = (YEXACT - Y)/YEXACT*100.
        PUNCH 997, X, Y, YEXACT, ERROR
        DEL1 = H*F(X,Y)
        DEL2 = H*F(X + H/2., Y + DEL1/2.)
        DEL3 = H*F(X + H/2., Y + DEL2/2.)
        DEL4 = H*F(X + H,   Y + DEL3)
        Y = Y + (DEL1 + 2.*DEL2 + 2.*DEL3 + DEL4)/6.
        X = X + H
        IF (X - XLAST) 1,1,2
    2   STOP 00002
C
  997   FORMAT(F7.2,3F14.7)
  998   FORMAT (// 14X, 24HRESULTS FROM PROGRAM 7.3 // 10X, 33HA FOURTH OR
       1DER RUNGE-KUTTA METHOD // 41X, 7HPERCENT / 5X, 1HX, 10X, 1HY 10X,
       2 7HEXACT Y 8X, 5HERROR)
  999   FORMAT (2F10.0)
        END
```

245

RESULTS FROM PROGRAM 7.3

A FOURTH ORDER RUNGE—KUTTA METHOD

X	Y	EXACT Y	PERCENT ERROR
0.00	1.0000000	1.0000000	0.0000000
.10	1.0554089	1.0554089	0.0000000
.20	1.1235954	1.1235955	.0000089
.30	1.2084590	1.2084592	.0000165
.40	1.3157891	1.3157894	.0000228
.50	1.4545446	1.4545454	.0000550
.60	1.6393420	1.6393442	.0001342
.70	1.8957274	1.8957345	.0003745
.80	2.2727002	2.2727272	.0011880
.90	2.8775694	2.8776978	.0044619
1.00	3.9991048	4.0000000	.0223800
1.10	6.7659921	6.7796610	.2016162
1.20	22.8154340	25.0000000	8.7382640

X	Y	EXACT Y	PERCENT ERROR
0.00	1.0000000	1.0000000	0.0000000
.05	1.0262989	1.0262989	0.0000000
.10	1.0554089	1.0554089	0.0000000
.15	1.0876953	1.0876954	.0000091
.20	1.1235953	1.1235955	.0000178
.25	1.1636361	1.1636363	.0000171
.30	1.2084589	1.2084592	.0000248
.35	1.2588509	1.2588512	.0000238
.40	1.3157890	1.3157894	.0000304
.45	1.3804999	1.3805004	.0000362
.50	1.4545448	1.4545454	.0000412
.55	1.5399414	1.5399422	.0000519
.60	1.6393432	1.6393442	.0000610
.65	1.7563104	1.7563117	.0000740
.70	1.8957328	1.8957345	.0000896
.75	2.0645136	2.0645161	.0001210
.80	2.2727235	2.2727272	.0001628
.85	2.5356515	2.5356576	.0002405
.90	2.8776863	2.8776978	.0003996
.95	3.3402670	3.3402922	.0007544
1.00	3.9999327	4.0000000	.0016825
1.05	5.0154439	5.0156739	.0045856
1.10	6.7785302	6.7796610	.0166793
1.15	10.5855550	10.5960260	.0988200
1.20	24.5671360	25.0000000	1.7314560

Flow Chart 7.3

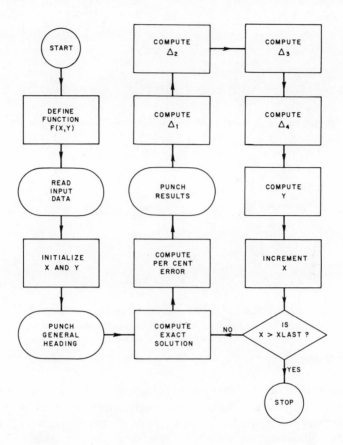

Program 7.4 solves the initial-value problem of Programs 7.1, 7.2, and 7.3 by the predictor-corrector method of Milne. The basic relations are (7.4.2) and (7.4.3):

$$y_{i+1,p} = y_{i-3} + \frac{4h}{3}\,(2f_{i-2} - f_{i-1} + 2f_i),$$

$$y_{i+1,c} = y_{i-1} + \frac{h}{3}\,(f_{i-1} + 4f_i + f_{i+1}).$$

The correspondence between these variables and those in the program is

$$y_{i+1,p} \longrightarrow \text{YP}$$
$$y_{i-3} \longrightarrow \text{Y3}$$
$$f_{i-2} \longrightarrow \text{F2}$$
$$f_{i-1} \longrightarrow \text{F1}$$
$$f_i \longrightarrow \text{F0}$$
$$f(x_i, y_{i+1,p}) \longrightarrow \text{FC}$$
$$y_{i-1} \longrightarrow \text{Y2}$$
$$Y_{i+1,c} \longrightarrow \text{Y0}$$

The output includes the predicted and corrected values of f_i and y_i at each value of x_i as well as the exact solution and the per cent error.

Beginner's Hint

Notice that the variable names for y_{i-1} and $y_{i+1,c}$ do not seem to be consistent with the other names. You might expect them to be named Y1 and YC instead of Y2 and Y0. Their names appear to be a step behind. The program makes the reason for this clear. As the calculation moves from x to $x + h$ each variable must be stepped back by one, e.g.,

$$\text{Y3} = \text{Y2}, \qquad \text{Y2} = \text{Y1}, \quad \text{etc.}$$

But the names Y2 and Y0 instead of Y1 and YC make this stepping back unnecessary for these two variables, and the program is shortened.

```
C        PROGRAM 7.4
C        PREDICTOR-CORRECTOR METHOD OF MILNE FOR DY/DX = F(X,Y)
C
         F(X,Y) = .5*(1. + X)*Y*Y
         READ 998, X, H, YO, Y1, Y2, Y3 , XLAST
         PUNCH 997
         XO = X + 3.*H
         X1 = X + 2.*H
         X2 = X +    H
         FO = F(XO,YO)
         F1 = F(X1,Y1)
         F2 = F(X2,Y2)
         PUNCH 996, X, Y3, X2, F2, Y2, X1, F1, Y1, XO, FO, YO
         X = X + 4.*H
   1     YP = Y3 + 4.*H/3.*(2.*F2 - F1 + 2.*FO)
         FC = F(X,YP)
         Y3 = Y2
         Y2 = Y1
         Y1 = YO
         YO = Y2 + H/3.*(F1 + 4.*FO + FC)
         F2 = F1
         F1 = FO
         FO = F(X,YO)
         YEXACT = 4./(4. - 2.*X - X*X)
         PUNCH 999, X, YP, FC, YO, FO, YEXACT
         X = X + H
         IF (X - XLAST) 1,1,2
   2     STOP
 996     FORMAT (F7.2, 48X, F12.6 / (F7.2, 36X, 2F12.6))
 997     FORMAT (// 23X, 24HRESULTS FROM PROGRAM 7.4 // 17X,
        1 35HPREDICTOR-CORRECTOR METHOD OF MILNE // 5X, 1HX 4X,
        2 9HPREDICTED 3X, 9HPREDICTED 3X, 9HCORRECTED 3X, 9HCORRECTED 5X,
        3 5HEXACT / 14X, 1HY 11X, 1HF 11X, 1HY 11X, 1HF 11X, 1HY)
 998     FORMAT(7F10.0)
 999     FORMAT (F7.2, 5F12.6)
         END
```

RESULTS FROM PROGRAM 7.4

PREDICTOR-CORRECTOR METHOD OF MILNE

X	PREDICTED Y	PREDICTED F	CORRECTED Y	CORRECTED F	EXACT Y
0.00					1.000000
.10				.612638	1.055408
.20				.757480	1.123595
.30				.949242	1.208459
.40	1.315504	1.211385	1.315790	1.211912	1.315789
.50	1.454014	1.585618	1.454542	1.586771	1.454545
.60	1.638277	2.147162	1.639328	2.149918	1.639344
.70	1.893377	3.047147	1.895662	3.054505	1.895734
.80	2.266807	4.624575	2.272412	4.647471	2.272727
.90	2.859912	7.770144	2.876146	7.858609	2.877697
1.00	3.929829	15.443559	3.989927	15.919523	4.000000
1.10	6.332379	42.103982	6.664169	46.631711	6.779661
1.20	14.680560	237.070720	18.640496	382.214880	25.000000

X	PREDICTED Y	PREDICTED F	CORRECTED Y	CORRECTED F	EXACT Y
0.00					1.000000
.05				.552976	1.026298
.10				.612638	1.055408
.15				.680271	1.087695
.20	1.123590	.757473	1.123595	.757480	1.123595
.25	1.163629	.846271	1.163636	.846281	1.163636
.30	1.208450	.949229	1.208459	.949243	1.208459
.35	1.258839	1.069657	1.258851	1.069677	1.258851
.40	1.315773	1.211882	1.315789	1.211911	1.315789
.45	1.380478	1.381647	1.380501	1.381692	1.380500
.50	1.454514	1.586709	1.454546	1.586778	1.454545
.55	1.539897	1.837744	1.539943	1.837855	1.539942
.60	1.639277	2.149784	1.639346	2.149964	1.639344
.65	1.756209	2.544524	1.756314	2.544826	1.756311
.70	1.895572	3.054217	1.895737	3.054747	1.895734
.75	2.064249	3.728486	2.064518	3.729458	2.064516
.80	2.272267	4.646879	2.272728	4.648764	2.272727
.85	2.534818	5.943405	2.535650	5.947310	2.535657
.90	2.876055	7.858110	2.877663	7.866899	2.877697
.95	3.336786	10.855791	3.340162	10.877767	3.340292
1.00	3.991611	15.932965	3.999512	15.996098	4.000000
1.05	4.992199	25.545104	5.013616	25.764760	5.015673
1.10	6.696927	47.091273	6.768618	48.104910	6.779661
1.15	10.169312	111.171020	10.502873	118.583610	10.596026
1.20	20.038967	441.716200	22.837876	573.725420	25.000000

Flow Chart 7.4

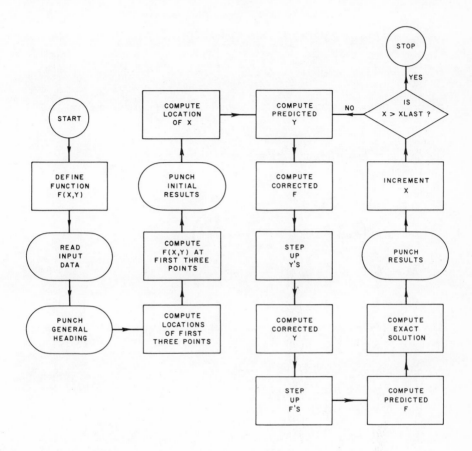

Program 7.5 integrates the initial-value problem for the two simultaneous equations

$$\frac{dy}{dx} = xyz, \qquad y(0) = \frac{1}{3},$$

$$\frac{dz}{dx} = \frac{xy}{z}, \qquad z(0) = \frac{1}{3},$$

by a second-order Runge-Kutta method. The basic relations are (7.5.1) and (7.5.2):

$$f(x, y, z) = xyz, \quad g(x, y, z) = \frac{xy}{z},$$

$$\Delta'y_i = hf(x_i, y_i, z_i),$$

$$\Delta'z_i = hg(x_i, y_i, z_i),$$

$$\overline{\Delta}y_i = hf\left(x_i + \frac{h}{2}, y_i + \frac{\Delta'y_i}{2}, z_i + \frac{\Delta'z_i}{2}\right),$$

$$\overline{\Delta}z_i = hg\left(x_i + \frac{h}{2}, y_i + \frac{\Delta'y_i}{2}, z_i + \frac{\Delta'z_i}{2}\right),$$

$$y_{i+1} = y_i + \overline{\Delta}y_i, \quad z_{i+1} = z_i + \overline{\Delta}z_i.$$

The correspondence between these variables and those in the program is

$$f(x, y, z) \longrightarrow F(X,Y,Z)$$
$$g(x, y, z) \longrightarrow G(X,Y,Z)$$
$$\Delta'y_i \longrightarrow DELY1$$
$$\Delta'z_i \longrightarrow DELZ1$$
$$\overline{\Delta}y_i \longrightarrow DELY2$$
$$\overline{\Delta}z_i \longrightarrow DELZ2$$

The output includes the computed and exact values of y_i and z_i at each x_i.

Beginner's Hint

Notice that more than one arithmetic statement function may be used in a program. The only restriction in their use requires that they appear in the program before any executable statement. (Some FORTRAN compilers also require that their names be at least four characters long, beginning with a letter and ending with an F.)

Program 7.5-A generalizes Program 7.5 by FUNCTION subprograms and an arbitrary starting point.

```
C       PROGRAM 7.5
C       SOLUTION OF SIMULTANEOUS FIRST ORDER EQUATIONS
C       BY SECOND ORDER RUNGE-KUTTA METHOD
C
        F(X, Y, Z) = X * Y * Z
        G(X, Y, Z) = X * Y/Z
        READ 999, H, XLAST
        X = 1.
        Y = 1./3.
        Z = 1.
        PUNCH 998
   1    YEXACT = 72./(7. - X * X) ** 3
        ZEXACT = 6./(7. - X * X)
        PUNCH 997, X, Y, YEXACT, Z, ZEXACT
        DELY1 = H * F(X, Y, Z)
        DELZ1 = H * G(X, Y, Z)
        DELY2 = H * F(X + H/2., Y + DELY1/2., Z + DELZ1/2.)
        DELZ2 = H * G(X + H/2., Y + DELY1/2., Z + DELZ1/2.)
        X = X + H
        Y = Y + DELY2
        Z = Z + DELZ2
        IF (X - XLAST) 1,1,2
   2    STOP
 997    FORMAT (F7.2, 4F14.7)
 998    FORMAT (// 21X, 24HRESULTS FROM PROGRAM 7.5 // 22X,
       1 22HSIMULTANEOUS EQUATIONS // 5X, 1HX 11X, 1HY 10X, 7HEXACT Y 9X,
       2 1HZ 10X, 7HEXACT Z)
 999    FORMAT (2F10.0)
        END
```

RESULTS FROM PROGRAM 7.5

SIMULTANEOUS EQUATIONS

X	Y	EXACT Y	Z	EXACT Z
1.00	.3333333	.3333333	1.0000000	1.0000000
1.10	.3706958	.3709341	1.0361475	1.0362694
1.20	.4182706	.4188978	1.0788245	1.0791366
1.30	.4796217	.4808935	1.1293360	1.1299435
1.40	.5600314	.5623942	1.1894098	1.1904761
1.50	.6675577	.6718180	1.2613729	1.2631578
1.60	.8149166	.8225903	1.3484247	1.3513513
1.70	1.0229883	1.0370675	1.4550749	1.4598540
1.80	1.3277194	1.3544686	1.5878714	1.5957446
1.90	1.7946094	1.8481337	1.7566682	1.7699115
2.00	2.5515750	2.6666666	1.9769547	2.0000000
2.10	3.8709589	4.1441284	2.2744266	2.3166023
2.20	6.4001646	7.1444901	2.6947103	2.7777777
2.30	11.9186340	14.3993920	3.3262763	3.5087719
2.40	26.3945230	37.7630820	4.3621035	4.8387096
2.50	76.5217440	170.6666600	6.2982755	8.0000000
2.60	349.1417000	5208.3333000	10.7597630	25.0000000

Flow Chart 7.5

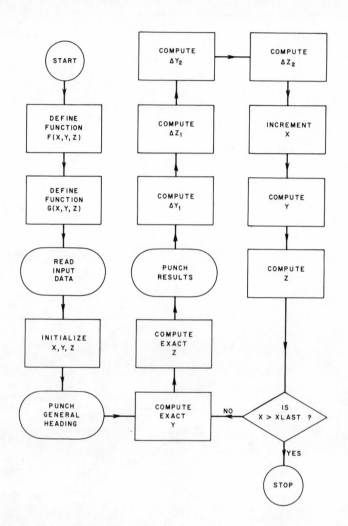

```
C      PROGRAM 7.5-A
C      SOLUTION OF SIMULTANEOUS FIRST ORDER EQUATIONS
C      BY SECOND ORDER RUNGE-KUTTA METHOD
C
       READ 999, H, XLAST, X, Y, Z
       PUNCH 998
  1    YEXACT = YSOLN(X)
       ZEXACT = ZSOLN(X)
       PUNCH 997, X, Y, YEXACT, Z, ZEXACT
       DELY1 = H * F(X, Y, Z)
       DELZ1 = H * G(X, Y, Z)
       DELY2 = H * F(X + H/2., Y + DELY1/2., Z + DELZ1/2.)
       DELZ2 = H * G(X + H/2., Y + DELY1/2., Z + DELZ1/2.)
       X = X + H
       Y = Y + DELY2
       Z = Z + DELZ2
       IF (X - XLAST) 1,1,2
  2    STOP
997    FORMAT (F7.2, 4F14.7)
998    FORMAT (// 21X, 26HRESULTS FROM PROGRAM 7.5-A // 22X,
      1 22HSIMULTANEOUS EQUATIONS // 5X, 1HX 11X, 1HY 10X, 7HEXACT Y 9X,
      2 1HZ 10X, 7HEXACT Z)
999    FORMAT (5E10.0)
       END



       FUNCTION F(X,Y,Z)
       F = X * Y * Z
       RETURN
       END



       FUNCTION G(X,Y,Z)
       G = X*Y/Z
       RETURN
       END



       FUNCTION YSOLN(X)
       YSOLN = 72./(7. - X * X) ** 3
       RETURN
       END



       FUNCTION ZSOLN(X)
       ZSOLN = 6./(7. - X * X)
       RETURN
       END
```

Program 7.6 integrates the second-order initial-value problem

$$\frac{d^2y}{dx^2} + \frac{dy}{dx} + y = c, \qquad y(0) = 1, \quad y'(0) = 0,$$

by reducing it to the two simultaneous first-order problems

$$\frac{dy}{dx} = p, \qquad\qquad y(0) = 1,$$

$$\frac{dp}{dx} = -p - y + c, \qquad p(0) = 0,$$

which are integrated by a second-order Runge-Kutta method. The basic equations and the naming of the FORTRAN variables follow closely those in Program 7.5. The results are for the case $c = 10$.

Beginner's Hint

Notice that *library subroutines* may be used on the right-hand side of an arithmetic expression without having been previously defined in the program or called from a subprogram. The library subroutines used in this program are

SQRTF,   EXPF,   COSF,   SINF

Program 7.6-A uses FUNCTION subprograms and an arbitrary starting point.

```
C       PROGRAM 7.6
C       INTEGRATION OF A SECOND-ORDER DIFFERENTIAL EQUATION
C       BY REDUCING IT TO TWO FIRST ORDER EQUATIONS
C       RUNGE-KUTTA SECOND ORDER METHOD
C
        F(X,Y,P)  =  C - Y - P
        PUNCH 998
        READ 999, H, XLAST, C, X, Y, P
        CON  =  SQRTF(3.)/2.
   1    YEXACT = (1.-C)*EXPF(-X/2.)*(COSF(CON*X) + SINF(CON*X)/(2.*CON))+C
        PEXACT =-(1.-C)*EXPF(-X/2.)*(CON + 1./(4.*CON))*SINF(CON*X)
        PUNCH 997,  X, Y, YEXACT, P, PEXACT
        DELY1   =  H * P
        DELP1   =  H * F(X, Y, P)
        DELY2   =  H * (P + DELP1/2.)
        DELP2   =  H * F(X + H/2., Y + DELY1/2., P + DELP1/2.)
        X   =  X + H
        Y   =  Y + DELY2
        P   =  P + DELP2
        IF (X - XLAST) 1,1,2
   2    STOP
C
 997    FORMAT (F7.2, 4F14.7)
 998    FORMAT (// 21X, 24HRESULTS FROM PROGRAM 7.6 ///
       1        5X, 1HX 11X, 1HY 10X, 7HEXACT Y 9X, 1HP 10X, 7HEXACT P)
 999    FORMAT (6E10.0)
        END
```

RESULTS FROM PROGRAM 7.6

X	Y	EXACT Y	P	EXACT P
0.00	1.0000000	1.0000000	0.0000000	0.0000000
.10	1.0450000	1.0435020	.8550000	.8550366
.20	1.1710000	1.1680240	1.6202250	1.6205758
.30	1.3690663	1.3646750	2.2969575	2.2978554
.40	1.6304319	1.6247180	2.8872004	2.8888345
.50	1.9465637	1.9396500	3.3935894	3.3961066
.70	2.7105098	2.7016470	4.1680001	4.1725662
.80	3.1429172	3.1333350	4.4437017	4.4493609
.90	3.5993542	3.5892310	4.6507544	4.6575092
1.00	4.0731790	4.0627000	4.7937404	4.8015643
1.10	4.5582184	4.5475650	4.8774143	4.8862561
1.20	5.0487816	5.0381330	4.9066421	4.9164278
1.30	5.5396686	5.5291970	4.8863438	4.8969818
1.40	6.0261729	6.0160390	4.8214410	4.8328239
1.50	6.5040789	6.4944330	4.7168106	4.7288195
1.60	6.9696555	6.9606340	4.5772421	4.5897492
1.70	7.4196452	7.4113700	4.4074007	4.4202723
1.80	7.8512500	7.8438260	4.2117944	4.2248938
1.90	8.2621142	8.2556290	3.9947463	4.0079363
2.00	8.6503045	8.6448310	3.7603709	3.7735163

Flow Chart 7.6

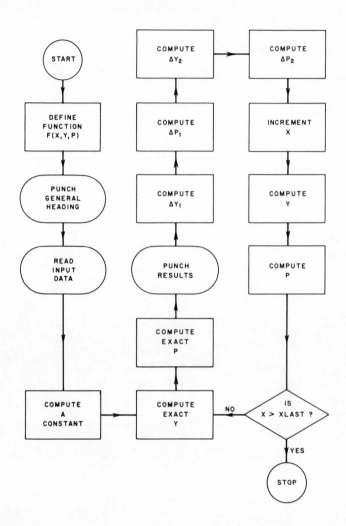

```
C       PROGRAM 7.6-A
C       INTEGRATION OF A SECOND-ORDER DIFFERENTIAL EQUATION
C       BY REDUCING IT TO TWO FIRST ORDER EQUATIONS
C       RUNGE-KUTTA SECOND ORDER METHOD
C
        PUNCH 998
        READ 999, H, XLAST, X, Y, P
   1    YEXACT = YSOLN(X)
        PEXACT = PSOLN(X)
        PUNCH 997 , X, Y, YEXACT, P, PEXACT
        DELY1  =  H * P
        DELP1  =  H * F(X, Y, P)
        DELY2  =  H * (P + DELP1/2.)
        DELP2  =  H * F(X + H/2., Y + DELY1/2., P + DELP1/2.)
        X  =  X + H
        Y  =  Y + DELY2
        P  =  P + DELP2
        IF (X - XLAST) 1,1,2
   2    STOP 00002
C
 997    FORMAT (F7.2, 4F14.7)
 998    FORMAT (// 21X, 26HRESULTS FROM PROGRAM 7.6-A ///
   1           5X, 1HX 11X, 1HY 10X, 7HEXACT Y 9X, 1HP 10X, 7HEXACT P)
 999    FORMAT (5E10.0)
        END




        FUNCTION F(X,Y,P)
        F = 10. - Y - P
        RETURN
        END




        FUNCTION YSOLN(X)
        CON  =  SQRTF(3.)/2.
        YSOLN =(1.-10.)*EXPF(-X/2.)*(COSF(CON*X)+SINF(CON*X)/(2.*CON))+10.
        RETURN
        END




        FUNCTION PSOLN(X)
        CON  =  SQRTF(3.)/2.
        PSOLN=-(1.-10.)*EXPF(-X/2.)*(CON + 1./(4.*CON))*SINF(CON*X)
        RETURN
        END
```

Program 7.7 integrates directly the second-order initial-value problem of Program 7.6 by the Milne predictor-corrector method. The basic relations are (7.6.2), (7.6.3), (7.6.4), (7.6.5), and (7.6.6):

$$y'_{i+1,p} = y'_{i-3} + \frac{4h}{3}(2f_i - f_{i-1} + 2f_{i-2}),$$

$$y_{i+1,p} = y_{i-1} + \frac{h}{3}(y'_{i-1} + 4y'_i + y'_{i+1,p}),$$

$$f_{i+1} = f(x, y_{i+1,p}, y'_{i+1,p}),$$

$$y'_{i+1,c} = y'_{i-1} + \frac{h}{3}(f_{i-1} + 4f_i + f_{i+1}),$$

$$y_{i+1,c} = y_{i-1} + \frac{h}{3}(y'_{i-1} + 4y'_i + y'_{i+1,c}).$$

The correspondence between these variables and those in the program is

$$y'_{i+1,p} \longrightarrow \mathsf{PP}$$
$$y'_{i-3} \longrightarrow \mathsf{P0}$$
$$f_i \longrightarrow \mathsf{F3}$$
$$f_{i-1} \longrightarrow \mathsf{F2}$$
$$f_{i-2} \longrightarrow \mathsf{F1}$$
$$y_{i+1,p} \longrightarrow \mathsf{YP}$$
$$y_{i-1} \longrightarrow \mathsf{Y2}$$
$$y'_{i-1} \longrightarrow \mathsf{P2}$$
$$y'_i \longrightarrow \mathsf{P3}$$
$$f_{i+1} \longrightarrow \mathsf{FP}$$
$$y'_{i+1,c} \longrightarrow \mathsf{PC}$$
$$y_{i+1,c} \longrightarrow \mathsf{YC}$$

The output includes the predicted, corrected, and exact values of y_i and y'_i at each x_i. The results shown are for the case $c = 10$.

```
C       PROGRAM 7.7
C       INTEGRATION OF A SECOND-ORDER DIFFERENTIAL EQUATION
C       DIRECTLY BY THE MILNE METHOD.           LET DY/DX = P.
C
        F(X, Y, P)  =  C - Y - P
        CON  =  SQRTF(3.)/2.
        READ 999, X, H, XLAST, C, YO, Y1, Y2, Y3, PO, P1, P2, P3
        X3 = X  - H
        X2 = X3 - H
        X1 = X2 - H
        XO = X1 - H
        PUNCH 998, XO, YO, PO, X1, Y1, P1, X2, Y2, P2, X3, Y3, P3
        F1 = F(X1, Y1, P1)
        F2 = F(X2, Y2, P2)
        F3 = F(X3, Y3, P3)
   1    PP = PO + 4. * H/3. *(2. * F3 - F2 + 2. * F1)
        YP = Y2 + H/3. * (P2 + 4. * P3 + PP)
        FP = F(X, YP, PP)
        PC = P2 + H/3. * (F2 + 4. * F3 + FP)
        YC = Y2 + H/3. * (P2 + 4. * P3 + PC)
        YEXACT = (1.-C)*EXPF(-X/2.)*(COSF(CON*X) + SINF(CON*X)/(2.*CON))+C
        PEXACT =-(1.-C)*EXPF(-X/2.)*(CON + 1./(4.*CON))*SINF(CON*X)
        PUNCH 997, X, YP, YC, YEXACT, PP, PC, PEXACT
        F1  =  F2
        F2  =  F3
        F3  =  F(X, YC, PC)
        PO  =  P1
        P1  =  P2
        P2  =  P3
        P3  =  PC
        Y2  =  Y3
        Y3  =  YC
        X = X + H
        IF (X- XLAST) 1,1,2
   2    STOP
C
 997    FORMAT (F6.2, 6F11.6)
 998    FORMAT (// 25X, 24HRESULTS FROM PROGRAM 7.7 // 26X,
       1 21HSECOND-ORDER EQUATION / 28X, 17HBY A MILNE METHOD // 24X, 1HY
       2 30X, 5HDY/DX //   4X, 1HX 4X, 62HPREDICTED  CORRECTED    EXACT
       3PREDICTED  CORRECTED    EXACT / (F6.2, 22X, F11.6, 22X, F11.6))
 999    FORMAT (8F10.0)
        END
```

Notice that any variable appearing on the right-hand side of an arithmetic statement function, which is *not* one of the arguments of the function, is *not* a *dummy* variable, but a true FORTRAN variable. Thus in the arithmetic statement function

F(X,Y,P) = C − Y − P

the variable C is not a dummy variable but has whatever value C may have when the function is used. Hence, in the statement

F3 = F(X,YC,PC)

the dummy variables Y and P are replaced by whatever values YC and PC have, but C retains whatever value it had when it was read in.

RESULTS FROM PROGRAM 7.7

SECOND—ORDER EQUATION
BY A MILNE METHOD

	Y			DY/DX		
X	PREDICTED	CORRECTED	EXACT	PREDICTED	CORRECTED	EXACT
0.00			1.000000			0.000000
.10			1.043502			.855036
.20			1.168024			1.620575
.30			1.364675			2.297855
.40	1.624719	1.624718	1.624718	2.888861	2.888832	2.888834
.50	1.939652	1.939651	1.939650	3.396133	3.396104	3.396106
.60	2.301254	2.301253	2.301253	3.822839	3.822810	3.822813
.70	2.701649	2.701648	2.701647	4.172592	4.172563	4.172566
.80	3.133334	3.133334	3.133335	4.449382	4.449355	4.449360
.90	3.589231	3.589231	3.589231	4.657532	4.657505	4.657509
1.00	4.062699	4.062698	4.062700	4.801582	4.801558	4.801564
1.10	4.547564	4.547563	4.547565	4.886275	4.886251	4.886256
1.20	5.038131	5.038131	5.038133	4.916443	4.916422	4.916427
1.30	5.529195	5.529194	5.529197	4.896997	4.896977	4.896981
1.40	6.016036	6.016036	6.016039	4.832835	4.832818	4.832823
1.50	6.494430	6.494429	6.494433	4.728832	4.728816	4.728819
1.60	6.960630	6.960630	6.960634	4.589758	4.589744	4.589749
1.70	7.411365	7.411365	7.411370	4.420282	4.420269	4.420272
1.80	7.843820	7.843820	7.843826	4.224900	4.224890	4.224893
1.90	8.255624	8.255623	8.255629	4.007944	4.007935	4.007936
2.00	8.644825	8.644825	8.644831	3.773521	3.773513	3.773516

Flow Chart 7.7

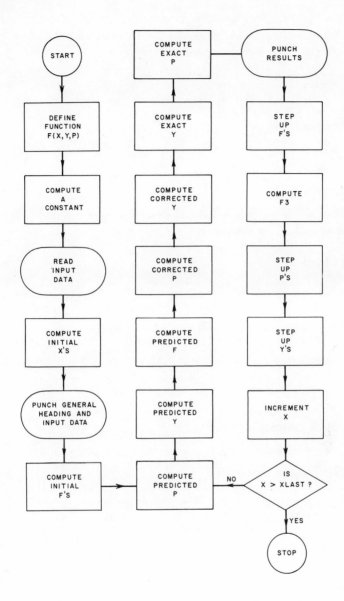

Program 7.8 integrates the second-order initial-value problem of Programs 7.6 and 7.7 by a finite difference approach (Sec. 7.6). The recurrence equation for this problem is

$$y_{i+1} = \frac{h^2 c + (2 - h^2)y_i - \left(1 - \dfrac{h}{2}\right)y_{i-1}}{1 + \dfrac{h}{2}}. \tag{a}$$

In the program,

$$y_{i+1} \longrightarrow Y$$
$$y_i \longrightarrow Y1$$
$$y_{i-1} \longrightarrow Y0$$

The results include the calculated and exact values of y_{i+1} and the percentage error at each x_i for the case $c = 10$.

Beginner's Hints

The value of y_i when $i = 1$ is computed from (a) applied at $i = 0$,

$$\left(1 + \frac{h}{2}\right)y_1 = h^2 c + (2 - h^2)y_0 - \left(1 - \frac{h}{2}\right)y_{-1}, \tag{b}$$

which, remembering that $y_0 = 1$ and $y'(0) = 0$ (i.e., $y_{-1} = y_1$) gives

$$y_1 = 1 + \frac{h^2}{2}(c - 1),$$

leading to the program statement

$$Y = 1. + H*H*(C-1.)/2.$$

for the first point.

```
C          PROGRAM 7.8
C          INTEGRATION OF A SECOND ORDER DIFFERENTIAL EQUATION
C          BY FINITE DIFFERENCES
C
           READ 999, H, XLAST, C
           X = 0.
           Y1 = 1.
           Y = 1. + H*H*(C - 1.)/2.
           CON = SQRTF(3.)/2.
           PUNCH 998, X, Y1
    1      X   = X + H
           YEXACT = (1.-C)*EXPF(-X/2.)*(COSF(CON*X) + SINF(CON*X)/(2.*CON))+C
           ERROR = (YEXACT - Y)/YEXACT*100.
           PUNCH 997, X, Y, YEXACT, ERROR
           YO = Y1
           Y1 = Y
           Y = (H*H*C +(2.-H*H)*Y1 -(1.-H/2.)*YO)/(1.+H/2.)
           IF (X - XLAST) 1,2,2
    2      STOP
C
  997      FORMAT (F7.2, 3F14.7)
  998      FORMAT (// 14X, 24HRESULTS FROM PROGRAM 7.8 /// 42X, 7HPERCENT
          1 / 5X, 1HX 11X, 1HY 10X, 7HEXACT Y 8X, 5HERROR / F7.2, 14X, F14.7)
  999      FORMAT (3E10.0)
           END
```

X	Y	EXACT Y	PERCENT ERROR
0.00		1.0000000	
.10	1.0450000	1.0435020	-.1435550
.20	1.1710000	1.1680240	-.2547892
.30	1.3690857	1.3646750	-.3232051
.40	1.6305052	1.6247180	-.3561971
.50	1.9467370	1.9396500	-.3653751
.60	2.3095492	2.3012530	-.3605079
.70	2.7110502	2.7016470	-.3480543
.80	3.1437315	3.1333350	-.3318030
.90	3.6005028	3.5892310	-.3140449
1.00	4.0747196	4.0627000	-.2958525
1.10	4.5602041	4.5475650	-.2779311
1.20	5.0512595	5.0381330	-.2605429
1.30	5.5426790	5.5291970	-.2438328
1.40	6.0297476	6.0160390	-.2278675
1.50	6.5082400	6.4944330	-.2125974
1.60	6.9744161	6.9606340	-.1980006
1.70	7.4250095	7.4113700	-.1840348
1.80	7.8572123	7.8438260	-.1706603
1.90	8.2686600	8.2556290	-.1578438
2.00	8.6574114	8.6448310	-.1455251

Flow Chart 7.8

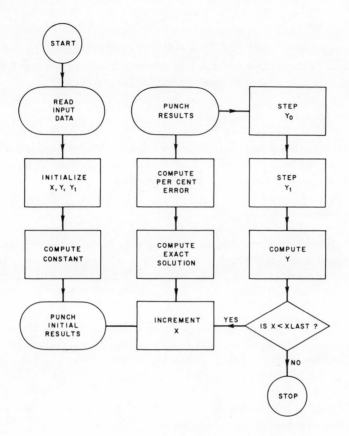

Program 8.1 computes the solution of Laplace's equation (8.3.3)

$$\frac{\partial^2 u}{\partial x^2} + \frac{\partial^2 u}{\partial y^2} = 0$$

in the interior of a square domain for given values of u on the boundary of the domain. The solution is obtained by iteration, i.e., at any point i, j the value of u_{ij} is found by averaging the four adjoining values:

$$u_{ij} = \frac{1}{4} \left(u_{i-1,j} + u_{i+1,j} + u_{i,j-1} + u_{i,j+1} \right).$$

The iteration stops when the counter reaches ITLAST, at which point the results are punched. A new value of ITLAST may then be read and the iteration continued if greater accuracy is required.

Beginner's Hints

(a) Notice that, instead of a 1, the $ sign has been used in the continuation column. Since any symbol in column 6 (except a zero or a blank) causes the statement to be continued, some programmers use a symbol like $ rather than a 1, which could be confused with a 1 in the continued statement.

(b) The A field specification in a FORMAT statement allows nonnumeric data to be given a variable name, usually for output purposes. The expression "J =" appears repeatedly in the output of Program 8.1; hence it is desirable to read this quantity in under the name EQUALJ and then simply punch the variable EQUALJ each time "J =" is required. The FORMAT specification for this variable is A3, indicating that in this case the nonnumeric data occupy three columns.

```
C       PROGRAM 8.1
C       SOLUTION OF LAPLACE-S EQUATION BY ITERATION
C
        DIMENSION U(25,25)
        PUNCH 996
        READ 999, ITLAST, N, EQUALJ
        M = N - 1
        READ 997, (U(1,J), J = 1,N), (U(N,J), J = 1,N), (U(I,1), I = 2,M),
     $            (U(I,N), I = 2,M)
        ITERA = 0
        DO 1 I = 2,M
        DO 1 J = 2,M
   1    U(I,J) = 0.
   2    DO 3 I = 2,M
        DO 3 J = 2,M
   3    U(I,J) = (U(I,J + 1) + U(I,J - 1) + U(I - 1,J) + U(I + 1,J))/4.
        ITERA = ITERA + 1
        IF ( ITERA - ITLAST) 2,5,5
   5    PUNCH 995, ITLAST, (EQUALJ, J, J = 1,N)
        DO 6 I = 1,N
   6    PUNCH 998, I, (U(I,J), J = 1,N)
        READ 999, ITLAST
        GO TO 2
C
 995    FORMAT ( // 29X, 14HSOLUTION AFTER / 29X, I2, 11H ITERATIONS //
     $            17X, 6(5X, A3, I2))
 996    FORMAT (// 24X, 24HRESULTS FROM PROGRAM 8.1 )
 997    FORMAT (8E10.0)
 998    FORMAT ( 13X, 3HI = I2, 6F10.4)
 999    FORMAT (2I5, A3)
        END
```

RESULTS FROM PROGRAM 8.1

SOLUTION AFTER
2 ITERATIONS

	J = 1	J = 2	J = 3	J = 4
I = 1	0.0000	30.0000	60.0000	90.0000
I = 2	60.0000	47.8125	53.9062	60.0000
I = 3	120.0000	83.9062	56.9531	30.0000
I = 4	180.0000	120.0000	60.0000	0.0000

SOLUTION AFTER
5 ITERATIONS

	J = 1	J = 2	J = 3	J = 4
I = 1	0.0000	30.0000	60.0000	90.0000
I = 2	60.0000	59.8095	59.9047	60.0000
I = 3	120.0000	89.9047	59.9523	30.0000
I = 4	180.0000	120.0000	60.0000	0.0000

SOLUTION AFTER
8 ITERATIONS

	J = 1	J = 2	J = 3	J = 4
I = 1	0.0000	30.0000	60.0000	90.0000
I = 2	60.0000	59.9970	59.9985	60.0000
I = 3	120.0000	89.9985	59.9992	30.0000
I = 4	180.0000	120.0000	60.0000	0.0000

SOLUTION AFTER
11 ITERATIONS

	J = 1	J = 2	J = 3	J = 4
I = 1	0.0000	30.0000	60.0000	90.0000
I = 2	60.0000	59.9999	59.9999	60.0000
I = 3	120.0000	89.9999	59.9999	30.0000
I = 4	180.0000	120.0000	60.0000	0.0000

Flow Chart 8.1

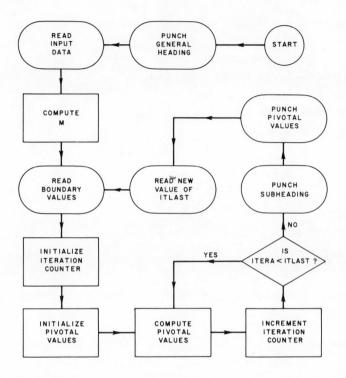

Program 8.2 computes the solution of the parabolic equation (8.4.1)

$$\kappa \frac{\partial^2 f}{\partial x^2} - \frac{\partial f}{\partial t} = 0$$

by the Bender-Schmidt recurrence equation (8.4.5)

$$f_{i,j+1} = \frac{1}{2}\left(f_{i+1,j} + f_{i-1,j}\right),$$

with the boundary conditions

$$f_1 = A, \qquad f_{n+1} = B,$$

and the initial condition

$$f_{i,0} = g_{0i} \qquad (i = 2, n).$$

The correspondence between variables is

$$f_{i,j+1} \longrightarrow \text{F1(I)}$$
$$f_{i,j} \longrightarrow \text{F0(I)}$$
$$g_{0i} \longrightarrow \text{G0(1)}$$

The process continues until the number of steps NSTEP becomes greater than NLAST.

Beginner's Hints

(a) Since only two values of i appear at each step of the integration process, the introduction of the variables F0(I), F1(I) allows them to be simply-subscripted rather than doubly-subscripted as $f_{i,j}$.

(b) Two variables with A-type format are used to introduce parentheses in the output of Program 8.2. The variable LEFT contains the two-character field, F(, while the variable RIGHT contains the one-character,) . Thus, the instruction

PUNCH n_1, LEFT, I, RIGHT

causes the output of F(I).

(c) Notice that it is possible to use either fixed-point variables (like LEFT) or floating-point variables (like RIGHT) with the A-type format. It is sometimes necessary to distinguish between these two types of variables when using a computer with variable word length, since the amount of storage assigned to a fixed-point variable may differ from that assigned to a floating-point variable.

```
C       PROGRAM 8.2
C       SOLUTION OF PARABOLIC DIFFERENTIAL EQUATION
C
        DIMENSION FO(25), F1(25)
        READ 999, N, NLAST, LEFT, RIGHT, A, B, (FO(I), I = 2,N)
        M = N + 1
        PUNCH 997, (LEFT, I, RIGHT, I = 1,M)
        NSTEP = 0
        FO(1) = A
        FO(M) = B
  1     PUNCH 998, NSTEP, (FO(I), I = 1,M)
        NSTEP = NSTEP + 1
        DO 10 I = 2,N
  10    F1(I) = (FO(I + 1) + FO(I - 1))/2.
        DO 20 I = 2,N
  20    FO(I) = F1(I)
        IF(NSTEP - NLAST) 1,1,30
  30    STOP
C
  997   FORMAT ( // 24X, 24HRESULTS FROM PROGRAM 8.2 //
      $          11X, 1HN 5X, 6(A2, I1, A1, 6X))
  998   FORMAT (7X, I5, 6F10.4)
  999   FORMAT (2I5, A2, A1/(8E10.0))
        END
```

N	F(1)	F(2)	F(3)	F(4)	F(5)	F(6)
0	-10.0000	-10.0000	-10.0000	-10.0000	-10.0000	10.0000
1	-10.0000	-10.0000	-10.0000	-10.0000	0.0000	10.0000
2	-10.0000	-10.0000	-10.0000	-5.0000	0.0000	10.0000
3	-10.0000	-10.0000	-7.5000	-5.0000	2.5000	10.0000
4	-10.0000	-8.7500	-7.5000	-2.5000	2.5000	10.0000
5	-10.0000	-8.7500	-5.6250	-2.5000	3.7500	10.0000
6	-10.0000	-7.8125	-5.6250	-.9375	3.7500	10.0000
7	-10.0000	-7.8125	-4.3750	-.9375	4.5312	10.0000
8	-10.0000	-7.1875	-4.3750	.0781	4.5312	10.0000
9	-10.0000	-7.1875	-3.5546	.0781	5.0390	10.0000
10	-10.0000	-6.7773	-3.5546	.7421	5.0390	10.0000
11	-10.0000	-6.7773	-3.0175	.7421	5.3710	10.0000
12	-10.0000	-6.5087	-3.0175	1.1767	5.3710	10.0000
13	-10.0000	-6.5087	-2.6660	1.1767	5.5883	10.0000
14	-10.0000	-6.3330	-2.6660	1.4611	5.5883	10.0000
15	-10.0000	-6.3330	-2.4359	1.4611	5.7305	10.0000
16	-10.0000	-6.2179	-2.4359	1.6473	5.7305	10.0000
17	-10.0000	-6.2179	-2.2853	1.6473	5.8236	10.0000
18	-10.0000	-6.1426	-2.2853	1.7691	5.8236	10.0000
19	-10.0000	-6.1426	-2.1867	1.7691	5.8845	10.0000
20	-10.0000	-6.0933	-2.1867	1.8489	5.8845	10.0000
21	-10.0000	-6.0933	-2.1222	1.8489	5.9244	10.0000
22	-10.0000	-6.0611	-2.1222	1.9011	5.9244	10.0000
23	-10.0000	-6.0611	-2.0799	1.9011	5.9505	10.0000
24	-10.0000	-6.0399	-2.0799	1.9352	5.9505	10.0000
25	-10.0000	-6.0399	-2.0523	1.9352	5.9676	10.0000
26	-10.0000	-6.0261	-2.0523	1.9576	5.9676	10.0000
27	-10.0000	-6.0261	-2.0342	1.9576	5.9788	10.0000
28	-10.0000	-6.0171	-2.0342	1.9722	5.9788	10.0000
29	-10.0000	-6.0171	-2.0224	1.9722	5.9861	10.0000
30	-10.0000	-6.0112	-2.0224	1.9818	5.9861	10.0000
31	-10.0000	-6.0112	-2.0146	1.9818	5.9909	10.0000
32	-10.0000	-6.0073	-2.0146	1.9881	5.9909	10.0000
33	-10.0000	-6.0073	-2.0096	1.9881	5.9940	10.0000
34	-10.0000	-6.0048	-2.0096	1.9922	5.9940	10.0000
35	-10.0000	-6.0048	-2.0062	1.9922	5.9961	10.0000
36	-10.0000	-6.0031	-2.0062	1.9949	5.9961	10.0000
37	-10.0000	-6.0031	-2.0041	1.9949	5.9974	10.0000
38	-10.0000	-6.0020	-2.0041	1.9966	5.9974	10.0000
39	-10.0000	-6.0020	-2.0026	1.9966	5.9983	10.0000
40	-10.0000	-6.0013	-2.0026	1.9978	5.9983	10.0000
41	-10.0000	-6.0013	-2.0017	1.9978	5.9989	10.0000
42	-10.0000	-6.0008	-2.0017	1.9985	5.9989	10.0000
43	-10.0000	-6.0008	-2.0011	1.9985	5.9992	10.0000
44	-10.0000	-6.0005	-2.0011	1.9990	5.9992	10.0000
45	-10.0000	-6.0005	-2.0007	1.9990	5.9995	10.0000

Flow Chart 8.2

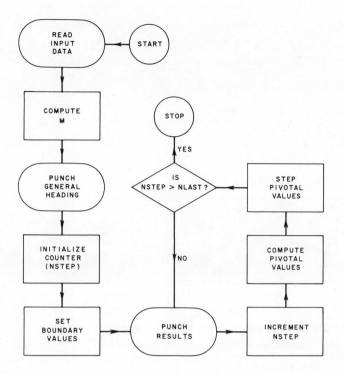

Program 8.3 computes the solution of the wave equation (8.5.1)

$$a^2 \frac{\partial^2 f}{\partial x^2} - \frac{\partial^2 f}{\partial t^2} = 0, \qquad\qquad\text{(a)}$$

using such spacings h in the x-direction and τ in the t-direction that $a^2\tau^2/h^2 = 1$. The recurrence equation for (a) becomes (8.5.3):

$$f_{i,j+1} = -f_{i,j-1} + f_{i+1,j} + f_{i-1,j}.$$

The boundary conditions are

$$f_{1,j} = f_{1,0}; \qquad f_{n,j} = f_{n,0}.$$

The initial conditions give

$$f_{i,0} = g_{0i} \qquad (i = 2, n - 1),$$

and the starting formula

$$f_{i,1} = \frac{1}{2}(f_{i+1,0} + f_{i-1,0}).$$

Beginner's Hint

The variables $f_{i,j}$ are singly-subscripted, not doubly-subscripted, because only three values of the j subscript need be considered at one time; the correspondence between $f_{i,j}$ and F is given by

$$f_{i,j+1} \longrightarrow \text{F2(I)}$$
$$f_{i,j} \longrightarrow \text{F1(I)}$$
$$f_{i,j-1} \longrightarrow \text{F0(I)}$$

```
C        PROGRAM 8.3
C        SOLUTION OF A HYPERBOLIC PARTIAL DIFFERENTIAL EQUATION
C
         DIMENSION F0(25), F1(25), F2(25)
         READ 999, N, NLAST, LEFT, RIGHT, (F0(I), I = 1,N)
         PUNCH 997, (LEFT, I, RIGHT, I = 1,N)
         M = N - 1
         F1(1) = F0(1)
         DO 1 I = 2,M
  1      F1(I) = (F0(I + 1) + F0(I - 1))/2.
         F1(N) = F0(N)
         NSTEP = 0
  2      PUNCH 998, NSTEP, (F0(I), I = 1,N)
         NSTEP = NSTEP + 1
         DO 3 I = 2,M
  3      F2(I) = -F0(I) + F1(I + 1) + F1(I - 1)
         DO 4 I = 2,M
         F0(I) = F1(I)
  4      F1(I) = F2(I)
         IF (NSTEP - NLAST) 2,2,5
  5      STOP
C
997      FORMAT ( // 24X, 24HRESULTS FROM PROGRAM 8.3 //
        $          11X, 1HN 5X, 6(A2, I1, A1, 6X))
998      FORMAT (7X, I5, 6F10.4)
999      FORMAT (2I5, A2, A1/(8E10.0))
         END
```

RESULTS FROM PROGRAM 8.3

N	F(1)	F(2)	F(3)	F(4)	F(5)
0	0.0000	3.0000	4.0000	3.0000	0.0000
1	0.0000	2.0000	3.0000	2.0000	0.0000
2	0.0000	0.0000	0.0000	0.0000	0.0000
3	0.0000	-2.0000	-3.0000	-2.0000	0.0000
4	0.0000	-3.0000	-4.0000	-3.0000	0.0000
5	0.0000	-2.0000	-3.0000	-2.0000	0.0000
6	0.0000	0.0000	0.0000	0.0000	0.0000
7	0.0000	2.0000	3.0000	2.0000	0.0000
8	0.0000	3.0000	4.0000	3.0000	0.0000
9	0.0000	2.0000	3.0000	2.0000	0.0000
10	0.0000	0.0000	0.0000	0.0000	0.0000
11	0.0000	-2.0000	-3.0000	-2.0000	0.0000
12	0.0000	-3.0000	-4.0000	-3.0000	0.0000

(ADDITIONAL)
RESULTS FROM PROGRAM 8.3

N	F(1)	F(2)	F(3)	F(4)	F(5)	F(6)
0	0.0000	15.0000	30.0000	45.0000	60.0000	30.0000
1	0.0000	15.0000	30.0000	45.0000	37.5000	30.0000
2	0.0000	15.0000	30.0000	22.5000	15.0000	30.0000
3	0.0000	15.0000	7.5000	0.0000	15.0000	30.0000
4	0.0000	-7.5000	-15.0000	0.0000	15.0000	30.0000
5	0.0000	-30.0000	-15.0000	0.0000	15.0000	30.0000
6	0.0000	-7.5000	-15.0000	0.0000	15.0000	30.0000
7	0.0000	15.0000	7.5000	0.0000	15.0000	30.0000
8	0.0000	15.0000	30.0000	22.5000	15.0000	30.0000
9	0.0000	15.0000	30.0000	45.0000	37.5000	30.0000
10	0.0000	15.0000	30.0000	45.0000	60.0000	30.0000
11	0.0000	15.0000	30.0000	45.0000	37.5000	30.0000
12	0.0000	15.0000	30.0000	22.5000	15.0000	30.0000
13	0.0000	15.0000	7.5000	0.0000	15.0000	30.0000
14	0.0000	-7.5000	-15.0000	0.0000	15.0000	30.0000
15	0.0000	-30.0000	-15.0000	0.0000	15.0000	30.0000
16	0.0000	-7.5000	-15.0000	0.0000	15.0000	30.0000
17	0.0000	15.0000	7.5000	0.0000	15.0000	30.0000
18	0.0000	15.0000	30.0000	22.5000	15.0000	30.0000
19	0.0000	15.0000	30.0000	45.0000	37.5000	30.0000
20	0.0000	15.0000	30.0000	45.0000	60.0000	30.0000
21	0.0000	15.0000	30.0000	45.0000	37.5000	30.0000
22	0.0000	15.0000	30.0000	22.5000	15.0000	30.0000
23	0.0000	15.0000	7.5000	0.0000	15.0000	30.0000
24	0.0000	-7.5000	-15.0000	0.0000	15.0000	30.0000
25	0.0000	-30.0000	-15.0000	0.0000	15.0000	30.0000
26	0.0000	-7.5000	-15.0000	0.0000	15.0000	30.0000
27	0.0000	15.0000	7.5000	0.0000	15.0000	30.0000
28	0.0000	15.0000	30.0000	22.5000	15.0000	30.0000
29	0.0000	15.0000	30.0000	45.0000	37.5000	30.0000
30	0.0000	15.0000	30.0000	45.0000	60.0000	30.0000

Flow Chart 8.3

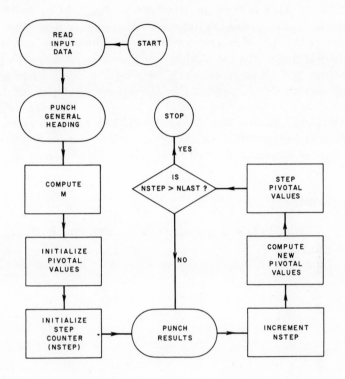

Program 8.4 computes the transverse deflections of a simply-supported rectangular plate. In the x-direction, the plate has a length of AL and N pivotal points, while in the y-direction, it has a length of BL and M pivotal points. The coefficients of the difference equations are A(I,J) and the constant vector is C(I,1). The program initially evaluates the coefficients at (N+4)(M+4) points (in the DO loops ending at statements 10 and 20). The exterior two points on each side are related to the interior points by the boundary conditions through the DO loops ending at statements 30 and 40, and the interior points are renumbered from 1 to N (in the x-direction) and from 1 to M (in the y-direction) in the DO loop ending at statement 50. The subroutine subprogram MATINV (Program 9.7) is called for the solution of the N × M simultaneous equations. The results are punched out together with the exact solution EXACT(I).

Beginner's Hint

The program could be generalized by using a FUNCTION subprogram for F(X,Y) instead of an arithmetic statement function.

```
C       PROGRAM 8.4
C       TWO DIMENSIONAL BOUNDARY VALUE PROBLEM
C       TRANSVERSE DEFLECTIONS OF RECTANGULAR PLATE
C       SINUSOIDALLY LOADED,  EQUAL SPACING
C
        DIMENSION A(18,110), B(18,18), C(18,1), EXACT(18), CX(18), CY(18)
        F(X,Y) = SINF(PI*X/AL)*SINF(PI*Y/BL)
        PI = 3.1415927
        PUNCH 995
1       READ 999, AL, BL
        CONST = (AL*BL/PI)**4/(AL*AL + BL*BL)**2
2       READ 998, N, M
        PUNCH 991, N, M
        XN = N + 1
        YM = M + 1
        HX = AL/XN
        HY = BL/YM
        H4 = HX**4
        X = HX
        Y = HY
        DO  20   I = 1, N
        DO  10   J = 1, M
        K = I + N*(J - 1)
        L1 = (N + 4)*(M + 4)
        DO   5   K1 = 1, L1
5       A(K,K1) = 0.
        L = I + 2 + (N + 4)*(J + 1)
        C(K,1) = F(X,Y)*H4
        LLL = L - 2*(N + 4)
        LL = L - N - 4
        LR = L + N + 4
        LRR = L + 2*(N + 4)
        A(K,LLL ) =    1.
        A(K,LL-1) =    2.
        A(K,LL  ) =   -8.
        A(K,LL+1) =    2.
        A(K,L-2 ) =    1.
        A(K,L-1 ) =   -8.
        A(K,L   ) =   20.
        A(K,L+1 ) =   -8.
        A(K,L+2 ) =    1.
        A(K,LR-1) =    2.
        A(K,LR  ) =   -8.
        A(K,LR+1) =    2.
        A(K,LRR ) =    1.
        CX(K) = X
        CY(K) = Y
        EXACT(K) = CONST*F(X,Y)
10      Y = Y + HY
        Y = HY
20      X = X + HX
```

```
        MAX = N*M
        IF (SENSE SWITCH 2)  24, 22
22      PUNCH 996, (I, C(I,1), I = 1, MAX)
24      IF (SENSE SWITCH 1) 26, 28
26      PUNCH 997, ((I, J, A(I,J), J = 1, L1), I = 1, L1)
28      DO  30    I = 1, N
        L1 = I + 2 + 2*(N + 4)
        A(I,L1) = A(I,L1) − A(I,I + 2)
        K1 = I + (M − 1)*N
        L1 = I + 2 + (M + 1)*(N + 4)
        L2 = I + 2 + (M + 3)*(N + 4)
30      A(K1,L1) = A(K1,L1) − A(K1,L2)
        DO  40    J = 1, M
        K1 = 1 + N*(J − 1)
        L1 = 1 + (N + 4)*(J + 1)
        L2 = 3 + (N + 4)*(J + 1)
        A(K1,L2) = A(K1,L2) − A(K1,L1)
        K1 = N + N*(J − 1)
        L1 = N + 2 + (N + 4)*(J + 1)
        L2 = N + 4 + (N + 4)*(J + 1)
40      A(K1,L1) = A(K1,L1) − A(K1,L2)
        DO  50    I = 1, N
        DO  50    J = 1, M
        K = I + N*(J − 1)
        DO  50   I1 = 1, N
        DO  50   J1 = 1, M
        K1 = I1 + N*(J1 − 1)
        L = I1 + 2 + (N + 4)*(J1 + 1)
50      B(K,K1) = A(K,L)
        IF (SENSE SWITCH 2)  54, 52
52      PUNCH 994, ((I, J, B(I,J), J = 1, MAX), I = 1, MAX)
54      CALL MATINV (B, MAX, C, 1, DETERM, ID)
        PUNCH 993, (I, CX(I), CY(I),   C(I,1), EXACT(I), I = 1, MAX)
        PUNCH 992
        IF (SENSE SWITCH 3)  1, 2
C
991     FORMAT (// 19X, 13HSOLUTION WITH / 12X, I3, 22H POINTS IN X DIRECT
       1ION / 12X, I3, 22H POINTS IN Y DIRECTION)
992     FORMAT (/ 8X, 37H************************************* /)
993     FORMAT ( / 4X, 1HI 4X, 1HX 5X, 1HY 5X,   11HAPPROXIMATE 8X, 5HEXACT
       1 / (2X, I3, 2F6.2, 2E16.7))
994     FORMAT (/ 15X, 22HMATRIX OF COEFFICIENTS / 14X, 1HI 4X, 1HJ 8X,
       1 6HA(I,J) / (10X, 2I5, E18.7))
995     FORMAT (// 14X, 24HRESULTS FROM PROGRAM 8.4 // 7X,
       1 38HTWO DIMENSIONAL BOUNDARY VALUE PROBLEM)
996     FORMAT (/ 19X, 15HCONSTANT VECTOR / 18X, 1HI 8X, 4HC(I) /
       1         (16X, I3, E16.7))
997     FORMAT (/(2I5, E16.7))
998     FORMAT (2I5)
999     FORMAT (2F10.0)
        END
```

Flow Chart 8.4

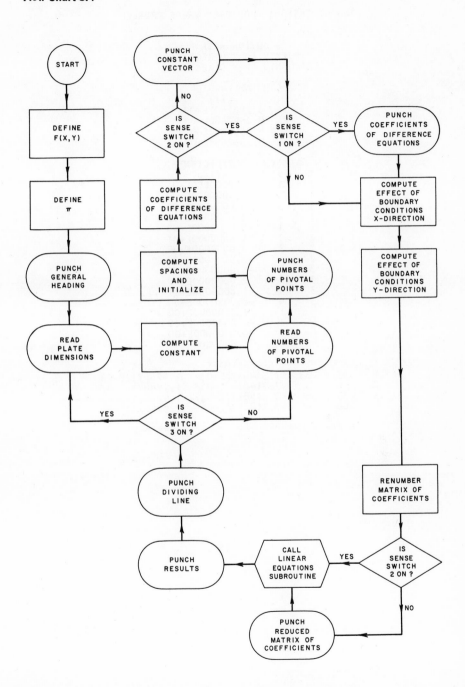

RESULTS FROM PROGRAM 8.4

TWO DIMENSIONAL BOUNDARY VALUE PROBLEM

SOLUTION WITH
2 POINTS IN X DIRECTION
2 POINTS IN Y DIRECTION

CONSTANT VECTOR

I	C(I)
1	9.2592577E-03
2	9.2592580E-03
3	9.2592580E-03
4	9.2592583E-03

MATRIX OF COEFFICIENTS

I	J	A(I,J)
1	1	1.8000000E+01
1	2	-8.0000000E+00
1	3	-8.0000000E+00
1	4	2.0000000E+00
2	1	-8.0000000E+00
2	2	1.8000000E+01
2	3	2.0000000E+00
2	4	-8.0000000E+00
3	1	-8.0000000E+00
3	2	2.0000000E+00
3	3	1.8000000E+01
3	4	-8.0000000E+00
4	1	2.0000000E+00
4	2	-8.0000000E+00
4	3	-8.0000000E+00
4	4	1.8000000E+01

I	X	Y	APPROXIMATE	EXACT
1	.33	.33	2.3148138E-03	1.9248712E-03
2	.66	.33	2.3148137E-03	1.9248712E-03
3	.33	.66	2.3148137E-03	1.9248712E-03
4	.66	.66	2.3148138E-03	1.9248713E-03

****

```
             SOLUTION WITH
         6 POINTS IN X DIRECTION
         3 POINTS IN Y DIRECTION

    I     X     Y     APPROXIMATE        EXACT
    1    .10   .10    4.9933538E-05    4.5820964E-05
    2    .20   .10    8.9977119E-05    8.2566527E-05
    3    .30   .10    1.1219961E-04    1.0295877E-04
    4    .40   .10    1.1219958E-04    1.0295877E-04
    5    .50   .10    8.9977081E-05    8.2566530E-05
    6    .60   .10    4.9933523E-05    4.5820965E-05
    7    .10   .20    7.0616677E-05    6.4800630E-05
    8    .20   .20    1.2724684E-04    1.1676670E-04
    9    .30   .20    1.5867418E-04    1.4560569E-04
   10    .40   .20    1.5867418E-04    1.4560570E-04
   11    .50   .20    1.2724682E-04    1.1676670E-04
   12    .60   .20    7.0616667E-05    6.4800632E-05
   13    .10   .30    4.9933528E-05    4.5820964E-05
   14    .20   .30    8.9977092E-05    8.2566526E-05
   15    .30   .30    1.1219958E-04    1.0295877E-04
   16    .40   .30    1.1219960E-04    1.0295877E-04
   17    .50   .30    8.9977101E-05    8.2566529E-05
   18    .60   .30    4.9933532E-05    4.5820964E-05


   *************************************
```

Program 9.1 is a SUBROUTINE subprogram (COMSQ) which computes one square root of the complex number

$$w = u + iv$$

by the formula

$$w^{1/2} = \left[\frac{(u^2 + v^2)^{1/2} + u}{2}\right]^{1/2} \pm i \left[\frac{(u^2 + v^2)^{1/2} - u}{2}\right]^{1/2}, \qquad \text{(a)}$$

where the sign of the imaginary part is positive or negative depending on whether v is positive or negative. The other root is the negative of the root computed by the program.

Beginner's Hints

(a) Whenever u is much greater in absolute value than v, (a) leads to significant loss of accuracy. In such a case, a more accurate result may be found from the formula

$$w^{1/2} = u^{1/2}(1 + iv/2u)$$

where $u^{1/2}$ is an imaginary number if u is negative; v may be positive or negative.

(b) The numbers in (a) may get very large when either u or v is large. This difficulty can be averted by dividing the entire Formula (a) by the absolute value of $u^{1/2}$ or $v^{1/2}$, whichever is greater.

```
C       PROGRAM 9.1
C       SQUARE ROOT OF A COMPLEX NUMBER
C
        SUBROUTINE COMSQ (U, V, REAL, AMAG)
        R = SQRTF (U*U + V*V)
        REAL = SQRTF ((R + U)/2.)
        AMAG = SQRTF ((R - U)/2.)
        IF(V) 20,25,25
20      AMAG = -AMAG
25      RETURN
        END
```

Flow Chart 9.1

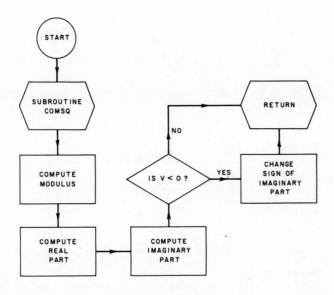

Program 9.2 writes a general heading on the output tape, reads the real and imaginary parts of a complex number from the input tape, calls Program 9.1 (COMSQ) for the computation of the square root, and writes the results on the output tape.

Flow Chart 9.2

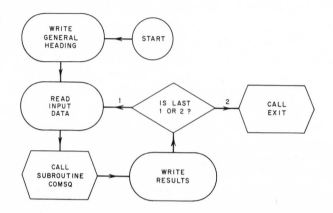

```
C         PROGRAM 9.2
C         CALLS COMPLEX SQUARE ROOT SUBROUTINE
C
          WRITE OUTPUT TAPE 6, 999
    1     READ INPUT TAPE 5, 998, U, V, LAST
          CALL COMSQ (U, V, X, Y)
          WRITE OUTPUT TAPE 6, 997, U, V, X, Y
          GO TO (1,2), LAST
    2     CALL EXIT
C
  997     FORMAT (/ 7X, 14HCOMPLEX NUMBER 2(4X, 1PE14.7)
    1            / 7X, 14HSQUARE  ROOT   2(4X, 1PE14.7))
  998     FORMAT (2F10.0)
  999     FORMAT (// 1H1 19X, 25HRESULTS FROM PROGRAM 9.2 // 28X,
    1 9HREAL PART 9X, 9HIMAGINARY)
          END
```

RESULTS FROM PROGRAM 9.2

	REAL PART	IMAGINARY
COMPLEX NUMBER	−1.0000000E+00	0.0000000E−99
SQUARE ROOT	0.0000000E−99	1.0000000E+00
COMPLEX NUMBER	3.0000000E+00	0.0000000E−99
SQUARE ROOT	1.7320508E+00	0.0000000E−99
COMPLEX NUMBER	0.0000000E−99	1.0000000E+00
SQUARE ROOT	7.0710678E−01	7.0710678E−01
COMPLEX NUMBER	0.0000000E−99	−1.0000000E+00
SQUARE ROOT	7.0710678E−01	−7.0710678E−01
COMPLEX NUMBER	1.0000000E+00	1.0000000E+00
SQUARE ROOT	1.0986840E+00	4.5508982E−01

(a) The instruction

READ INPUT TAPE 5, 998, U, V, LAST

causes the computer to read the values of U, V, and LAST (according to FORMAT statement 998) from tape number 5. This is the usual form of input when a large computer is used. A smaller computer is used to read the input cards and place their contents on the magnetic tape. For large computers this procedure is generally more efficient than to have the input cards read from the on-line reader by a READ statement. Many tapes are used in a large computer; hence, one must specify which tape is to be read at any time. In the case shown, the input data will be found on tape number 5.

(b) Similarly, it is usually more efficient to have the output of large computers written on tapes by instructions such as

WRITE OUTPUT TAPE 6, 999

and

WRITE OUTPUT TAPE 6, 997, U, V, X, Y

rather than to have it printed on-line by a PRINT statement or punched on cards on-line by a PUNCH statement. The output on tape or tapes (tape 6, in this case) is then converted into printed sheets or punched cards, or both, by a smaller computer and other auxiliary equipment.

(c) Notice that the FORMAT statements do not depend on the method of input or output. They may be the same, for example, for READ INPUT TAPE as for READ statements.

(d) The 1H1 in FORMAT statement 999 is a signal often used in connection with the printer. The digit 1 in the first column causes the printer to skip to the top of the next page before continuing to print.

(e) Some versions of FORTRAN specify that E-type numbers begin with a zero followed by the decimal point. For example, the number 9941. would appear as

0.9941E+04

if its format were E11.4. The scale factor wP moves the decimal point w places to the right. Thus for a format 1PE11.4, the number 9941. would appear as

9.9410E+03

(f) The CALL EXIT statement is used to indicate that the computation of this program is finished; the computer may then begin processing another program.

Program 9.3 computes values of the Bessel functions of the first and second kinds, $J_n(x)$ and $Y_n(x)$, and of the modified Bessel functions of the first and second kinds, $I_n(x)$ and $K_n(x)$, of integral orders n for any value of the argument x. Power series expansions are used for $x \leq n + 6$ and asymptotic expansions for $x > n + 6$.

The correspondence between the arguments of the subroutine and the mathematical variable is

$$x \longrightarrow \mathsf{X}$$
$$n \longrightarrow \mathsf{NORD}$$
$$J_n(x) \longrightarrow \mathsf{BJN}$$
$$Y_n(x) \longrightarrow \mathsf{BY}$$
$$I_n(x) \longrightarrow \mathsf{BIN}$$
$$K_n(x) \longrightarrow \mathsf{BK}$$

For small x, the values of $J_0(x)$ and $I_0(x)$ are computed first in a subroutine, by power series. The values of $Y_0(x)$ and $K_0(x)$ are then computed in a subroutine from power series involving $J_0(x)$ and $I_0(x)$. When the results for $n = 0$ are desired, these results are returned to the mainline program. $J_1(x)$ and $I_1(x)$ are next computed by power series, and $Y_1(x)$ and $K_1(x)$ by Wronskian formulas in subroutines. These results are returned to the main program when $n = 1$ is considered. For $n > 1$, the program computes $Y_n(x)$ and $K_n(x)$ for increasing n from $Y_{n-1}(x)$, $Y_{n-2}(x)$, $K_{n-1}(x)$, and $K_{n-2}(x)$ by recurrence relations until the desired n is reached. The program then computes in subroutines $J_n(x)$ and $I_n(x)$ by power series, and returns these results to the calling program. The recurrence relations are not used to compute $J_n(x)$ and $I_n(x)$ for high orders n, because there is significant loss of accuracy for high values of n; for $x \leq n + 6$ these functions are computed by power series for all orders n. For $x > n + 6$, asymptotic expansions are used to compute simultaneously all four functions $J_n(x)$, $I_n(x)$, $Y_n(x)$, $K_n(x)$. The number of terms used in the asymptotic expansions is

$$m = x + 1 + (x^2 + n^2)^{1/2},$$

unless earlier terms in the series do not affect the results, in which case a test terminates the process.

(a) The program computes $I_n(x)$ together with $J_n(x)$, because their power series are the same except for an alternating sign.

(b) The test for terminating the power series for $J_n(x)$ and $I_n(x)$ is

IF((BJN + T) − BJN) 25,50,25

which stops the calculation as soon as T no longer affects the value of BJN, i.e., as soon as the last calculated term in the series doesn't change any of the significant figures in the answer. This is a more logical and less restrictive test than

IF(T)25,50,25

which terminates the calculation only when T reaches zero, i.e., is smaller than 10^{-99} on many computers. A test to terminate a calculation when a single floating-point variable reaches zero is a poor test. It is more practical to use in the test a difference between terms of like magnitude.

(c) Either one of the statements

DO   30 K = 1, K

or

DO 110 K = 2, K

causes endless looping since the index (K) can never exceed its terminal value (which is also K). The loop is broken only by an IF statement, e.g.

IF ((BJN + T) − BJN) 25,50,25

This artifice succeeds only in those versions of FORTRAN where the index K and the terminal value K occupy the same memory location; in other versions of FORTRAN the terminal value K must be replaced by some large integer.

```
C        PROGRAM 9.3
C        SUBROUTINE FOR COMPUTING  J-N, Y-N, I-N, AND K-N
C        ASYMPTOTIC EXPANSION IS USED FOR LARGE ARGUMENT
C
         SUBROUTINE BESSEL (X, NORD, BJN, BY, BIN, BK)
         PI  = 3.1415927
         GAM =  .57721566
C
         FN = NORD
         IF(X - FN - 6.) 1,200,200
       1 XA = X/2.
         XB = XA*XA
C
C        COMPUTATION OF J-ZERO AND I-ZERO
C
         N = 0
C
C        COMPUTATION OF J-N AND I-N BY POWER SERIES
C
       3 AN = N
         T = 1.
         S = -1.
      10 IF(AN) 9999,20,12
      12 T = T*XA/AN
         AN = AN - 1.
         GO TO 10
      20 BJN = T
         BIN = T
         DO 30 K = 1,K
         DEN = K*(K + N)
         T = T*XB/DEN
         IF((BJN + T) - BJN)  25,50,25
      25 BJN = BJN + T*S
         BIN = BIN + T
      30 S = -S
C
C
C
      50 IF(N - 1) 75,130,55
C
C        K-N IS COMPUTED FROM ASYMPTOTIC EXPANSION
C        IF X IS GREATER THAN N + 3
C
      55 IF(X - FN - 3.) 1111,1111,200
C
C        CALCULATION OF J-1 AND I-1
C
      65 N = 1
         BJO = BJN
         BIO = BIN
         BYO = BY
         BKO = BK
         GO TO 3
C
```

```
C      COMPUTATION OF K-ZERO AND Y-ZERO
C
   75 BY = 2./PI*(GAM + LOGF(XA))*BJN
      BK =        -(GAM + LOGF(XA))*BIN
      T = XB
      S = 1.
      XI = 1.
      DO 110 K = 2,K
      AK = K
      IF((BY + T*XI) - BY) 100,120,100
  100 BK = BK + T*XI
      BY = BY + 2./PI*S*T*XI
      T = T*XB/(AK*AK)
      XI = XI + 1./AK
  110 S = -S
C
C
  120 IF(NORD) 9999,55,65
C
C      COMPUTATION OF Y-1 AND K-1 BY WRONSKIAN FORMULAS
C
  130 BY  = (BJN*BYO- 2./(PI*X))/BJO
      BK  = (1./X - BIN*BKO)/BIO
C
C      Y-N AND K-N BY RECURSION FORMULAS FOR ORDERS HIGHER THAN ONE
C
      P = 1.
      IF(NORD - 1) 9999,55,140
  140 BY1 = BY
      BK1 = BK
      BY  =  2.*P/X*BY1 - BYO
      BK  =  2.*P/X*BK1 + BKO
C
      P = P + 1.
C
      IF(NORD -2) 9999,150,146
  146 BYO = BY1
      BKO = BK1
      NORD = NORD - 1
      GO TO 140
C
  150 N = P
      GO TO 3
C
```

```
C       COMPUTATION OF J-N, I-N, K-N, AND Y-N BY ASYMPTOTIC EXPANSIONS
C
  200 C = 4*NORD*NORD
      D = 8.*X
      CON1 = SQRTF(2./(PI*X))
      CON2 = 1./SQRTF(2.*PI*X)
      CON3 = SQRTF(PI/(2.*X))
      AN = NORD
      PHI = X - (2.*AN + 1.)/4.*PI
      M = X + 1. + SQRTF(X*X + AN*AN)
      T = (C - 1.)/D
      S = 1.
      U = 1.
      PN = 1.
      QN = T
      BK = 1. + T
      BI = 1. - T
C
      DO 240 I = 2,M
      AI = I
      T = (C - (2.*AI - 1.)**2)/D*T/AI
      BK = BK + T
      BI = BI + T*S
      IF(S) 220,9999,210
  210 PN = PN - T*S*U
      U = - U
      GO TO 230
  220 QN = QN - T*S*U
      IF((QN + T) - QN) 230,241,230
  230 S = -S
  240 CONTINUE
  241 BK  = EXPF(-X)*CON3*BK
C
C       ASYMPTOTIC EXPANSION IS USED ONLY FOR K-N
C       IF X IS BETWEEN N + 3 AND N + 6
C
      IF(X - FN - 6.) 1111,250,250
  250 BJN = CON1*(PN*COSF(PHI) - QN*SINF(PHI))
      BY  = CON1*(PN*SINF(PHI) + QN*COSF(PHI))
      BIN = EXPF( X)*CON2*BI
C
 1111 NORD = FN
      RETURN
C
 9999 STOP
C
      END
```

Flow Chart 9.3

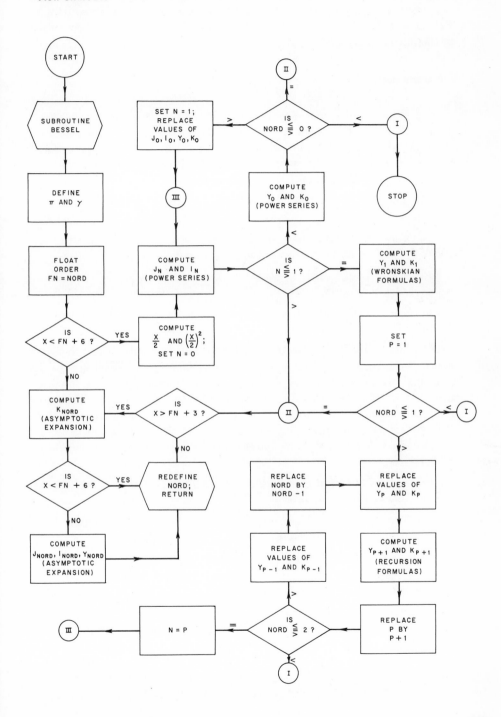

Program 9.4 writes a general heading on the output tape, reads the order and argument of the Bessel functions from the input tape, calls Program 9.3 (BESSEL) for the computation of the Bessel functions, and writes the results on the output tape.

Beginner's Hints

(a) When a program is to be run under the control of a computer system, there must be some means of giving instructions to the system. The IBM Monitor system, for example, uses control cards for this purpose. A control card is identified by an * in the first column. The typical control cards shown with Program 9.4 are explained below.

(b) The * DATE card is used to indicate the date when the program was run.

(c) The * I.D. card is used to identify the job. It usually contains the title of the project and the name of the programmer.

(d) The * PAUSE card causes the computer to halt, e.g., to obtain a pause for tape mounting.

(e) The * XEQ card will cause the system to execute the program, provided it is successfully compiled.

(f) The * CHAIN (1,A4) card indicates to the system that this program (and its subprograms) is only one "link" in a "chain job." A job (or link) is one mainline program together with all its subprograms. A chain job is a succession of jobs, each called a link, to be executed sequentially. The two numbers in the parentheses (1,A4) indicate respectively the number of the link and the tape on which that link is to be stored. A chain job is often used to break a job that is too large (for the computer's memory) into smaller jobs.

(g) The * PACK card causes the output to be written in a condensed format ("packed") on the tape.

(h) The * LIST8 card causes the machine-language coding of the program to be included in the listing.

(i) The * SYMBOL TABLE card causes a list of all the symbols (and their addresses) used in the program to be placed on cards immediately before the object program. The symbol table is useful in "debugging" procedures.

(j) The * LABEL card causes the binary object deck to be numbered and labeled with the program name. For a mainline program this name is obtained from the first six characters following the C on a comment card which follows the control cards. It may be seen that this program will be labeled "P94". It is advisable to limit the program label to three characters when the * SYMBOL TABLE card is used, because the symbol table is labeled

"ST" following the program name. Thus, if this program had a symbol table of three cards, the object deck would be numbered

P94 ST00
P94 ST01
P94 ST02
P9400000
P9400001

. . . .

The numbering would then continue sequentially throughout the rest of the object deck.

(k) It is usual practice to have all source decks, which are being compiled for the first time, preceded by the * LIST8, * SYMBOL TABLE, and * LABEL cards. The order of their appearance is immaterial.

(l) The * DATA card indicates the end of the symbolic and source decks and is followed by the data for all the jobs.

(m) The CALL CHAIN (2,A4) statement tells the monitor system to transfer control to the link in the chain that is identified by CHAIN (2,A4). No such link is shown here; in fact CHAIN (1,A4) is incomplete as shown. The coding of the subprogram BESSEL must be included in the link, and the * DATA card and the data must follow the physically last link in the chain.

```
*       DATE 3/29/64
*       PROGRAM 9.4       MC CORMICK-SALVADORI
*       PAUSE
*       XEQ
*       CHAIN(1,A4)
*       PACK
*       LIST8
*       SYMBOL TABLE
*       LABEL
CP94
C       CALLS BESSEL FUNCTION SUBROUTINE
C
        WRITE OUTPUT TAPE 6, 999
    1   READ INPUT TAPE 5, 998, X, N, LAST
        CALL BESSEL (X, N, BJ, Y, BI, BK)
        WRITE OUTPUT TAPE 6, 997, X, N, BJ, Y, BI, BK
        GO TO (1,2), LAST
    2   CALL CHAIN (2,A4)
C
997     FORMAT (F8.2, I4, 4(3X, 1PE12.5))
998     FORMAT (E10.0, 2I5)
999     FORMAT (// 25X, 25HRESULTS FROM PROGRAM 9.4 // 29X,
    1   16HBESSEL FUNCTIONS //5X, 1HX, 5X, 1HN, 6X, 6HJ(N,X) 9X, 6HY(N,X)
    2   9X, 6HI(N,X) 9X, 6HK(N,X) /)
        END


*       DATA
         1.    0   1
         4.    0   1
         7.    0   1
        10.    0   1
         1.    1   1
        11.    1   1
         .5    2   1
        13.    2   1
         2.    5   2
```

Flow Chart 9.4

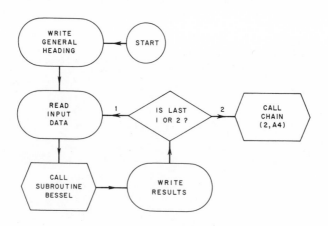

RESULTS FROM PROGRAM 9.4

BESSEL FUNCTIONS

X	N	J(N,X)	Y(N,X)	I(N,X)	K(N,X)
1.00	0	7.65197E-01	8.82569E-02	1.26606E-00	4.21024E-01
4.00	0	-3.97149E-01	-1.69408E-02	1.13019E+01	1.11591E-02
7.00	0	3.00079E-01	-2.59496E-02	1.68593E+02	4.24795E-04
10.00	0	-2.45935E-01	5.56711E-02	2.81571E+03	1.77800E-05
1.00	1	4.40050E-01	-7.81212E-01	5.65159E-01	6.01907E-01
11.00	1	-1.76785E-01	1.63705E-01	6.94885E+03	6.52086E-06
.50	2	3.06040E-02	-5.44137E-00	3.19061E-02	7.55018E-00
13.00	2	-2.17744E-01	4.58874E-02	4.21363E+04	9.02740E-07
2.00	5	7.03962E-03	-9.93599E-00	9.82567E-03	9.43104E-00

Program 9.5 is a subroutine subprogram which solves a system of linear simultaneous equations whose coeff.cients and constant vector may be complex:

$$\sum_{j=1}^{N} (\mathrm{Re}\, a_{ij} + \mathrm{Im}\, a_{ij})(\mathrm{Re}\, x_j + \mathrm{Im}\, x_j) = \mathrm{Re}\, y_i + \mathrm{Im}\, y_i$$
$$(i = 1, 2, \ldots, N).$$

The matrix of the real parts of the coeff.cients is represented by AR(I,J), the matrix of the imaginary parts by AI(I,J). The real and imaginary parts of the constant vector are designated by YR and YI, respectively, while the real and imaginary parts of the solution vector are XR and XI, respectively. The program uses the subroutine subprogram MATINV (Program 9.7) twice to invert matrices.

Flow Chart 9.5

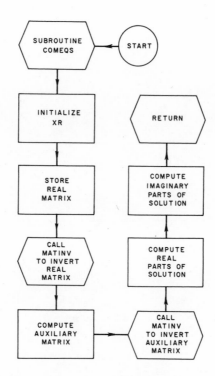

```
*       PROGRAM 9.5
*       PAUSE
*       CHAIN(1,A4)
*       LABEL
*       PACK
*       LIST8
*       SYMBOL TABLE
        SUBROUTINE COMEQS (N, AR, AI, YR, YI, XR, XI)
C       PROGRAM 9.5
C       SOLUTION OF COMPLEX SIMULTANEOUS EQUATIONS
C       A(I,J)*X(J,1) = Y(I,1)
        DIMENSION AR(54,54), AI(54,54), ARI(54,54),
     1  XR(54,1), XI(54,1), YR(54,1), YI(54,1)
        DO  10    I = 1, N
        XR(I,1) = 0.
        DO  10    J = 1, N
   10 ARI(I,J) = AR(I,J)
        CALL MATINV (ARI, N, XR, 1, DETERM, ID)
        DO  20    I = 1, N
        DO  20    J = 1, N
        DO  20    L = 1, N
        DO  20    K = 1, N
   20 AR(I,J) = AR(I,J) + AI(I,L)*ARI(L,K)*AI(K,J)
        CALL MATINV (AR, N, XR, 1, DETERM, ID)
        DO  30    L = 1, N
        XR(L,1) = 0.
        DO  30    I = 1, N
        XR(L,1) = XR(L,1) + AR(L,I)*YR(I,1)
        DO  30    K = 1, N
        DO  30    M = 1, N
   30 XR(L,1) = XR(L,1) + AR(L,I)*AI(I,M)*ARI(M,K)*YI(K,1)
        DO  40    L = 1, N
        XI(L,1) = 0.
        DO  40    K = 1, N
        XI(L,1) = XI(L,1) + ARI(L,K)*YI(K,1)
        DO  40    J = 1, N
   40 XI(L,1) = XI(L,1) - ARI(L,K)*AI(K,J)*XR(J,1)
        RETURN
        END
```

Program 9.6 reads the matrices of the complex coefficients and the complex constant vector of a complex system of simultaneous linear equations, calls the subroutine subprogram COMEQS (Program 9.5) to solve the complex linear equations, computes a check vector by substituting the solution vector into the original equations, and punches the matrices, the constant vector, the solution vector, and the check vector.

Beginner's Hint

Notice that the program sets the matrices BR and BI equal to AR and AI, respectively, then calls COMEQS with arguments including BR and BI. This is done because COMEQS changes the original values of BR and BI during the computation and returns to the calling program with these changed values, which, therefore, cannot be used in evaluating the check vector. The check vector can be evaluated because the original values of the coefficients in AR and AI were saved in memory.

Flow Chart 9.6

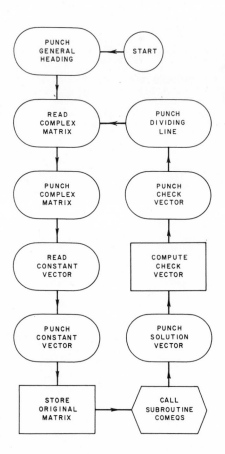

```
C       PROGRAM 9.6
C       CALLS SUBROUTINE FOR SOLUTION OF COMPLEX SIMULTANEOUS EQUATIONS
C
        DIMENSION AR(18,18), AI(18,18), BR(18,18), BI(18,18), YR(18,1),
       1         YI(18,1), XR(18,1), XI(18,1)
        PUNCH 999
   1    READ 998, N, ((AR(I,J), AI(I,J), I = 1, N), J = 1, N)
        PUNCH 997, N, ((J, I, AR(I,J), AI(I,J), I = 1, N), J = 1, N)
        READ 996, (YR(I,1), YI(I,1), I = 1, N)
        PUNCH 995, (I, YR(I,1), YI(I,1), I = 1, N)
        DO 10   I = 1, N
        DO 10   J = 1, N
        BR(I,J) = AR(I,J)
  10    BI(I,J) = AI(I,J)
        CALL COMEQS (N, BR, BI, YR, YI, XR, XI)
        PUNCH 994, (I, XR(I,1), XI(I,1), I = 1, N)
        DO 20   I = 1, N
        YR(I,1) = 0.
        YI(I,1) = 0.
        DO 20   J = 1, N
        YR(I,1) = YR(I,1) + AR(I,J)*XR(J,1) - AI(I,J)*XI(J,1)
  20    YI(I,1) = YI(I,1) + AR(I,J)*XI(J,1) + AI(I,J)*XR(J,1)
        PUNCH 993, (I, YR(I,1), YI(I,1), I = 1, N)
        PUNCH 992
        GO TO 1
C
 992    FORMAT (/ 46H*********************************************** /)
 993    FORMAT (// 17X, 12HCHECK VECTOR // 6X, 3HROW 5X, 9HREAL PART 8X,
       1 9HIMAGINARY / (I8, 2E17.7))
 994    FORMAT (// 16X, 15HSOLUTION VECTOR // 6X, 3HROW 5X, 9HREAL PART
       1 8X, 9HIMAGINARY / (I8, 2E17.7))
 995    FORMAT (// 16X, 15HCONSTANT VECTOR // 6X, 3HROW 5X, 9HREAL PART
       1 8X, 9HIMAGINARY / (I8, 2E17.7))
 996    FORMAT (8F10.0)
 997    FORMAT (// 15X, 15HMATRIX OF ORDER I2 // 3X, 3HCOL 2X, 3HROW 5X,
       1 9HREAL PART 8X, 9HIMAGINARY / (2I5, 2E17.7))
 998    FORMAT (I5 / (8F10.0))
 999    FORMAT (// 11X, 24HRESULTS FROM PROGRAM 9.6
       1          // 11X, 24HCOMPLEX LINEAR EQUATIONS)
        END
```

RESULTS FROM PROGRAM 9.6

COMPLEX LINEAR EQUATIONS

MATRIX OF ORDER 3

COL	ROW	REAL PART	IMAGINARY
1	1	0.0000000E-99	1.0000000E+00
1	2	0.0000000E-99	2.0000000E+00
1	3	3.0000000E+00	0.0000000E-99
2	1	2.0000000E+00	0.0000000E-99
2	2	1.0000000E+00	0.0000000E-99
2	3	2.0000000E+00	0.0000000E-99
3	1	2.0000000E+00	0.0000000E-99
3	2	0.0000000E-99	1.0000000E+00
3	3	2.0000000E+00	0.0000000E-99

CONSTANT VECTOR

ROW	REAL PART	IMAGINARY
1	-1.0000000E+00	8.0000000E+00
2	1.0000000E+00	6.0000000E+00
3	0.0000000E-99	7.0000000E+00

SOLUTION VECTOR

ROW	REAL PART	IMAGINARY
1	4.0000003E-01	-2.0000000E-01
2	-7.0000000E-01	5.0999999E+00
3	1.0000010E-01	-1.2999999E+00

CHECK VECTOR

ROW	REAL PART	IMAGINARY
1	-9.9999980E-01	8.0000000E+00
2	9.9999990E-01	6.0000000E+00
3	2.0000000E-07	6.9999992E+00

****

Program 9.7 is a subprogram for inverting a matrix or solving a system of simultaneous linear equations by the Gauss-Jordan method. At each stage the largest element of the submatrix under consideration is found, rows and columns are interchanged to make this the pivot element, and all elements are divided by it.*

* The authors are indebted to Mrs. Sharon Good of the David Taylor Model Basin for permission to publish this program.

Beginner's Hint

The program has been designed to accept a number, say M, of constant vectors for a matrix of given order, say N. The constant vector is thus designated as a two-dimensional variable $B(N,M)$. In this program M has been set equal to unity since none of the programs in this book requires more than a single constant vector for a given matrix. Accordingly, the constant vectors used as arguments of MATINV are always of the form $Y(I,1)$.

Flow Chart 9.7

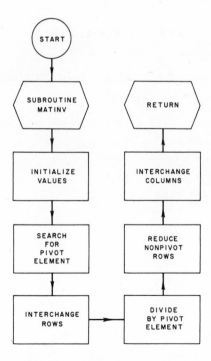

```
C       PROGRAM 9.7
        SUBROUTINE MATINV(A,N1,B,M1,DETERM,ID)
C       MATRIX INVERSION WITH ACCOMPANYING SOLUTION OF LINEAR EQUATIONS
C
C
C       GENERAL FORM OF DIMENSION STATEMENT
C       DIMENSION    A(  ,  ),B(  ,  ),INDEX(  ,3)
C
        DIMENSION  A(18,18), B(18,1), INDEX(18,3)
        EQUIVALENCE (IROW,JROW), (ICOLUM,JCOLUM), (AMAX, T, SWAP)
C
C       INITIALIZATION
C
        M=M1
        N=N1
     10 DETERM=1.0
     15 DO 20 J=1,N
     20 INDEX(J,3) = 0
     30 DO 550 I=1,N
C
C       SEARCH FOR PIVOT ELEMENT
C
     40 AMAX=0.0
     45 DO 105 J=1,N
        IF(INDEX(J,3)-1) 60, 105, 60
     60 DO 100 K=1,N
        IF(INDEX(K,3)-1) 80, 100, 715
     80 IF (AMAX - ABSF(A(J,K))) 85, 100, 100
     85 IROW=J
     90 ICOLUM=K
        AMAX = ABSF(A(J,K))
    100 CONTINUE
    105 CONTINUE
        INDEX(ICOLUM,3) = INDEX(ICOLUM,3) +1
    260 INDEX(I,1)=IROW
    270 INDEX(I,2)=ICOLUM
C
C       INTERCHANGE ROWS TO PUT PIVOT ELEMENT ON DIAGONAL
C
    130 IF (IROW-ICOLUM) 140, 310, 140
    140 DETERM=-DETERM
    150 DO 200 L=1,N
    160 SWAP=A(IROW,L)
    170 A(IROW,L)=A(ICOLUM,L)
    200 A(ICOLUM,L)=SWAP
        IF(M) 310, 310, 210
    210 DO 250 L=1, M
    220 SWAP=B(IROW,L)
    230 B(IROW,L)=B(ICOLUM,L)
    250 B(ICOLUM,L)=SWAP
```

```
C
C      DIVIDE PIVOT ROW BY PIVOT ELEMENT
C
 310  PIVOT    =A(ICOLUM,ICOLUM)
      DETERM=DETERM*PIVOT
 330  A(ICOLUM,ICOLUM)=1.0
 340  DO 350 L=1,N
 350  A(ICOLUM,L)=A(ICOLUM,L)/PIVOT
 355  IF(M) 380, 380, 360
 360  DO 370 L=1,M
 370  B(ICOLUM,L)=B(ICOLUM,L)/PIVOT
C
C      REDUCE NON-PIVOT ROWS
C
 380  DO 550 L1=1,N
 390  IF(L1-ICOLUM) 400, 550, 400
 400  T=A(L1,ICOLUM)
 420  A(L1,ICOLUM)=0.0
 430  DO 450 L=1,N
 450  A(L1,L)=A(L1,L)-A(ICOLUM,L)*T
 455  IF(M) 550, 550, 460
 460  DO 500 L=1,M
 500  B(L1,L)=B(L1,L)-B(ICOLUM,L)*T
 550  CONTINUE
C
C      INTERCHANGE COLUMNS
C
 600  DO 710 I=1,N
 610  L=N+1-I
 620  IF (INDEX(L,1)-INDEX(L,2)) 630, 710, 630
 630  JROW=INDEX(L,1)
 640  JCOLUM=INDEX(L,2)
 650  DO 705 K=1,N
 660  SWAP=A(K,JROW)
 670  A(K,JROW)=A(K,JCOLUM)
 700  A(K,JCOLUM)=SWAP
 705  CONTINUE
 710  CONTINUE
      DO 730 K = 1,N
      IF(INDEX(K,3) -1) 715,720,715
 715  ID =2
      GO TO 740
 720  CONTINUE
 730  CONTINUE
      ID =1
 740  RETURN
C      LAST CARD OF PROGRAM
      END
```

Program 9.8 may be used for the inversion of a square matrix or for the solution of a system of linear simultaneous equations. The input must give the variable M as either 1 or 2 depending on which problem is to be solved; if M is 1, the program will perform only the matrix inversion, and skip all operations (reading the constant vector, punching the solution vector, etc.) concerned solely with the solution of linear equations. Program 9.7 (MATINV) is called for the actual computation of the inverse matrix or the solution of the linear equations. The variable ID is 2 or 1 according to whether MATINV found the matrix to be singular or not. If the matrix is singular, this information is outputted and the rest of the program skipped. If the matrix is nonsingular, its determinant is punched, and the inverse of the matrix will be punched if sense switch 1 is on. The program ends on a PAUSE statement.

Beginner's Hint

A blank card must follow the data card containing the control number M. This is because the I5 specification is followed by a slash in the format statement 999. Notice that no blank card follows the data card containing the matrix order N, even though the same format statement is used. The slash in this case merely causes the next card to be read. The effect of the slash thus depends on where it is encountered in the input list.

```
C      PROGRAM 9.8
C      CALLS MATRIX INVERSION SUBROUTINE
C
       DIMENSION A(18,18), B(18,1)
       PUNCH 995
  1    READ 999, N, ((A(I,J), J=1,N), I=1,N)
       PUNCH 994
       PUNCH 997, ((A(I,J), J=1,N), I=1,N)
C      M = 1 FOR MATRIX INVERSION ONLY
C      M = 2 FOR SOLUTION OF SIMULTANEOUS EQUATIONS
       READ 999, M
       GO TO (20,10), M
 10    READ 998, (B(I,1), I=1,N)
       PUNCH 993
       PUNCH 997, (B(I,1), I=1,N)
 20    CALL MATINV (A,N,B,1,DETERM,ID)
       GO TO (24,22), ID
 22    PUNCH 990
       GO TO 60
 24    PUNCH 996, DETERM
       IF (SENSE SWITCH 1) 30,40
 30    PUNCH 992
       PUNCH 997, ((A(I,J), J=1,N), I=1,N)
 40    GO TO (60,50), M
 50    PUNCH 991
       PUNCH 997, (B(I,1), I=1,N)
 60    PAUSE 00060
       GO TO 1
C
990    FORMAT (// 22X, 22HTHE MATRIX IS SINGULAR)
991    FORMAT (// 25X, 15HSOLUTION VECTOR)
992    FORMAT (// 24X, 17HINVERSE OF MATRIX)
993    FORMAT (// 25X, 15HCONSTANT VECTOR)
994    FORMAT (// 30X, 6HMATRIX)
995    FORMAT (// 21X, 24HRESULTS FROM PROGRAM 9.8)
996    FORMAT (// 17X, 19HTHE DETERMINANT IS E14.7)
997    FORMAT (/(4E16.7))
998    FORMAT (8F10.0)
999    FORMAT (I5/(8F10.0))
       END
```

MATRIX

1.0000000E+00	1.0000000E+00	1.0000000E+00	1.0000000E+00
1.0000000E+00	2.0000000E+00	3.0000000E+00	4.0000000E+00
1.0000000E+00	4.0000000E+00	9.0000000E+00	1.6000000E+01
1.0000000E+00	8.0000000E+00	2.7000000E+01	6.4000000E+01

CONSTANT VECTOR

1.0000000E+01	3.0000000E+01	1.0000000E+02	3.5400000E+02

THE DETERMINANT IS 1.2000007E+01

INVERSE OF MATRIX

3.9999981E+00	−4.3333308E+00	1.4999990E+00	−1.6666652E−01
−5.9999961E+00	9.4999943E+00	−3.9999976E+00	4.9999967E−01
3.9999972E+00	−6.9999957E+00	3.4999981E+00	−4.9999974E−01
−9.9999920E−01	1.8333321E+00	−9.9999949E−01	1.6666659E−01

SOLUTION VECTOR

1.0000002E+00	1.9999996E+00	3.0000004E+00	3.9999999E+00

MATRIX

1.0000000E+00	1.0000000E+00	1.0000000E+00	1.0000000E+00
1.0000000E+00	8.0000000E+00	2.7000000E+01	6.4000000E+01
1.0000000E+00	1.0000000E+00	1.0000000E+00	1.0000000E+00
1.0000000E+00	1.0000000E+00	1.0000000E+00	1.0000000E+00

THE MATRIX IS SINGULAR

Flow Chart 9.8

Program 9.9 uses Simpson's 1/3 rule to evaluate the integral of a function FUN(X) between the limits X = A and X = B. The program differs from Program 3.2 in two important respects:

(a) The function to be integrated, FUN(X), is defined by a FUNCTION subprogram rather than by an arithmetic statement function. It is thus not necessary to recompile the mainline Program 9.9 in order to integrate a different function. It is necessary only to compile the shorter FUNCTION subprogram for the new function, if its object deck is not already available.

(b) The program halves the interval and computes automatically the integral with the smaller interval. This process of halving and recomputing is continued until the difference between two successive computations is less than a specified amount EPS.

Program 9.9-A performs two-dimensional integration by Simpson's 1/3 rule (Sec. 8.2) by shifting the operator in the y-direction for each pair of strips in the x-direction. Three different spacings and Richardson's extrapolations are used to improve the results.

```
C           PROGRAM 9.9
C           SIMPSON-S RULE INTEGRATION WITH AUTOMATIC HALVING OF INTERVAL
C
            PRINT 999
     1      READ 998, A, B, H, CUTOFF
            PRINT 997, A, B
C
C           COMPUTE SUM1 (SUM OF THE VALUES TO BE MULTIPLIED BY ONE)
C
            SUM1 = FUN(A) + FUN(B)
            SUMA = 0.
C
C           COMPUTE INITIAL SUM2 (SUM OF THE VALUES TO BE MULTIPLIED BY TWO)
C
            SUM2 = 0.
            X = A + H
     3      SUM2 = SUM2 + FUN(X)
            X = X + H
            IF (X + H/2. - B) 3,50,4
C
C           COMPUTE SUM4 (SUM OF THE VALUES TO BE MULTIPLIED BY FOUR)
C
     4      SUM4 = 0.
            X = A + H/2.
    10      SUM4 = SUM4 + FUN(X)
            X = X + H
            IF (X - B) 10,50,20
C
C           COMPUTE VALUE OF THE INTEGRAL
C
    20      SIMP = H/6.*(SUM1 + 2.*SUM2 + 4.*SUM4)
            PRINT 996, H, SIMP
C
C           TEST WHETHER THE RELATIVE DIFFERENCE BETWEEN THE LAST TWO VALUES
C           OF THE INTEGRAL IS GREATER THAN THE ASSIGNED CUTOFF VALUE
C
            IF (ABSF((SIMP - SUMA)/SIMP) - CUTOFF) 1,1,30
C
C           COMPUTE NEW SUM2
C
    30      SUM2 = SUM2 + SUM4
            SUMA = SIMP
            H = H/2.
            GO TO 4
    50      STOP 00050
C
   996      FORMAT ( 25X, F6.4, 3X, E13.7 )
   997      FORMAT ( / 14X, 27HINTEGRAL OF FUN(X) FROM X = F5.2
          1          7H TO X = F5.2 // 25X, 19HINTERVAL      RESULT )
   998      FORMAT ( 4E10.0 )
   999      FORMAT ( // 24X, 24HRESULTS FROM PROGRAM 9.9 )
            END
```

```
FUNCTION FUN(X)
FUN = X**2*EXPF(-X**3)
RETURN
END
```

RESULTS FROM PROGRAM 9.9

INTEGRAL OF FUN(X) FROM X = 0.00 TO X = 1.00

INTERVAL	RESULT
.5000	.2109031E-00
.2500	.2107176E-00
.1250	.2107074E-00
.0625	.2107068E-00

INTEGRAL OF FUN(X) FROM X = 1.00 TO X = 2.00

INTERVAL	RESULT
.5000	.1222719E-00
.2500	.1225019E-00
.1250	.1225138E-00
.0625	.1225145E-00
.0312	.1225146E-00

```
     FUNCTION FUN(X)
     IF(X - .000001) 10,10,20
10   FUN = 1.
     RETURN
20   FUN = SINF(X)/X
     RETURN
     END
```

RESULTS FROM PROGRAM 9.9

INTEGRAL OF FUN(X) FROM X = 0.00 TO X = 1.00

INTERVAL	RESULT
.5000	.9460868E-00
.2500	.9460831E-00
.1250	.9460829E-00
.0625	.9460827E-00
.0312	.9460826E-00
.0156	.9460825E-00

INTEGRAL OF FUN(X) FROM X = 0.00 TO X = 8.00

INTERVAL	RESULT
.5000	.1574187E+01
.2500	.1574186E+01
.1250	.1574186E+01

Flow Chart 9.9

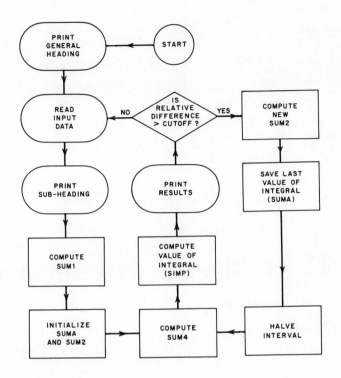

315

```
C       PROGRAM 9.9-A
C       TWO DIMENSIONAL SIMPSON-S RULE (SEE SECTION 8.2)
C
        DIMENSION SUMM(3)
   1    READ  999, NUMX, NUMY, XA, XB, YA, YB
        PRINT 998,              XA, XB, YA, YB
        DO 200 K = 1,3
        NUMMX = NUMX*K
        NUMMY = NUMY*K
        XSTRIP = 2*NUMMX
        YSTRIP = 2*NUMMY
        XH = (XB - XA)/XSTRIP
        YH = (YB - YA)/YSTRIP
        SUM = 0.
        X1 = XA
        X2 = X1 + XH
        X3 = X2 + XH
        DO 100 I = 1,NUMMX
        Y1 = YA
        Y2 = Y1 + YH
        Y3 = Y2 + YH
        F1 = F(X1,Y1)
        F2 = F(X2,Y1)
        F3 = F(X3,Y1)
        DO 80 J = 1,NUMMY
        F4 = F(X1,Y2)
        F5 = F(X2,Y2)
        F6 = F(X3,Y2)
        F7 = F(X1,Y3)
        F8 = F(X2,Y3)
        F9 = F(X3,Y3)
        SUM = SUM + XH*YH/9.*(F1 +F3 +F7 +F9 +4.*(F2 +F4 +F6 +F8) +16.*F5)
        F1 = F7
        F2 = F8
        F3 = F9
        Y2 = Y3 + YH
  80    Y3 = Y2 + YH
        X1 = X3
        X2 = X1 + XH
  100   X3 = X2 + XH
        PRINT 997, K, XH, YH, SUM
  200   SUMM(K) = SUM
C
C       RICHARDSON-S EXTRAPOLATIONS (SEE SECTION 3.5)
C
        EXTR21 = (16.*SUMM(2) - SUMM(1))/15.
        EXTR31 = (81.*SUMM(3) - SUMM(1))/80.
        EXTR32 = (81.*SUMM(3) - 16.*SUMM(2))/65.
        PRINT 996, EXTR21, EXTR31, EXTR32
        GO TO 1
C
  996   FORMAT (/ 19X, 19HEXTRAPOLATION 2,1 = E14.7 / 33X, 5H3,1 = E14.7 /
       $                                    33X, 5H3,2 = E14.7 )
  997   FORMAT (I18, 2F10.5, E17.7)
  998   FORMAT (// 23X, 26HRESULTS FROM PROGRAM 9.9-A // 25X, 21HLIMITS OF
       $ INTEGRATION / 16X, 4HXA = E14.7, 4X, 4HXB = E14.7 / 16X,4HYA = E1
       $4.7, 4X, 4HYB = E14.7 // 17X, 1HK 6X, 2HXH 8X, 2HYH 8X,8HINTEGRAL)
  999   FORMAT (2I5 / 4E10.3)
        END
```

316

```
FUNCTION F(X,Y)
F = EXPF(X + Y)
RETURN
END
```

RESULTS FROM PROGRAM 9.9-A

LIMITS OF INTEGRATION
XA = 0.0000000E-99   XB = 1.0000000E+00
YA = 0.0000000E-99   YB = 1.5000000E+00

K	XH	YH	INTEGRAL
1	.50000	.37500	5.9851861E+00
2	.25000	.18750	5.9826922E+00
3	.16666	.12500	5.9825550E+00

EXTRAPOLATION 2,1 = 5.9825259E+00
             3,1 = 5.9825221E+00
             3,2 = 5.9825212E+00

```
FUNCTION F(X,Y)
F = X*Y*EXPF(X*X + Y*Y)
RETURN
END
```

RESULTS FROM PROGRAM 9.9-A

LIMITS OF INTEGRATION
XA = 2.0000000E-01   XB = 1.2000000E+00
YA =-3.0000000E-01   YB = 1.4000000E+00

K	XH	YH	INTEGRAL
1	.50000	.85000	5.8512601E+00
2	.25000	.42500	4.9007915E+00
3	.16666	.28333	4.8041138E+00

EXTRAPOLATION 2,1 = 4.8374269E+00
             3,1 = 4.7910243E+00
             3,2 = 4.7803161E+00

317

Index

FORTRAN Programs,
Flow Charts,
Beginner's Hints,
and Examples